ILLUSTRATED GEOGRAPHY OF
COSTA RICA

This work was inspired by the original Illustrated Geography of Costa Rica written by Juan Trejos-Quirós whose final edition (the twenty-second) was published in 1968.

ILLUSTRATED GEOGRAPHY OF
COSTA RICA

Alonso Trejos
EDITOR

Trejos Editores
San José
1991

First edition: 1991

The content of this book was edited by:	Alonso Trejos
With the collaboration of:	Sinaí Badilla - Geography Ronulfo Jiménez - Economics Vivienne Solís - Zoology Patricia Ramírez and Pablo Manso - Climatology
Final editing was done by:	José Joaquín Trejos Fernández Alonso Trejos
Photography:	John Skiffington III
(The index on page 265 indicates the photographer for each individual photo):	Humberto Trejos Alonso Trejos Guillermo Navarro Marco Tulio Saborío
Photograph selection	Alonso Trejos Ricardo Baudrit
Design:	Alonso Trejos
Cover design:	Sylvia Troyo
Layout:	Jorge Guido
Technical publishing advice:	Ricardo Baudrit - Guillermo Navarro
Maps:	Guillermo Navarro - Sinaí Badilla
Assistant Editor:	Ileana Zamora
Translated:	Harry Spencer
Spanish title	Geografía Ilustrada - Costa Rica

917.86
T787i   Trejos Fonseca, Alonso
        Illustrated Geography of Costa Rica / Alonso
Trejos Fonseca. – 1st ed. - San José:
Trejos 1991.
      272 pp. : ill. (some colored), maps; 28 cm.

      ISBN 9977-54-030-6

      1. Costa Rica - Geography. I. Title.

Cover photograph: (John Skiffington III)	Above: Below, left: Below right:	Braulio Carrillo National Park Sixaola River Guayabo National Monument, Turrialba

Printed by Trejos Hermanos Sucesores, S.A.
San José, Costa Rica

Table of Contens ━━━━

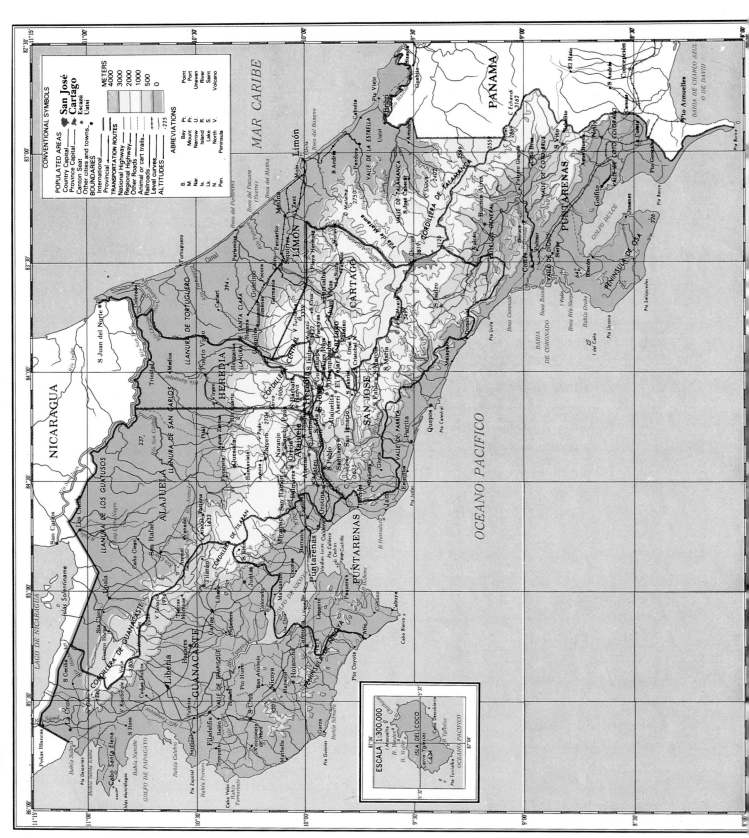

Adapted from the School Map of Costa Rica, with permission from the National Geographic Institute.

1 Geographical Position and Boundaries

LOCATION

Costa Rica, the southernmost of the five republics that comprise Central America, extends approximately from eight to eleven degrees north latitude and between eighty-three and eighty-six degrees west longitude. Hence, the country is located in the northwest quadrant of the planet.

GLOBAL POSITION

According to the latitudes mentioned, Costa Rica is located practically in the center of the inter-tropical zone 10° north of the equator. This zone is also referred to as the "Hot Zone", due to its prevailing warm temperatures throughout. It is also located on the North American Continent, on the Central American Isthmus. It is six hours west of Greenwich.

BOUNDARIES

Costa Rica's boundaries are natural, conventional and mixed. On the east and northeast it is bounded by the Caribbean Sea, and on the west and south by the Pacific Ocean; on the southeast it borders with the country of Panama. It is separated from its northern neighbor, Nicaragua, by natural boundaries: the little Sapoá River, the southern shore of Lake Nicaragua and the San Juan River. But by virtue of the Cañas-Jerez Treaty signed in 1858, this border was defined as a line starting from the Caribbean Sea, exactly from the tip of Punta Castilla at the mouth of the San Juan River; the

Page 5: Tambor, Paquera, Puntarenas Province

Page 6: National Theater, in the capital city San José

To the east and northeast Costa Rica is bounded by the Caribbean Sea. Below, a beach in Puerto Viejo on the Caribbean Sea

line continues along the right bank of the river, upstream, to a point three English miles from Fort Castillo Viejo; from there it continues west, making an equidistant curve at three miles radius from the fort, and then continues two English miles south of the right bank of the same river; then it continues two miles south of the shore of Lake Nicaragua until it meets the Sapoá River. From this point on, it follows an astronomically straight line to the center of Salinas Bay (see Map No. 1).

The validity of this treaty was disputed by the two sister republics for several years, until 1888, when, through the arbitrated decision of the President of the United States of America, this boundary was definitively accepted. The southeast boundary is also mixed.

Costa Rica borders with present-day Panama (which had been a department of Colombia until 1903). This border issue **went on unresolved for many years**, with Costa Rica claiming as part of its territory the littoral of Chiriquí Lagoon. Later, however, to end the dispute, Costa Rica and Colombia submitted the matter for French President Loubet to decide, but he suggested an equivocal border that failed to resolve the issue. Once Panama was established as a republic, the matter was submitted to the Chief Justice of the United States, Edward Douglas White, who presented his verdict on September 12, 1914. It pleased the Costa Ricans but was not altogether satisfactory to the Panamanians.

In 1941 Panama and Costa Rica arrived at a border agreement through the Echandi-Montero/Fernández-Jaén Treaty signed on May 1 of that year. Then the respective legislative bodies of both countries simultaneously approved a boundary described as: "starting from the present mouth of the Sixaola at the Caribbean Sea, following along the lowest part of the river valley upstream to its confluence with the Yorkín River; from there it follows the lowest part of that river valley upstream to the parallel at longitude 9°30', north of the ecuador; then it continues south 76°37', west, to the meridian at longitude 82°58'10", west of Greenwich; from there it continues along this meridian south to the mountain ridge that separates the waters of the Caribbean Sea from those of the Pacific; it follows this mountain ridge to Cerro Pando, where it meets the spur dividing the waters of the tributaries of the Gulf Dulce and the Charco Azul Bay; from there it follows this spur until it ends at Punta Burica on the Pacific Ocean." (See Map No. 1.)

Opposite page: Sunset at Hermosa Beach, Guanacaste.

Sixaola River. Part of this river serves a natural and conventional boundary with the country of Panama.

10

2 Physical Geography

LIE OF THE LAND

The most recent hypothesis explaining the overall physiography of Costa Rica states that some hundred million years ago starting from a few volcanic islands, located in what we now know as the large peninsulas on the Pacific, the land began to expand, due to volcanic activity arising first in the sector of the Talamanca Mountain Range, and, later in the areas now occupied by volcanic mountains. Even as the mountains were being formed, the process of erosion began wearing away at them. The resulting sediments helped to fill in the sea bottom and then cover the surface, giving rise to the plains. A sort of intrusive volcanism has been elevating the Talamanca Mountain Range and surrounding areas. For this reason, today we find sediments that had previously been on the ocean floor, several hundred meters above sea level.

All these processes along with others such as seismic activity have contributed to the present shape of the land.

Costa Rica is an elongated form that stretches from northeast to southeast; its

Opposite page: Potrero Beach and Bay, Santa Cruz, Guanacaste.

Brasilito and Conchal Beaches, Santa Cruz, Guanacaste.

northern half begins wide but gradually tapers southward. The highest regions are in the center of the country and its lowlands are more extensive and flat on the Caribbean side and to the north, than on the Pacific side where the declivity is much sharper.

COASTS

Costa Rica has the advantage of access to both the Pacific Ocean and the Caribbean Sea. (See Map No. 1.)

CONTOUR OF THE CARIBBEAN COAST

The Caribbean coastline, two hundred twelve kilometers long, stretches from

northeast to southeast, defining two distinct parts: San Juan River-Limón and Limón-Sixaola River.

The first, a long straight coastal strip consisting of a broad alluvial plain of recent deposit, separates the sea from a series of freshwater lagoons fed by multiple rivers. The southeast tip of this large beach area is comprised of the rocky headlands of Limón, surrounded by very deteriorated corral reefs. In front of Limon rises the only islet on this side of the country, Uvita.

From Limón going southeast there is another wide stretch of beach, but unlike those to the north, there are no notable lagoons behind it, and the alluvial plains are narrow. This beach is interrupted by the corral headlands of Cahuita, on whose protruding tip has developed the most splendid reef in the region. Continuing southward there is a beach whose sands have a high content of magnetite, and farther on there is Puerto Viejo where there begins a stretch of beach, interrupted every so often by low cliffs and reefs. South of Punta Mona the beach becomes regular again, with alluvial plains and some marshes behind them. (*Statistical Atlas*, 1982).

CONTOUR OF THE PACIFIC COAST

Just as the predominance of recent depositional forms on Caribbean side have determined a extremely uniform coastline, vulcanism, tectonic activity, tertiary deposits, and a long erosive period have made for great variety on the Pacific side along its over 1,000 km long coastline, with capes, inlets, peninsulas, gulfs, islands, points, and marshes.

Generalizing a bit to categorize the Pacific coastal area into sectors, it could be divided into seven parts, each of which display a degree of uniformity with respect to geological structure, morphology, origin, exposure to the ocean, and climate. Starting from the north, these sectors would be: 1) Santa Elena, from Salinas Bay to Punta Mala; 2) Nicoya, from Culebra Bays through Los Negritos to the Barranca River, taking in all of the gulf interior; 3) Herradura, from the Barranca River to Punta Judas; 4) Quepos, from Punta Judas to Boca Sierpe; 5) Osa-Burica, from Boca Sierpe to Cabo Matapalo, through the gulf; 6) from Punta Blanca to Punta Burica; 7) the Dulce Gulf area.

Each of these sectors presents unique distinguishing characteristics: Santa Elena is geologically the oldest zone of Costa Rica, its predominant traits being broad, high cliffs and rock clusters jutting out to sea. In some parts the cliffs have receded giving rise to small cape-bay

inlets. Nicoya is somewhat varied. In the northern part, its transverse geological structure has given rise to many inlets separated by high rocky hills. The central part is more exposed to the beating of the waves and there are more extensive positional forms, one over another, making for long beaches, occasionally interrupted by relatively low cliffs. At the southern end, between Cabo Blanco and Los Negritos there are high cliffs, a spacious bay, with mangroves developing within it transverse structures that form several chains of islands and islets. Both the Gulf of Nicoya and Gulf Dulce offer protected coastline that has allowed great mud deposits on the shores and the development of mangroves, but this trend has been more pronounced in the Gulf of Nicoya. Herradura has characteristics similar to those of northern Nicoya, while Quepos-Coronado presents a long, uniform coastal strip bordering a broad alluvial plain. This uniformity is interrupted only by the headlands of Quepos and Uvita and the thriving

Cabo Velas, Santa Cruz, Guanacaste.

Punta Cahuita, Talamanca, Limón Province

mangroves of the Terraba River delta. In Osa-Burica, the next sector, the Osa beaches predominate, with an rugged topography that extends almost to the seashore in Burica (Eusebio Flores, 1979).

PENINSULAS

The major peninsulas are on the Pacific. The northernmost of these is Santa Elena Peninsula (formed by the cape bearing the same name). Continuing south there is Nicoya Peninsula, which reminds one of a robust arm upon which Costa Rica rests. The map reveals that this peninsula contributes much to the pleasing shape of the country as a whole, unique among all other countries of the world. Finally, the Osa Peninsula is sparsely inhabited, low-lying, and fertile, although somewhat marshy in its northern part. (See Map No. 2)

CAPES AND POINTS

On the Caribbean are: Punta Castilla, at the Nicaraguan border; continuing south, Punta Blanca, which forms the small harbor at Puerto Limón; then Punta Cahuita and Punta Mona.

On the Pacific we have: Punta Descartes, Punta Blanca, Cabo Santa Elena, Punta Mala, Punta Gorda, Cabo Velas, Punta Guiones, Cabo Blanco, Punta Morales, Punta Arenas, with the town and port of Puntarenas; continuing south, Punta Caldera, today known as Puerto Caldera, Punta Herradura, Punta Judas, Punta Quepos, Punta Dominical, Punta Llorona, Cabo Matapalo, and Punta Burica at the Panamanian border. (See Map No. 2)

BAYS, GULFS, AND HARBORS

On the eastern coast, only Moín Bay and Limón Bay are noteworthy. Located on the latter is the city of Limón, the principal port of the country.

This harbor handles most of the sea trade for the country. At Moín Bay there is a new port bearing the same name, which also has a river terminal for the

Moín river. The Costa Rican Petroleum Refinery (*Refinadora Costarricense de Petróleo, RECOPE*) has its main facilities here.

Limón is Costa Rica's only seaport that offers direct docking and ferrying. It handles general merchandise and homogeneous cargo, such as bananas, fertilizers, sugar, and heavy machinery, and others. In addition, through Moín, its complementary port, crude oil is received for processing in the refinery. Limón has four docks: the smallest is called "Muelle Nacional", and the others, "Muelle Metálico", "Muelle 70" and "Muelle Alemán". It also has a barge service making it possible to attend ships anchored in the bay when no docking space is available. Port movement at Limón has been experiencing a rapid increase over the last few years.

The "Muelle Alemán" dock consists of two 420-meter side landing stages a roll-on-roll-off ship stop, warehouses, containers yards, and other facilities. This dock was built inside a 725-meter breakwater north of the Muelle Nacional, which was built to protect the Muelle Metálico and Muelle 70 from the high waves that were frequently hampered the docking of ships (MOPT, *Ministerio de Obras Públicas y Transportes* = Ministry of Public Works and Transportation, 1984).

On the Pacific Ocean, north of Salinas Bay, we have Santa Elena and Culebra which meet the necessary conditions that would allow them to become some the finest ports in the world. In recent years, due to its natural beauty, planning has been underway to make this bay a major tourist center.

Next, to the south is the Gulf of Nicoya, formed by the Nicoya Peninsula. Filled with a myriad of bays, points, and islands, it is one of the most picturesque spots in Costa Rica.

There is also the port of Puntarenas, which due to its age, state of deterioration,

Cabo Blanco, Cóbano, Puntarenas Province

and lack of capacity, has forfeited its position to Port Caldera, also located on the Gulf of Nicoya, just a half hour from the town of Puntarenas. It has become a modern port complex. Further, there is the conveyor of Punta Morales, which has facilities and docks to accommodate ships that transport sugar and alcohol.

Caldera will be linked to San José and the rest of the metropolitan area by means of a freeway. Several stretches of it have already been constructed, one of which runs between San José and Ciudad Colón.

Also touching this gulf, there are many small ports that carry traffic for the various regions of the peninsula and the rest of the country.

In Puntarenas movement is handled mainly by the "*muellecito*" ("little dock"), but there are two other docks used for costal traffic: Y Griega and El Cocal.

Finally, there is the Gulf of Osa or Gulf Dulce, which is also a very scenic spot, having several inlets, including Rincón Bay and Golfito, whose harbor conditions were first utilized for banana company activities. Now Golfito has been declared a free port. (See Map No. 2).

ISLANDS

South of Cabo Santa Elena there is a small archipelago called Murciélago, followed by a string of islands of small import scattered all along the western

Tortugas (Tortoise) Islands, Gulf of Nicoya, Puntarenas Province

18

Cabo Matapalo, Osa Peninsula, Puntarenas Province

coast of the Nicoya Peninsula. In the Gulf of Nicoya are the biggest islands, Chira Island being the largest of these, and San Lucas the second largest.

The other islands in this gulf are: Venado Island, Bejuco, Caballos, Negritos, Cedros, Tortuga, and Alcatraz.

Along the western coast of the country there is another insignificant string of islands, of which only Caño Island, northwest of the Osa Peninsula and Violin Island at the mouth of the Sierpe River are worth mentioning.

In the Caribbean Sea there is the islet La Uvita, in front of Puerto Limón. The only islet on the Caribbean side, it is a lovely place for excursions and hiking. The beach which extends southeast of Limón is interrupted by the corral headlands of Cahuita.

La Uvita Islet, Limón Province, sole islet off the Caribbean shore.

19

There are no more important islands off Costa Rica's east coast, except an occasional reef rising above the surface of the sea. (See Map No. 2)

Coco Island, off the Pacific coast, is the only one that does not arise out of the continental platform, but, rather, out of the ocean platform that stretches from the Osa Peninsula toward the southeast. Some 500 kms separate it from the continental shore, it covers only 47 kms^2, and its greatest height is around 600 mts at Mount Yglesias. It is comprised of volcanic materials, relatively old and diverse (lava, pebbles, pumice, etc.). Its topography is quite irregular, with impressive costal cliffs and lush plant cover. It is a strategic zone for Costa Rican ocean sovereignty, and the meteorological information it provides is greatly useful for weather studies and forecasts pertaining to the Central American isthmus. Currently investigations are being made on a treasure the Spaniards possibly left there at the time of the conquest.

TOTAL LAND AREA OF COSTA RICA

As of 1975, with an amendment to Article 6 of the Constitution, Costa Rica's boundary was established at 12 nautical miles from the coast (around 22 kilometers off shore). The area within these twelve nautical miles is referred to as "Territorial Waters" over which Costa Rica exercises the same sovereignty as it does over its continental territory. According to measurements taken by the National Geographical Institute, Costa Rica has a sea surface in the Caribbean Sea of 4,326 kms^2, and 13,669 kms^2 in the Pacific Ocean. This area added to a total land surface of 51,000 kms^2, gives Costa Rica a total area of 69,095 kms^2. Nonetheless, its continental surface is one of the smallest of all the countries on the Central American isthmus, larger only than that of El Salvador and Belize.

Law No. 5,699 of June 5, 1975 modified Article 6 of the Constitution fixing the Territorial Waters, in addition to establishing its "Patrimonial Waters", now called its "Exclusive Economic Zone", which extends 188 nautical miles from shore (around 370 kms). This, as it connects with the Territorial Waters determined by Coco Island situated at 496 kms southeast of Cabo Blanco, gives a total area of approximately half a million square kilometers. According to a maritime law convention, this enormous area constituted by the Patrimonial Waters, referred to as an "Exclusive Economic Zone", represents an economic potential of extraordinary magnitude. (Cevo Juan and others, 1988).

Opposite page: Puerto Viejo, Talamanca, Limón Province.

Blanca Beach (Flamingo), Santa Cruz, Guanacaste Province.

3 The Terrain

MOUNTAIN SYSTEM

The mountains of Costa Rica form a group independent from the rest of the Central American mountains, although all of these are of more recent origin than the others in North and South American.

The mountain system of Costa Rica can be divided into two distinct units, separated in the middle of the country by two valleys, those of the Río Grande de Tárcoles and the Reventazón.

This spinal column, running from northeast to southeast, is comprised of the following sections: a) the *Sierra Volcánica de Guanacaste* (Volcanic Mountain Chain of Guanacaste, containing the prominent volcanoes of Orosí, Góngora, Rincón de la Vieja, Miravalles, Tenorio, and Arenal); b) the *Sierra Minera de Tilarán* (Mountain Chain of Tilarán, including Abangares,

Aguacate, Cedral, and Miramar peaks); c) the *Sierra Volcánica Central* (Central Volcanic Mountain Chain, including the volcanoes, Poás, Barva, Irazú, Turrialba); d) the last section, the mountain hub of the country is the most striking –the *Cordillera de Talamanca* (Talamanca Mountain Range), which ends in Panamanian territory. This is a complete mountain system in its own right, due to its breadth, complexity of formation processes, heights (including the peaks of Escazú, Urán, Cabécar, Chirripó, Kamuk), and other reasons. Linked to this mountain range is a chain of hills that follows that coastline known as the *brunqueña*. (See Map No. 3)

Volcanic Mountains

These mountains, formed from eruptive rocks, can be divided into two main groups. The first begins at the

San Roque Hill, canton of Liberia, Guanacaste Province.

Opposite page: Arenal Volcano in eruption. Its elevation is 1,633 meters and is located west of the plains of San Carlos.

23

northeast border, stretches toward the southeast and ends at the *Cerros del Aguacate*. The the most important mountains of the group, called the *Sierra Volcánica de Guanacaste*, are: Orosí, Rincón de la Vieja, Miravalles, Tenorio, and Arenal (all are volcanic). The highest of these, Miravalles, rises 2,028 meters above sea level.

THE ARENAL VOLCANO

The Arenal Volcano, with an altitude of 1,633 meters, located west of the Plains of San Carlos, conically shaped, has been active since 1968, a year of heavy eruptions accompanied by seismic movements. Gases with temperatures of 600 to 800°C formed "clouds of fire" that deposited ash and lava fragments over an area of 1,850 kms^2 (Hall, 1984) (Chávez and Sáenz, 1970). It is the only volcano in Costa Rica that produces intermittent *peleanas* (eruptions, characterized by "clouds of fire", Hall, 1984). History records that this was a sacred place for the Indians during the pre-Columbian period.

Until 1968 from time immemorial, Arenal had been considered a calm volcano. There is no record of any activity during the colonial days nor in subsequent years, until the thirties, when an expeditionary group discovered some fumarole activity. Then in July 1968, one side of the volcano exploded, and from the new crater poured out balls of fire and gases that razed everything in their path –people, houses, trees, animals. The only thing that remained were a few twisted sheets of corrugated tin from the peasants houses and the thoroughly baked naked corpses of some 80 former dwellers of Tabacón and surrounding areas. (Salguero, 1982).

Although the volcano has quieted down, it is still active. The lava thrown from it is forming new mountains. Now the volcano has another crater near the top, according to observers' reports. Moreover, it can be shown that the crater has deepened, and it is assumed that the top will eventually sink down. (Volcanological Observatory, UNA).

Of the other four volcanoes, two are in a solfatarian state –Rincón de la Vieja and Miravalles– and two are dormant –Orosí and Tenorio.

RINCON DE LA VIEJA

As for volcanic activity in the past century, according to Carlos von Seebach, a scientist who climbed the volcano for

Arenal Volcano, San Carlos, Alajuela Province

the first time in 1865, the crater had poured out smoke for several days in 1863.

In 1922 an expedition made up of Fidel Tristán, and Ricardo and Alvaro Fernández-Peralta, made it to the summit. For the first time photographs were taken and the volcano was completely surveyed, which actually has two peaks, one of which is called "Santa María" in recent maps of the National Geographical Institute, and appears as a separate volcano. "It is situated 40 kms northeast of Liberia and its highest point reaches 1,907 meters above sea level.

At the summit there are several extinguished craters and one active one. At the foot of these craters there is a lagoon 100 meters long by 40 meters wide, containing crystal clear water. Two of the three craters are conically shaped The active one is elliptic but almost circular, with a diameter of 500 meters and a depth of 100 meters. The walls stand vertical. The bottom is indented in the form of a funnel, with a diameter

of some 20 meters at its top and eight meters at the bottom. In the past, this volcano mightily hurled great clouds of hot smoke, of no less than 250°C, through this opening, up to 300 meters into the air. Around the crater there are frequent vestiges of rocks having been thrown so high that they hit the ground as sticks of dynamite, leaving only holes in the ground to mark their collision. There is no vegetation surrounding the crater, and at the top all that can be found are unequivocal signs of powerful eruptions of the past. The solfataras, crevices through which sulfurous vapors are expelled, commonly called '*hornillas*' ('hot plates'), which extend down the side of the volcano, are the remains of what was once a caldron of activity."

The volcano began on May 8, 1991 moderate eruptive activity, accompanied by volcanic tremors, which triggered a series of "*lahares*" (mixture of ash, fragments of rock, and water that slide down the sides of the volcano).

Rincón de la Vieja Volcano, elevation at its highest point, 1,907 meters above sea level. Situated 40 kilometers northeast of Liberia.

25

*The Solfataras of Rincón de la Vieja are cracks through which sulfurous gases are expelled; they are commonly called **hornillas**.*

from the base of the cone itself, no more than a kilometer from where the ascent begins. There are several volcanic centers at which small mud volcanoes have tiny eruptions. Also, there are many scorched spots on the ground that maintain high temperatures (Salguero, 1982). (See also pages 162-163)

OROSI

This first peak in the Volcanic Mountain Range of Guanacaste, has a altitude of 1,487 meters. Examination of aerial photographs of the mountain mass of Orosí –graphs prepared by the National Geographic Institute– reveals no signs of craters in their original form, although deteriorated craters are seen as enormous *"canforros"* (hollows). This volcano "sleeps the sleep of the righteous" since its eruptive activity has long ceased, evidenced by the fact that no record has been left of any activity during the conquest, colonial days, or modern times.

TENORIO

Located north of the town of Cañas, its highest peak has a elevation of 1,916 meters.

Its mountain mass is made up of several peaks, and in aerial photographs several extinguished craters are clearly visible. Their shape is unequivocal; one of them has become a lagoon. There are also enormous *"canforros"* or *"guindos"* (gullies), probably formed by the erosion of old craters. None of these hollows, however, show any signs of recent volcanic activity.

El Tenorio has probably been dormant since many centuries before the conquest of our territory, judging from the presence of important aborigine population centers at the base of the mountain. (Salguero, 1982).

SIERRA MINERA

Going south, the next important mountains are the *Sierra Minera de Tilarán,* where there are no volcanic centers. Some gold has been mined in these mountains.

The *Cerros del Aguacate* in the *Sierra Minera de Tilarán* are located along the

MIRAVALLES

Located 15 kilometers north of the town of Bagaces, the volcano is dormant in its cone but rumblings and *"hornillas"* (solfataras) continue.

Heavy erosion observed around the crater show that the volcano has had no signs of activity, although the whole region at the base of the volcano does show numerous evidences of volcanic activity: *hornillas*, thermal springs, mineral or "Vichy" water, and the Blanco River of recent origin.

The largest group of *hornillas* is concentrated in one spot, a short distance

26

edge of the *Sierra Volcánica Central*. These mountains, too, have had gold mines but no volcanoes. Some of its peaks rise to over 1,500 meters above sea level.

The third group is comprised of three large mountain masses: Poás, including the Poás Volcano and surrounding hills; Barva, separated from the previous one by a pass, called El Desengaño, and after that, slightly to the southeast, the mountain mass of the Irazú, including two volcanoes, the Irazú and the Turrialba. This group is called the *Sierra Volcánica Central* (Central Volcanic Mountain Chain).

POAS

This volcano, situated between the dormant Viejo Volcano and the Barva, is the culminating point of the Central Volcanic Mountain Range, and is now a national park. With an elevation of 2,704 meters, it attracts thousands of visitors. It has a lagoon filled with cold, transparent water, evidence that it was once a crater. According to observations, however, the waters of the volcano's lagoon have for several years been receding, and continue to do so. The extensive forests cover this volcano and the wildlife found in them make this spot even more attractive.

The Indian name for the volcano was "Chibuzú", but, according to León Fernández, the name was subsequently changed to Poás, derived from the an early name "Púas", of a mountainside village now called San Pedro de Poás.

Some of the oldest data we have on the volcano was gathered by Miguel Alfaro, an explorer from the town of Alajuela. He was there in 1828 and wrote that at that time the activity of the volcano was quite intense. The size he reported of the lagoon, was apparently smaller than it is today. He also stated that there was an abundance of sulfur "that readily burned, giving off a blue flame". At that time, the volcano heaved ash that fell as far away as the town of Esparza.

Carlos Sapper, in his report on the volcanos of Central America, mentions

The Poás Volcano, in Alajuela Province, rises to 2,704 meters above sea level.

27

that "when Frantzius (another scientist) climbed the volcano in March of 1860, the temperature of the lake was 39.1°C. The water had a high sulfuric acid content. Occasionally, at intervals of approximately 10 minutes, the water would bubble. Then he describes, that around 1880 there was another ash eruption, that covered the sides of the volcano down to San Pedro de Poás. "From October 11, 1888 until February 1889, there occurred a series of strong tremors that caused many landslides and left large crevices, especially close to the volcano." This activity was responsible for forming another lagoon above San Pedro de Poás, right at a place called Fraijanes. (Volcanoes of Costa Rica, 1985).

According to a recent description given by Dr. Sapper, the Poás Volcano is a cone of relatively gentle slopes to the south, and sharp ones to the north. It has three craters. The one farthest to the north, is the oldest; only half of this one remains intact. The one farthest south is rocky and now contains a lake with a diameter of some 500 meters and drains into the Sarapiquí River. The crater in the center is active. It is sunken between the the south and north walls of the volcano. This would explain why the south

wall of this crater, the youngest, is much higher than the others. Those walls are formed of alternating layers of loose volcanic material and others of thoroughly decomposed volcanic rock."

In this century the Poás Volcano has experienced two strong eruptions, one in 1910 and another in 1953. Lately its activity has been increasing, and the acid content of the crater lagoon (relatively hot) has been rising while the water level in it has gone down by 15 meters. Over time, the high temperatures of the fumaroles and alterations of the sides of the volcano may be considered as indications of a possible ensuing eruption. Observations have shown that resultant contaminated water and acid rains affect the animal species, and burn the vegetation. As this phenomenon has been taking place since 1986, we can only conclude that the volcano is about to undergo another phase in its evolution.

The volcano is currently accessible by way of a good road, passible all year round. It goes from San Pedro de Poás in Alajuela province all the way to the volcano, which is today a national park. At the volcano itself there are information booths, a visitors' center, a management area, picnic and camping areas, hiking

Irazú Volcano: the highest peak in the Central Volcanic Mountains −3,432 meters above sea level−. It is located in Cartago Province.

trails, lookout points, and guides, as well as other facilities and attractions.

BARVA

Also called Las Tres Marías Peak (elevation 2,906 meters), there is no data available pertaining to its eruptive activity. Its crater is occupied by a splendid lagoon, although considerably smaller than the one at Poás. It is surrounded by a thick forest accessible only during the dry season.

The National Geographic Institute, based on studies done by Ricardo Fernández-Peralta, changed the spelling of the name from "Barba" to "Barva" as it appears in all early documents.

THE IRAZU AND TURRIALBA VOLCANOES

The Irazú is the highest mountain of the Central Volcanic Mountain Chain (elevation of 3,432 meters). Below, for historical purposes, is a description of the volcano, that was included by the author in the previous editions, followed by a revised description to account for subsequent events.

"The ascent up the Irazú volcano can be made with little difficulty. Leaving the city of Cartago on horseback, passing through the village of Tierra Blanca, you can make it to the top in five or six hours. At first you will see lush vegetation around the mountain; then past the forest belt, some large expanses of sand, with patches of brushwood, crowns the top of the volcano. The panorama at the top is grandiose; if the sky is clear, the view is delightful: multi-shaded green hills and valleys highlighted by the diverse colors and tones of assorted crops; in the distance, blended into the horizon you can make out on one side the Pacific Ocean and on the other the Atlantic (today called the Caribbean Sea); if the weather is misty, you behold a vast sea of clouds whose curly waves bump the sides of the mountains with each gust of wind.

Then, at your feet there is an immense cirque of rocks of over 1,000 meters in diameter. At the bottom of this first

crater, other smaller ones have successively formed: the oldest of these funnels is now obstructed; the second one still displays three chimneys of which two are partially obstructed and the third was breathing out sulfurous vapors until only a short while ago; the third funnel appeared at the beginning of 1918, and since then it has constantly bellowed huge columns of smoke and ash.

On the northern slope of the Irazú there are hot springs and numerous solfataras, but the lack of roads make these spots difficult to access."

Today the volcano is a cone with five craters, young colonies of myrtles, an extraordinary view in all directions, and a paved road all the way to the craters. There is an entrance booth, signs, well-marked hiking paths, and guides. From 1963 to 1965 the volcano was in

The Barva Volcano, elevation 2,906 meters, also called Las Tres Marías Mountain.

Mount Pelado, Cañas, Guanacaste.

View of Mount Echandi, Coto Brus, Puntarenas Province

eruption. Its intense activity propelled ashes far from their origin. Subsequently, the activity has been fumarolic. The Volcanological Observatory of the National University with the support of staff from the National Parks Service makes periodic observations of the volcano's state of activity.

The Irazú crater complex forms with the Turrialba and the Poás the most impressive "trinity" of the Central Volcanic Mountain Range. One of today's "visible" craters was the source of the eruptions of the sixties, and indeed caused a great visible impact, as it is gigantic and appears to open up before us as fauces to an underworld of fire and death. But alas, the fury that overwhelmed us for several years has now disappeared. The crater called "Diego de la Haya Fernández", in honor of the Spanish governor, has been dormant now for many years. But then, if you look around the volcano, that is, the visible craters, you will see many hollows covered with vegetation which undoubtedly were once active craters.

The crater called Reventado, where the river of the same name originates, was the cause of serious damages to the city of Cartago –particularly to the community of Taras– when accumulated ash formed a dam, that subsequently ruptured toward the southeast, not only caused flooding, but it also left enormous thick walls on which today vegetation thrives, as it does at the bottom of the

crater. The Department of Civil Defense reforested the entire watershed of the Reventado River up to the Derrumbe Crater, where today Australian eucalyptus trees and Honduran pines grow. This Reventado watershed is today a an emergency zone, given the large number of landslides occurring there.

Presently, there is no evidence of eruptive activity, and observers report that no reverberation is heard nor is anything noted other than total calm.

El Turrialba: to the northeast, with an altitude of 3,325 meters, it is the last volcano of the Central Volcanic Mountains, and, as it shares the same platform as the Irazú, it is often said that the two are twins.

The base of the volcano, according to Henry Pittier, is at 2,270 meters elevation, and the top at 3,325. El Turrialba was already spewing out smoke before 1723. Testimonies indicate activity in the years 1847, 1853, 1855, and 1861.

The Spaniards baptized this cone with the name "*Torre alba*" ("White Tower") because the great columns of white smoke and steam from its eruptions in the previous centuries resembled an enormous white tower. Today there are no signs of eruptions, except for the presence of internal fire visible from some of the cracks near the principal crater.

The Turrialba volcano forms an almost perfect sandy cone, from the vantage point of an observer situated at one of the neighboring cattle ranches.

For a long time the Turrialba was thought inaccessible, but now a road goes all the way to the sandy summit, completely devoid of vegetation. The volcano is presently in the solfatarian state.

THE TALAMANCA MOUNTAIN RANGE

Just before the Talamanca Mountain Range itself, there are some mountain chains surrounding the south side of the Central Tectonic Depression, called the *Cerros de Turrubares*, which start at the Pacific coast with Mount Herradura (altitude 860 meters). Then continuing east there are the *Cerros de Puriscal, Cerros de Escazú* (2,391 meters), *Cerros de Candelaria,* El Tablazo (1,858 meters) and La Carpintera (1,740 meters). With respect to formation, these mountains are partly eruptive and partly sedimentary; their slopes are formed of calcareous rocks, which are often mined to produce lime.

A short distance south of Cerros de Escazú are the Cerros de Bustamante (2,400 meters) and the Dota Mountains which shelter the valleys of Santa María (1,600 meters) and El Copey (1,800 meters).

Coming out of Cerro Tablazo, a mountain cluster called Cerro de las Cruces, extends to Cerro de las Vueltas, a peak 3,033 meters above sea level; Cerro Buenavista (3,480 meters), Cerro Chirripó Grande, the highest peak in the country (3,832 meters); Durica and Kamuk or Pico Blanco (3,595 meters), Cerro Echandi (3,168 meters), and Cerro Pando, at the Panamanian border.

Between Durica and Kamuk, on a hill separating the Arari and Ceibo rivers there is a large cross, "Cruz del Obispo" (at 2775 meters elevation), placed there by Bishop Thiel when he crossed the mountain range for the first time on his way to Talamanca.

None of the mountains of the Talamanca Mountain Range is considered volcanic.

Its complete geological structure includes marine sediments, lava, and igneous intrusions (Hall, 1984), of over 3,400 meters; in the massif of Chirripó and Kamuk, there was formed during the last glacial period Wisconsin or Würn, a landscape of cirques, artes, horns, U-shaped valleys, and lagoons full of glacial debris (Hall, 1984; Weyll, 1955; Bergoing, 1977).

Small mountain chains

Independent from the *Cordillera de Talamanca* (Talamanca Mountain Range) there are other small mountain chains, most of which are on the Nicoya Peninsula. Those in Nicoya are the *Cerros*

de San Blas, whose highest peak is 1,017 meters, *Cerros de Habana,* and *Cerros de Hoz.* In the Osa Peninsula are the *Cerros de Salsipuedes,* and parallel to the Talamanca Mountain Range on the west is the Fila Costeña or Brunqueña.

SEISMIC ACTIVITY IN COSTA RICA

According to the ISC (Instituto de Sismiscidad Costarricense = Costa Rican Institute of Seismology) (1974-1970), seismic activity in the country stemming from concentrations of hypocenters along the Benioff zone and the regional and local faults, shows a seismic frequency distribution that can be summarized as follows:

1) Most of the epicenters are distributed along the Pacific coast;
2) The most frequent seismic activity occurs on the southern and southeastern flanks of the Talamanca Mountain Range, in the vicinity of the Burica Peninsula and Punta Herradura toward the south and east.
3) Seismic frequency is lighter around the Nicoya Peninsula and tends to diminish toward the north and east of the territory, although in the region northeast of the territory in front of the Santa Elena Peninsula out in the Pacific Ocean, toward Nicaragua, there has been a notable concentration of epicenters of diverse depths (30-100 kms) with magnitudes strong enough to be felt or affect the region. (Castillo 1985)

Generally, it can be said that violent earthquakes are rare in this country, and are in no way comparable with the cataclysms that have occurred in the history of the Andes and north of Central America.

Among the events recorded that have caused disasters in Costa Rica are: the destruction of the city of Cartago in 1841, and again at the end of December 1888, a strong earthquake believed to have been caused by simultaneous activity in the Poás and Irazú, inflicted heavy damage throughout the whole Central Tectonic Depression; another destruction of Cartago on May 4, 1910; the Irazú Volcano did great damage during its eruptions that occurred from 1963 to 1965; similar damage was caused by the Arenal Volcano in its 1968 eruption; recent disasters include the earthquakes of Cóbano, and Paquera and Mata Limón, as well as Puriscal and Limón.

Seventy percent of Costa Rica's present population live in regions affected by seismic movements and Cenozoic volcanism. These areas are attractive due to their fertile soils and relatively dry climate. In the future, the large number of dormant volcanoes could constitute as much of a threat as those that have recently erupted (Hall, 1984).

According to data gathered historically and in recent years, our country can be divided into three different seismic regions, depending on the geological processes that cause the tremors, their magnitude and depth, occurrence, and

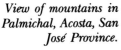

View of mountains in Palmichal, Acosta, San José Province.

extent of destruction (*Setiembre Centífico*, 1985)

Region I

Corresponding to the strip along the Pacific Ocean, it is affected by the process of subduction, through which the ocean plate Cocos slides under the Caribbean plate generating great tectonic forces; upon overcoming elastic resistance, the result is earth tremors or quakes. These have not, however, caused major damage, as they occur at depths greater than 20 kms, and rarely exceed seven on the Mercalli modified intensity scale. The only earthquakes recorded are that of April 2, 1983, which did not cause serious damage since it was not centered in a populous area; one that affected Cóbano, Paquera and Mata Limón in 1989; one that caused the disasters of Puriscal in 1990.

Region II

This region corresponds to the valleys and mountain ranges in the interior of

Cartago Valley along with San José Valley make up the Central Tectonic Depression.

the country. The tremors generated in this zone mainly stem from local faults, and, although they are moderate in magnitude, since their centers are near the surface and often near population centers, their effects are more destructive, not only because of quake intensity, but also because they trigger off other geological hazards, such as landslides and flooding caused by dammed rivers. The most destructive seismic events in Costa Rica have occurred in this region, especially at the edge of the valleys.

The Cartago earthquake of May 4, 1910 constitutes the greatest seismic disaster to date. The last earthquake occurred in this region on July 3, 1983 at División-Buena Vista, north of San Isidro, in the canton Pérez Zeledón.

Region III

This region includes the northern region of the country and the Caribbean plains. For years it had been the quietest region in the country, until April 22, 1991, when a violent earthquake (over seven on the Richter scale) worked havoc throughout the province of Limón. This was not the first time, however, that Limón had been hit by a sizable earthquake; one had also occurred on January 7, 1955 that caused considerable damage.

LOW-LYING INTER-MOUNTAIN AREAS

Between some mountainous sections, as a result of a tectonic process of sinking blocks, there is another unit of terrain referred to as "tectonic depressions". The most important cases of these are:
1) The Central Tectonic Depression
2) The El General and Coto Brus Depression
3) The Gulf of Nicoya-Tempisque Depression (see Map No. 5)

1) *The Central Tectonic Depression* called the Central Valley or Central Plateau is bounded on the north by the Central Volcanic Mountain Range; it is enclosed on the south by the Hills of Escazú, Candelaria and El Tablazo and on the west by the Cerros del Aguacate.

The average breadth of the depression is 20 kilometers, and its average length measured over a straight line drawn from Paraíso to Naranjo is 70 kilometers. The total area is estimated at 1,500 kms^2.

The Ochomogo and La Carpintera Hills divide the Central Tectonic Depression into two parts: the eastern or Cartago Valley, slightly more elevated,

which occupies a third of the total area; the western section, the San José Valley occupies the remaining 1,000 kms². Both sections have easy access to the coastal plains through a gradual descent: the first along the Reventazón River valley and the second along the Grande de Tárcoles River. The country's greatest population density is concentrated in this section.

This depression is mainly filled in with volcanic materials, but its topography is uneven due to fluvial cuts and fills, old lake deposits, and volcanoes.

2) *The depression of General and Coto Brus* corresponds to the Grande de Térraba River watershed. These are tectonic depressions of lower elevation than the first. They are used by Grande de Térraba and Coto Brus rivers to conduct their waters to sea, draining and filling the area; hence, the rolling terrain is of uniform composition –basically of homogeneous materials deposited by the rivers.

"The moderate elevation makes for a temperate climate, which is one reason the area has been a center of demographic attraction."

This rectangle is 100 kilometers long; its width is somewhat greater to the south. Its total area is around 3,000 kms².

It is comprised of four converging inclined planes. They are subdivided into small transverse valleys determined by a number of streams descending from the mountains. The great variety of levels that characterize such a configuration make for a diversity of terrains, climates, and agricultural aptitudes.

In this zone, so favored by nature, there are warm, chilly or pleasantly cool regions; they are low or moderately elevated, of warm, somewhat humid but healthy climates; drainage is adequate, and the condition and slope of the terrain prevent the formation of swamps.

3) *The depression of the Gulf of Nicoya*: The Gulf of Nicoya and the Tempisque River up to its watershed, also originated as a result of sinking blocks for tectonic reasons. This sinking occurred in lowlands, which allowed the sea to come in and fill what is now the gulf, as well as affect the entire course of the Tempisque River.

LOWLANDS AND HOT CLIMATES

Another large unit of land consists of the lowlands with hot climates, which are the "result of materials thrown from volcanoes, the erosion of the mountain

The plains of Guanacaste occupy a little over a third of the total area of Guanacaste Province.

systems, and changes in the elevations with respect to sea level. Around the mountains many materials have been accumulating which the rivers carry downstream. This has led to the formation of lowlands or plains, the third type of terrain in our country, and the most important."

Northern Plains

These were formed by the watersheds of the rivers Frío, San Carlos, and Sarapiquí. Previously these plains, stretching to the northern border at the San Juan River, were considered to be main routes of access to the San Juan River, Upala, Los Chiles, and the Sarapiquí River. Today they are linked by good roads, passable all year round.

Beginning between 1815 and 1820, the first access route was the Sarapiquí River via a trek of road that went from Heredia to Vara Blanca. In 1948 a highway was built that reached the Cuarto River, and in 1957 it was lengthened to Sarapiquí.

Another access route was the San Carlos River. People from San Ramón and Palmares had settled these areas during the last quarter century establishing such villages as Florencia, El Muelle, La Unión, and Arenal, which remained isolated for years. The other

access route, Upala and Los Chiles, utilized rivers to Limón, and since 1977, the construction of several bridges enabled access to the Inter-American Highway and the rest of the country.

Today the region is equipped with an important network of highways and local roads, including the highways Cañas-Upala, Heredia-Sarapiquí; Naranjo-Los Chiles; Florencia-El Muelle-Boca de Arenal (from this point the San Carlos River is navigable to its confluence with the San Juan River). Moreover, there are highways that cross this region, for example, one that goes from San Miguel de Sarapiquí toward Río Cuarto then to Venecia, then to Aguas Zarcas, where it crosses the highway between La Marina y Pital de San Carlos, and from San Miguel de Sarapiquí it goes on to Ciudad Quesada. Other roads link the following towns: Florencia-Fortuna, Fortuna-Arenal, Arenal-Tilarán.

These lands are dedicated to cattle raising. The area around San Carlos devotes from 50% to 70% of its territory to grazing lands, Guatuso and Sarapiquí 30-50%, and the canton of Los Chiles close to 30%. Previously, in the San Carlos area most of the cattle were raised for meat production, but by 1963 it had switched to primarily dairy farming. This was due to the scarcity of grazing lands brought on by ash eruptions of the Irazú Volcano, in the Central Tectonic Depression. Today there is a milk dehydration plant owned by a milk producers cooperative (Cooperativa de Productores de Leche, R.L.) with a daily production capacity of 200,000 liters of liquid milk. The region shows a great potential for milk production, particularly if it uses mestizo livestock or livestock cross-breeded with European strains, such as Jersey, Holstein, Pardo Suizo, and Guernsey. (Dirección General de Estadística y Censos, DGEC = General Bureau of Statistics and Censuses, 1984).

In the northern zone is the greatest expanse of forest lands, as well as a substantial area of brush lands (DGEC, 1984). Numerous squatters, however, have invaded these lands on a large scale, destroying the forests with the greatest productive potential for the country.

The Northern and Southern Caribbean Plains (Northern and Southern Atlantic)

The Caribbean Plains, north of Puerto Limón, comprise the Matina, Pacuare, Reventazón, and Tortuguero, stretching inward until they merge into the Sarapiquí plain, joining those of the Reventazón with those of Santa Clara. These lands are partly devoted to banana growing, a crop especially suited to the region.

These plains are essentially formed of fluvial sediments from the basins between the Chirripó and the Matina rivers; because they are quite flat and low-lying, the rivers contain many curves (meanders), and they are prone to overflow. These plains have very accessible means of communication through several branches of the National Atlantic Railway, several gravel roads, and a navigable canal running from Moín to Barra de Colorado, thus, providing access to the plains of the Tortuguero as well.

South of Limón there are other plains that drain into the rivers Banano, Bananito, and La Estrella; but the most important ones on this side are the plains of the Sixaola River basin, called the Llanuras de Talamanca (Plains of Talamanca).

These lands are partly occupied by banana plantations, and a railroad running from Limón to La Estrella crosses them. There is also a two-lane asphalt road, Route 36, that runs from Limón, through Penhurst, Cahuita, Horn Creek, Bribrí, and ends at Sixaola.

This plain is very narrow but of varied morphology. It is narrow because some of the foothills of the Talamanca Mountain Range extend almost to the coast. Contributing to its greatly varied morphology are numerous river valleys (such as La Estrella Valley), as well as corral deposits and reefs.

The Pacific Plains

The Pacific plains include:

"The Plains of Guanacaste which occupy a little over a third of Guanacaste Province. They extend from the shores of the Gulf of Nicoya and the Pacific Ocean, especially including the Tempisque River basin up to the Colorado River, it comprises one of the country's most valuable regions, covered by forest interspersed with cultivated lands consisting mainly of sugarcane, staple crops, and pastures. It is slightly higher and hillier than the the ones described in the last section, being essentially marine terraces covered by volcanic deposits.

The Central and Southern Pacific Plains. These consist mainly of marine terraces with broad, overlapping river valleys that

Another view of the plains of Guanacaste.

36

extend from the Tárcoles Valley to Punta Burica. There are plantations of cacao, teak, and mahogany, and, most prominently, oil palm. Rice, papaya, corn, and livestock are also produced. These plains are accessible through highways via San José-Santiago de Puriscal-Parrita-Quepos; San José-Atenas-San Mateo-Orotina-Herradura-Quepos; Puerto Caldera-Orotina. Part of route comprised of these highways was formerly called Costanera Sur, but today has been renamed Ruta de los Conquistadores (Route of the Conquistadores). These roads have opened up this region to tourism and recreation.

The plains that surround Gulf Dulce are exclusively river plains and are highly fertile. They are accessible by the Inter-American Highway. Until recently they were mainly devoted to banana plantations, but this activity has greatly diminished due to the United Fruit Company's pull-out, which included the dismantling of the Southern Railway whose 147 kms of railroad linked Palmar on the west, Golfito in the middle, and Coto-Colorado on the east. Off the Inter-American Highway first runs Route 245, an asphalt road that goes from Piedras Blancas, follows the innermost coast of Gulf Dulce, passes through Rincón to Puerto Jiménez, and ends at Carate on the coast of the Osa Peninsula bordering on the open sea. Then Route 14, another asphalt road, comes off the Inter-American Highway at Río Claro and ends in Golfito, passing through Unión, where it meets asphalt Route 238, which passes through Pueblo Nuevo, Laurel, La Cuesta, and ends at Paso Canoas on the Panamanian border.

Peninsular Plains of the Pacific. On the large peninsulas, the oldest mountains of the country have frequently been eroded and broken down. Around them, too, plains have developed, but with a very rough topography. Thus, they do not present great expanses, except on the Osa Peninsula." (Cevo Juan and others, 1988).

San José Valley: makes up part of Central Tectonic Depression, which is 20 kms wide and 70 kms long, measured on a straight line from Paraíso to Naranjo.

37

4 Rivers and Streams

"The existence of mountainous sectors and abundant rainfall, afford a great number of rivers to Costa Rica in spite of its small size."

Costa Rica's fluvial system comprises two versants, one on the Pacific side and another on the Caribbean side.

"The latter is usually subdivided into two parts: the northern sub-versant, that carries waters toward Lake Nicaragua and the San Juan River, and through it to the Caribbean (through the rivers Frío, San Carlos, Sarapiquí, and the Chirripó Norte). The Caribbean or Atlantic sub-versant, carries waters directly to the Caribbean (via the rivers Pacuare, Matina, Estrella)."

THE CARIBBEAN VERSANT

The Colorado River, a branch coming off the San Juan River some 30 kilometers before its mouth, crosses a marshy region of Costa Rica and then empties into the Caribbean Sea; it is fed by waters from the Negro River, originating from the Guápiles River and other small streams on the slopes of the Turrialba Volcano. All along the Caribbean coast from the Colorado to the Matina River, a series of lagoons and swamps make the region impassible, but, in addition, the rivers often overflow their banks as their waters come into this low, practically flat zone. The lagoons are called the Tortuguero Lagoons, which today form a canal system, unique in the country, and of great natural beauty, running from north to south through the Tortuguero National Park.

The principal rivers that drain through this system are: the Jiménez River, that receives tributaries whose sources are on the northern slopes of the Turrialba Volcano; the Reventazón, originating in Cerros de Las Cruces, gathers all the waters of the Cartago Valley and finally is enlarged as the Parismina River joins it; farther south the Pacuare and the Matina, carry waters from the slopes of the Talamanca Mountain Range.

Southeast of Puerto Limón the following rivers flow into the Caribbean

Opposite page: view of the Sarapiquí River (84 kms long) pertaining to the northern sub-versant.

Tortuguero Canals: now one can travel from the Pacuare River in Siquirres to Moín, and from there to the Colorado River.

The Reventazón River (145 kms long) in the Caribbean versant, originates in the Cerros de Las Cruces.

Sea: the Banano, Bananito, La Estrella, Puerto Viejo, and finally, the Telire or Sixaola, which originates on the Chirripó Grande Mountain. Farther downstream the Sixaola serves as a natural boundary with the country of Panama.

Canalization of Tortuguero

During the Orlich administration (1962-1966) a canal, one and a quarter kilometer long, was dug to lengthen another natural canal 2.2 kilometers long. This provided a waterway between the Matina River and Urpeano Lake.

During the Trejos administration (1966-1970) canals were dug through solid ground in four sections totalling 11.3 kilometers, to link natural canals and give a total length of 83.76 kilometers. Also during this administration a loan was procured to complete canalization to the Colorado River, as well as to build a river terminal at Moín.

Thanks to these canals, one can now travel from the Pacuare River, a short distance from Siquirres, eastward to Moín, northward to Caño Penitencia, and from

there to the Colorado River, which in turn connects with the San Juan River. Hence, by means of this system of waterways (canals and rivers) a vast, rich region was incorporated into national production. Now the tourist trade is expanding in that region, with boats travelling up and down the canals as far as Barra del Colorado (world famous for its shad fishing). Also, several first-class hotels and cabin complexes have been installed to provide lodging for the national and foreign tourists visiting those parts.

The Northern Sub-Versant

The rivers of the northern slopes are the most important due to the volume of water they carry. Three major arteries can be distinguished in this sub-versant: the Frío, San Carlos, and Sarapiquí rivers.

The Frío River traverses the Guatuso plains and empties into Lake Nicaragua, precisely at the lake's outlet to the San Juan River. The Frío River's main tributary is the Sobogal.

The San Carlos River flows into the San Juan, approximately midway along the

40

latter. Two-thirds of its course is navigable by shallow-water crafts, and its two main tributaries are the Arenal and Peñas Blancas.

The Arenal River originates from the Arenal Lagoon, in Guanacaste Province, northeast of Tilarán.

Other tributaries of the San Carlos are: Tres Amigos, San Rafael, Río Peje, and some others of minor import.

The Sarapiquí River, which descends from the Barva Volcano is a very important tributary of the San Juan. It was formerly the most travelled route to go from the central area to the Caribbean Sea. On the left it receives waters from the Toro River (originating on the Poás Volcano), as well as the Puerto Viejo, Sucio, and San José rivers.

The Sucio River originates on the northern slopes of the Irazú Volcano, carrying iron-laden waters and receiving those of the Honduras River, the Blanco, and other sub-tributaries.

From the Volcanic Mountain Range of Guanacaste many other rivers descend

into Lake Nicaragua –the Sapoá, Orosi, Cucaracha, and Zapote. Flowing into the San Juan River are the Poco-Sol and Las Marías, as well as other less important ones.

THE PACIFIC VERSANT

To the north is the Tempisque River, that flows into the Gulf of Nicoya. Much

Chirripó Atlántico River: in the Caribbean versant; the length of this river combined with Matina is 92 kms.

Frío River: in the Northern sub-versant; it crosses the plains of Guatuso and empties into Lake Nicaragua.

The Toro Amarillo River originates in Cartago Province, drains the watershed of the Chirripó in the northern sub-versant, and finally joins that river.

irrigated by a multitude of streams, some of which descend from the Central Volcanic Mountain Range and others from La Carpintera Hills, as well as the mountains of Candelaria, Escazú, and Puriscal. Those streams join the Virilla, a tributary of the Grande de Tárcoles River, which also empties into the Gulf of Nicoya.

Into the Pacific Ocean flows the river Pirrís or Parrita, which brings its waters from the hills of Bustamante and Santa María. At the mouth of this river there once was the small port of Parrita. Also flowing into the Pacific Ocean are the rivers Palo Seco, Paquita, Savegre, Naranjo, and other minor ones, all of which descend from the coastal hills and the Talamanca Mountain Range. In addition, there is the Diquís or Río Grande de Térraba, which is fed by the waters of the Diquís Valley, including those of the General River.

Into the Gulf of Osa empty the rivers Esquinas and Coto, that come down from the mountains that separate Costa Rica from Panama.

Due to the narrowness of its territory, Costa Rica has relatively small watersheds. The largest (with over 2,000 kms^2) are: Grande de Térraba (5,000 kms^2); Tempisque (3,400 kms^2); Reventazón-Parismina (3,000 kms^2); Sixaola (2,700 kms^2); San Carlos (2,650 kms^2); Grande de Tárcoles (2,150 kms^2); and Sarapiquí (2,150 kms^2).

The following table shows the country's principal rivers and their length in kilometers.

of this river is navigable. Its main tributaries are: Las Piedras, which is also navigable for much of its course, the Bagaces, Liberia, Bebedero, Cañas, and Belén.

Farther to the south, emptying into the Gulf of Nicoya and originating in the Volcanic Mountain Range are the rivers Abangares, Guacimal, Naranjo, Barranca, and other lesser important ones.

On the Nicoya Peninsula there is another river, the Matina, that empties into the Gulf.

The Central Tectonic Depression, starting from La Carpintera Hills, is

COSTA RICA'S PRINCIPAL RIVERS

Name of River	Length Kms	Versant
Térraba	160	Pacific
Sixaola	146	Caribbean
Reventazón-Parismina	145	Caribbean
Tempisque	136	Pacific
San Carlos	135	Northern sub
Parrita	108	Pacific
Pacuare	108	Caribbean

Chirripó-Colorado	96	Northern sub
Grande de Tárcoles	94	Pacific
Matina-Chirripó	92	Caribbean
Sarapiquí	84	Northern sub
Bebedero	62	Pacific
Estrella	52	Caribbean
Río Frío	52	Northern sub

— The Grande de Térraba River is both swift and long; it measures 160 kilometers from its source at Buena Vista on the Talamanca Mountain Range to its mouth at Boca Coronado, the name of its principal mouth, although to the south, one of its branches ends up as Boca Brava.

It receives the name Grande de Térraba as it joins the General River; its main tributary, is the Coto Brus near Paso Real. The mouth area of this river is poorly drained and is consequently a marshy area with mangroves.

— The Sixaola River, 146 kilometers long, begins at the confluence of the rivers Telire and Jorkin in the canton of Talamanca, and is the main watershed draining this canton.

This river, and the Jorkin, are natural international boundaries with the country of Panama. The main characteristic of these rivers is that they are constantly changing their course.

— The Reventazón-Parismina River, 145 kilometers long, is one of the best utilized, with large hydroelectric plants (Río Macho, Cachí, Tapantí, and Birrís). Its most important tributaries are the Grande de Orosi, Macho, and Pejibaye, that originate in the Talamanca Mountains. It its called the Reventazón from the point where the latter two rivers join; some 12 kilometers before its mouth the Parismina joins it.

— The Tempisque is the most important river in Guanacaste Province. Its source, called Tempisquito is located on the western slopes of the Volcanic Mountain Range of Guanacaste. It empties into an estuary about three kilometers wide inside the Gulf of Nicoya. These rivers, along with its tributaries Cañas, Las Palmas, and

Pacuare River: 108 kms long, located in the Caribbean versant.

43

Sixaola River: Originates on Mount Chirripó Grande and belongs to the Caribbean versant.

Opposite page: (above) the Estrella River, 52 kms long, empties into the Caribbean southeast of Puerto Limón; (below) the Sarapiquí River, which comes down from the Barva Volcano and is an important tributary of the San Juan.

Grande de Orosi River: one of the most important tributaries of the Reventazón-Parismina.

Bebedero, causes great difficulties due to flooding. The watershed of the Tempisque is located in the irrigating district of Moracia.

In general, due to the small geographical area of the country, the rivers are not very long and the mountains come quite close to the oceans.

All of the country's rivers are fed by rains, but it is important to point out that there are two general areas with distinct fluvial regimes, due to the fact that in one region of the country it rains throughout the whole year while in the other in rains only during part of the year.

The first regime involves the rivers of the Caribbean versant with the greatest flows from November to March. The rivers of the second regime are subject to a long dry season, except for those that drain the southeast region, such as the Grande de Térraba River.

On the remaining Pacific slopes, the rivers present their maximum flows in October and minimum flows from January to April.

5 General Climatic Conditions

Being a tropical country situated between two oceans and having complex mountain systems, Costa Rica offers a great variety of climatic conditions.

TEMPERATURE

Temperatures in any given place do not vary much throughout the year. Generally speaking, the difference in the mean temperature of the warmest and coolest months is no more than five degrees celsius.

More important than annual temperature variations are those that are related to altitude. In the lowlands, with elevations under 800 meters, the average annual temperatures vary from 22 to 27°C, in regions of altitude between 800 and 2,500 the temperatures vary from 14 and 22°C, and above 2,500 the temperatures are below 14°C.

RAINFALL

Costa Rica presents two clearly defined rainfall regimes: one on the Caribbean side and another on the Pacific side.

On the Pacific side, including the northern, central, and southern regions, as well as the Central Plateau, there are two distinct seasons: the rainy and the dry.

The rainy season goes from May to the middle of November in the northern half, and from April to December in the south. The dry season takes in the rest of the year.

The dry season is characterized by two phases. The first (December, January, February) is comparatively cool with cloudy skies and chilly winds. During the second (March and April) the sky remains clear for most of the day, with light

Opposite page: Cataract on the Pacacua River, near Ciudad Colón, Mora Canton, San José Province.

El Angel Cataract, in the Sarapiquí region.

breezes, and the highest temperatures of the year are reached. The light breezes and absence of rain favors the formation of fog due to the accumulation of dust and pollutants in air.

During the dry season, the differences between the maximum, day temperatures and minimum, night temperatures are more pronounced than those of the rest of the year.

The rainiest month of the rainy season in the north, and in the Central Tectonic Depression is September, while it is October in the south. Throughout this whole region the rains usually occur in the afternoon or evening.

During July and August there are short dry spells called *"veranillos"* ("little summers").

On the Caribbean side, including the northern and Caribbean regions, there

El Rodeo, Mora, San José Province.

Opposite page: Road to El Rodeo, Mora, seen from behind a savannah oak (Tabebuia rosea - Bignoniaceae).

is no definite dry season. In the coastal zone there are, however, relatively dry periods, one in March and April and the other in September and October. Here the rain usually occurs at night or in the early morning. In the mountainous parts the rains diminish only during March and April.

The moisture in the air that turns into rain comes primarily from the two oceans touching Costa Rica. Due to its complex mountain arrangement, the annual rain distribution varies greatly among the different regions of the country. The zones that receive the least annual rainfall are: the central part and coastal region of Guanacaste Province and the Guarco Valley. Those that receive the greatest annual rainfall are: the northern part of the Caribbean coastal region, the Osa Peninsula, and the upper part of the Reventazón River basin.

WINDS

The trade winds blowing from the east to the northeast, prevail in Costa Rica throughout the year. Usually, their velocity is below 15 kms per hour, but in January and February they may reach 30 kms per hour with gusts of up to 100 kms per hour. On the Pacific side breezes come out of West from April to October, favoring the formation of rain. These breezes are light with velocities of under 10 kms per hour.

Based on the climatic components of terrain, precipitation, vegetation, and hydrographic characteristics, five natural regions have been defined in the country:
a) Central
b) Northern Pacific
c) Southern Pacific
d) Atlantic
e) Northern Atlantic.

48

6 Natural Resources

MINERALS

Mineral resources of are not abundant in Costa Rica. Some gold and silver has been found in the hills of Tilarán and El Aguacate, as well as on the Osa Peninsula, and there are probably deposits in the Talamanca Mountains. Other potentially exploitable mineral resources include manganese in the Nicoya Peninsula, magnetite sand on the Atlantic shores of the south, bauxite (35% Al_2O_3) in the El General Valley, copper in the Talamanca Mountains, and sulfur in the Congo Mountain. Through solar evaporation of sea water, all along the Pacific coast, several thousand tons of salt are produced annually (Tropical Science Center, AID 1982).

Costa Rica has a number of mineral and hot springs, such as the ones found on the Arenal and Miravalles volcanoes. Some springs have been used for swimming resorts that attract thousands of tourists, due to the beneficial health properties of the water.

The most important mineral deposits (all non-metallic) include limestone, sandstone, silica, and diatomite, as well as travertine and kaolin. Other minerals found in the country are copper, silver, chromite, zinc sulphide, and lead.

Except for very few cases, however, minerals are known to exist, but there is little knowledge available as to their abundance or the conditions in which they are found. The exceptions include the metallic minerals, bauxite, magnetite sands, and non-metallic ones, such as sulphur, limestone, and diatomite. Some research projects have been started to this end, but much more needs to be done to discover the full mineral potential of the country.

For example, several explorations have been done to locate copper deposits in the *Cordillera de Talamanca*, but none has succeeded in determining the extent of the reserves. There are, however, companies interested in conducting other studies.

The known limestone reserves amount to some 13 billion metric tons. This resource benefits the country economically mainly through the production of cement. Most of the limestone is taken from quarries in Coris and Colorado de Abangares. The known reserves at Colorado de Abangares are around 532.7 million tons –enough to keep the cement plant there supplied for many years to come. (DGEC = *Dirección General de Estadísticas y Censos*, 1984)

Hydrocarbons such as petroleum are found in the country, mainly in the Limón watershed and the continental platform of the Caribbean. Thus far, however, no

Opposite page: San Gerardo de Dota, near the region known as Savegre, because of the Savegre River crosses it.

Oil exploration in Talamanca, Limón Province.

gas or oil deposits of any great commercial interest have been discovered. There are also some deposits of lignite in several parts of the country, particularly in Baja Talamanca, and recent explorations have turned up deposits of peat which could have substantial economic value.

PLANTS

Plants in every part of the country are extremely abundant and varied, thanks to the geographical position of the country, the topographical variety of its soils, and its climatic diversity, as well as other reasons.

It is said that the flora of Costa Rica forms a link between North and South America, with many endemic species from both continents found together here.

Tropical plants appear in all their splendor in the lowlands with heavy rainfall. This region still has virgin forests where one can find palm trees, arborescent ferns, high, full-foliaged

Platanilla (Heliconia wagneriana-musaceae). The tropical flora grows in the lowlands with heavy rainfall.

trees, hundreds of varieties of bushes, reeds, orchids, and likens. The most typical trees of these forests are ceibo, laurel, nargusta (*Terminalia chiriquensis*), pejibaye, palmetto (*palmito*), wild fig (*Ficus sp.*), ceder, and rubber. On many of these lands, however, the forests have been cleared to make way for bananas, cacao, African palm, and pastures.

The dry tropical forest of the northern Pacific region of the country is distinguished by a great variety of fruit species, some of which are native, such as the sapodilla (*zapote*), *caimito*, soursop (*guanábana*), papaya, cashew, and jocote. Also grown there are a variety of exotic fruits: tamarind, mango, watermelon, and cantaloupe. Some of the most typical trees include the guanacaste (the national tree), the *cenízaro* , *mahogany, spiny cedar* (*Bombacopsis quinatuma*), wild fig, and the savannah oak. Most of the forests of this region have been burned or cut down to make room for cotton, corn, sorghum, and pastures (DGEC, 1981).

The intermediate lands are located at heights of 600 to 1,500 meters. Vegetation on these lands constitutes the mountainside forest and jungle regions, both on the Caribbean and Pacific sides of the country. Those on the east are thicker, and have straighter trees. Those on the west are not as dense, and the trees there have fairly even foliage on all sides making for excellent shade. Some of trees in those forests are: ceders, *guachipelín, jocotes, higuerones, itabos,* guava, cas (a tart yellow variety of guava), as well as non-native trees, such as orange, lemon, lime, and mango. Some areas of these forests have been cleared to plant coffee, sugarcane, pastures, etc. (DGEC, 1981).

On higher ground, before reaching the tree line, there is cloud-covered, and therefore, very damp forest. Some of the trees in these forests are oak, holm oak, *candelillo, copey.*

Also found are small trees with twisted, sturdy trunks and leathery leaves, such as myrtles, *senecio, ciprecillo* (dwarf

White ibis
(Euduocimus albus).

cypresses) as well as plants such as cardoons and thistles.

At 3,500 meters there are wide subalpine prairies (*páramos*) whose predominant growth consists of grasses, composites, evergreen bushes and perennial flowers, and other species common to this altitude and climate. At this altitude there are no trees —only gigantic rocks. Other plants include mosses, ferns, and likens (DGEC, 1981).

All the existing natural forests are, for the most part, heterogeneous with broad-leaved trees.

The deciduous trees, consisting mainly of fancy woods and hardwoods, have been practically eradicated, although some are still found in small areas on the Pacific side, especially in the northern and central zones. The leafy evergreens, the most abundant, consisting mostly of light-colored woods, are found principally in the Caribbean regions and the southern part of the Pacific region.

The lumber industry, agricultural expansion, and, especially livestock raising, have contributed to the destruction of much of the forest wealth. However, the efforts of some institutions and individuals, who have tried to make the public and government aware of this situation, have led to the passing of the Forest Law of 1969, and in 1970, the creation of the National Parks Service, which initiated an active program of establishment, development, and protection of wildlife areas through parks and equivalent reserves (MIDEPLAN, 1983).

ANIMALS

Costa Rica's great biodiversity (its wide variety and diversity of animal organisms and ecosystems in which they live) owes itself to several factors: the country's intermediate position between the two Americas (serving as a land bridge for the passing of animals between the two continents); irregular geomorphological formation, resulting from the tectonic activity of past geological ages; and its proximity to the equator.

The animal species of Costa Rica include over 1,449 vertebrates. Excluding fish, there are 376 species of reptiles and amphibians, 868 of birds, and 216 of mammals (Janzen, 1983). Moreover, there are thousands of invertebrate species (butterflies and moths, snails, beetles,

53

Leatherback turtle
(Dermochelys coriacea).

wasps, ants, etc.). For example, considering butterflies and moths alone, some 1,200 butterflies and 1,500 moth species have been collected.

Our animal species could be classified into four categories for study and management purposes (Vaughan and Solís, 1984), which are described below.

Endangered species: those with diminishing populations whose survival requires active human intervention. Examples of these are: the *danta* or tapir whose hide and meat are greatly prized, and the jaguar, which needs for its survival large expanses of virgin forest, difficult to find today in the country.

Red lapa (Ara macao)

54

Yellow-billed heron (Egretta thula).

Species of economic importance: first, the *exploitable species* (for meat, hides, etc.), and second, *pest species* (considered harmful at the national level, due to their effect on crops and the national economy). Examples of exploitable species are the white-tailed deer, the most hunted species in the country; the caiman for its prized leather; and sea turtles. Examples of pest species are rats and mice, parrots, and *taltuzas* (small rodents).

Ecologically important species: includes all those species that do not fit into the other two categories but play a vital ecological role in the environment where they live. Examples of these include a great variety of hummingbirds (pollinators of many species of plants); vultures, which provide an indirect benefit by feeding on carrion; and a large number of insects.

The wild fauna in Costa Rica not only has high aesthetic value, but throughout our history, the use of animal resources has made an enormous economic contribution —as food for rural dwellers (for example, meat from the tepeizcuintle and the tapir), for sport (for example, pigeons and wild pigs), and for commercial purposes involving the whole animal or parts (e.g., butterflies, deer pelts). Hence, over the long term, the maintenance and conservation of these species is extremely important if Costa Ricans in the future are to have available various options open as to the use of these resources.

One approach to conserving these species involves the conservation of their habitats (rivers, forests, oceans, etc.). Protected wildlife areas have been set aside in the country (national parks and preserves and the like) which indirectly address this purpose. It is important to consider, however, that beyond preservation, conservation involves maintenance, restoration, and improvement of natural habitats —all essential to preserving these species.

The negative effect of man on renewable natural resources (including wild animals) has become more evident in the last few decades. This has increased the importance of all kinds of research related to conserving these resources. The main difficulties the wild fauna of Costa Rica have had, as in other parts of the world are: the loss of natural habitat (including a lack of space for mating, feeding, etc.), as well as man's needs to exploit natural resources.

55

An approach to maintaining a happy medium between the needs of wildlife and man's needs is referred to as wildlife management. As an example of the management of a particular animal species in this country, there is the White Tail Deer Restoration Project, aimed at repopulating this native species. This project holds out as one alternative the establishment of deer breeding farms having several basic objectives: the rational use of this resource (meat and leather production); an educational campaign to re-establish the bond between the inhabitants of the dry Pacific region of the country and this species; the re-establishment of the biological function of this species within the tropical dry forest (as a natural reforester, and prey for large mammals); and the improvement of the quality of life of the rural dwellers. For the first time in the history of the nation, there is a scientifically directed project to transport white-tailed deer from San Lucas Island in the Gulf of Nicoya to areas in Guanacaste. Some of the breeding farms will allow an economic evaluation of the productivity of the species with respect to local consumption; others will provide animals to be released in natural habitats in order to re-establish populations of this animal in the region.

The beautiful and fascinating wildlife of our country, that attracts hundreds of tourists each year to the wildlife areas that protect these species, are truly the hallmark displayed before the world of Costa Rica's genuine concern for its natural heritage. Today, the animal species that inhabit the national territory depend on our attitudes for their survival. But, in addition to becoming familiar with and appreciating these species, Costa Ricans ought to rescue all those values that could re-establish a balance between their needs and those of wildlife. The country should give priority to the conservation, maintenance, and restoration of biological diversity, as well as ensuring that animal resources will be used rationally based on the long-term needs of the future.

NATIONAL PARKS

Currently the National Parks Service is in charge of managing 14 national parks, eight biological reserves, and two national monuments. The Forestry Department is responsible for 18 protected zones, 12 forest reserves, 10 national wildlife reserves, and one national reserve. Certainly, these agencies have contributed and will continue to contribute to the protection of our flora and fauna. Costa Rica's system of national parks and reserves and similar entities involve 28 units covering 524,917 hectares, which corresponds to 10.27% of the national territory (Boza L., Mario, 1986). Hence, Costa Rica has, in proportion to its total area, more protected land than any other country in the world.

A national park is understood to be, according to the Forestry Law of 1969, Article 74, all "those areas of historical significance, which for their natural scenic beauty, or for their nationally or internationally important flora and fauna found within boundaries specified by executive decree, are destined for recreation and education of the public, for tourism, or for scientific research." Further, according to the International Union for the Conservation of Nature, it should be a relatively extensive area of certain environmental beauty, presenting one or more undisturbed ecosystems with few modifications, and having the proper authority to adopt the necessary measures to prevent or halt the exploitation of resources.

The principle national parks with some of their most notable characteristics are listed below (DGEC, 1981). (See Map No. 8)

Irazú Volcano National Park

Located northeast of Cartago, with a paved road leading up to the craters, it is a compound volcano with five craters. Its location near the center of the country, its extraordinary panoramic views, its breathtaking craters, and its geological history, are the main reasons that warrant its classification as a national park.

Opposite page: Cavern in Barra Honda National Park, Nicoya, Guanacaste.

57

Coco Island National Park

This is the only pre-mountain rainforest; it has numerous endemic species, and great scenic beauties. It is located in the Pacific Ocean.

Santa Ana National Recreational Area

It is accessible via the Piedades de Santa Ana Highway. This zone is close to San José, where the National Zoo is located. It has luxuriant vegetation and it contains the Cañon Island of the Uruca River.

Laguna de Fraijanes Recreation Park

It encompasses a lovely lagoon, cypress forests, and spacious meadows. The road leading up to the park is gravel from San Isidro de Alajuela.

Manuel Antonio National Park

Located in Puntarenas Province, seven kilometers south of Puerto Quepos, and accessible by good highway, it has splendid beaches, which are considered to be the best in the country. There are also undisturbed primary forests in it containing gigantic trees. Its abundant fauna includes the famous tití?? monkey. Marine birds are also abundant, greatly enhancing the scenic beauty.

Tortuguero National Park

This is the most important spawning area for the green turtle. The park has diverse natural ecosystems, including extensive marshy rainforests with great plant and animal variety. Moreover, it has a canal system, unique in the country, running through the park from north to south. This park is located in Limón Province, 70 kilometers northeast of the city of Limón. It is accessible by boat through the canals and by light plane from the landing strip in Limón.

Corcovado National Park

With respect to flora and fauna, this area is one of the most diverse and ichest in the Americas. Its marshy rainforests

Laguna de Fraijanes Recreational Park, Alajuela

Pájaros Island in the Tempisque River, Palo Verde National Park, Guanacaste. Inhabiting in this park are over 150 species of birds, as well as many species of mammals, amphibians, and reptiles. (See page 163).

protect a number of endangered species. This park is located on Caño Island, which is one of the most archaeologically rich zones in the country. It is within Puntarenas Province, next to the Osa Peninsula. It accessible by light plane.

Cahuita National Park

It is located in Limón Province, 35 kilometers southeast of the city of Limón, and is accessible by a good highway. Its beaches are extraordinarily beautiful, and it contains the only corral reef in the country. It also has marshy forests with a great diversity of plants and animals.

Barra Honda National Park

Located in Guanacaste Province, 15 kilometers northeast of Nicoya, it is accessible by a good highway. Its main attraction is a network of caverns with magnificent stalactites and stalagmites and other remarkable rock formations. Moreover, the panoramic view from the top of the hill is gorgeous.

Braulio Carrillo National Park

It has five types of forest, a great variety of wild animals, with an abundance of bird species. It is devoted to the protection of watersheds, as well as preserving the historic heritage left by citizens who for over 100 years longed and worked for a project to link the central region of the country with the Caribbean. The Guápiles-Siquirres-Limón Highway that crosses it today allows visitors to see firsthand the flora of both sides of the Central Volcanic Mountain Range, and behold the breathtaking sights all along the way. The Zurquí Tunnel, located at the top of Moravia, is a new attraction of the park.

Historic mansion, Santa Rosa National Park, canton of La Cruz, Guanacaste.

Santa Rosa National Park

Located in Guanacaste Province, 43 kilometers north of Liberia, it is accessible by a road that is passible all year round. This park protects the setting of the Battle of Santa Rosa of March 20, 1856, including the historical mansion and the stonewall corrals. Moreover, it protects the savannah and a deciduous forest, marshlands, and mangroves, and abundant animal life, including several endangered species. It also has lovely recreational beaches.

Rincón de la Vieja National Park

Situated in Guanacaste Province and partly in Alajuela Province, one can get to this park by going 5 kilometers north from Liberia on the Inter-American Highway and then taking the road to the east. The park protects numerous watersheds. It has an active volcano with geyser eruptions and fumaroles, very active on the walls of the crater near the bottom. These eruptions have been causing acid rains. There is also a beautiful lagoon that is now drying up. Many bird species thrive here.

Chirripó National Park

It is located in the Talamanca Mountains, between the provinces of Limón and San José. The entrance to the park is near the town of San Isidro, El General. The highest mountain in the country, it has lakes of glacial origin, extensive open spaces (*páramos*), and cloud forests. Its flora and fauna are highly diversified. The park protects an extensive system of watersheds.

In addition to the National Parks, the country has a number of "equivalent reserves", i.e., wildlife areas protected because of their biological treasures or their importance as wildlife refuges, or because they serve as habitats for plant or animal relics of singular value in the world. These reserves include biological preserves, national monuments, and buffer zones. Several of these are summarized below.

Guayabo National Monument

Located in Cartago Province on the slopes of the Turrialba Volcano. The most important archeological zone in the country, it contains ancient roadways, burial mounds, aqueducts, and other stone structures left by early Indians.

Biological Reserves of the Guayabo, Negritos, and Pájaros Islands

These islands are located in the Gulf of Nicoya. Eight kms south of the town of Puntarenas is Guayabos Island, 16.5 kms south is Negritos Island and 13 kms northeast is Pájaros Island. These picturesque islands protect large colonies of marine birds. Their dry forests contain a great variety of plants, but few animal species.

Cabo Blanco Total Natural Reserve

Located at the extreme south of the Nicoya Peninsula, the reserve includes the Cabo Blanco Island, located two kilometers off the coast of the peninsular part of the reserve. Cabo Blanco protects large colonies of marine birds, provides habitats for numerous plants and animals in its dry forests, and has lovely scenic beaches and rocky cliffs.

Hitoy-Cerere Biological Reserve

This is one of the best specimens of wet tropical forest, and serves as habitat for abundant birds species. It is surrounded by three indigenous reservations: Talamanca, Telire, and Estrella, which in turn are surrounded by very steep, treacherous mountains, making the reservations almost inaccessible.

Carara Biological Reserve

Located at the mouth of the Grande de Tárcoles River, it is accessible by the southern coastal highway. It is the home of a wide diversity of wildlife, with a tropical forest in transition from wet to rainforest. It is surrounded by areas completely transformed by the action of precipitation. Hence, this reserve ensures the conservation of the region's wealth of flora and fauna.

Caño Island Biological Reserve

Located in the Pacific Ocean, facing the Corcovado National Park, 15 kms offshore,

it is, archaeologically speaking, one of the country's most valuable areas. It is also of great biological interest.

All of these reserves and parks described here, as well as many others, such as the buffer zone of the hills of Escazú, Carpintera, the Huetar de Zapatón Indian Reservation, Los Santos Forest Reserve, the buffer zones of Caraigres, Rodeo, and the Central Volcanic Mountains, constitute the primary wealth of the nation, which we must strive to conserve for the benefit of the land and its citizens.

Tortuga National Park.

61

7 Human Aspects

POPULATION

The current population of Costa Rica, according to the 1984 census is 2,416,809, comprised of 1,208,216 males and 1,208,593 females, with population density of 47 inhabitants per square kilometer. That census also indicates that 47.4% of the population is economically active, the unemployment rate is 7.1%, the birthrate is 29.3 per thousand, and the mortality rate is 3.8 per thousand. The 1990 population is estimated to be around 3 million.

The largest number of the country's inhabitants have settled in the provinces of San José, and the least in Limón with 890,434 and 168,076 inhabitants respectively.

ETHNIC GROUPS

As all the other peoples of Latin America, Costa Rica cannot be understood apart from its ethnic roots, which begin with the Amerindians. This land was not virgin soil when the Spaniards arrived here; indeed, these lands were inhabited by indigenous peoples with considerably developed cultures. Some important indigenous groups, in fact, had reached high levels of civilization –for example, the Aztecs, Mayas, and Incas. But, by the end of the Fifteenth Century the Spaniards were landing on the Antilles, and within a half a century of constant, rapid advance, they had dominated a large part of the New World. Thus, the course of the Amerindian world was broken. The predominating culture that resulted was a mixture of European (especially from Ibero-America in Latin America) and Amerindian elements. Nonetheless, throughout the Americas populations of autochthonous indigenous cultures persist even today.

Opposite page: View of Playa Hermosa, Carrillo Guanacaste.

Monument to the Farmer, located on near the Juan Santamaría International Airport in Alajuela.

63

A chilamate tree (Ficus goldmannii-movaceae), Liberia, Guanacaste Province.

The Amerindians have, for the most part, disappeared from Costa Rica, although some tribes still exist on the plains of Guatuso (canton of Grecia), along the rivers, Chirripó, Taire and Estrella from their sources to mid-course, along the Térraba, Boruca, Salitre, and the Cabagra (canto of Buenos Aires), in the canton of Pérez Zeledón, and in Sixaola River region (canton of Talamanca), between Ciudad Colón and Puriscal.

There are, in all, twenty indigenous communities, corresponding to eight different ethnic groups: Bribí, Bunca, Cabécar, Chorotega, Guayamí, Huetar, Malekur, and Térraba. (See Map No. 8).

The white race is predominate in the Costa Rica, but the union of the two races is evident throughout the country. As in the rest of Latin America, Costa Rica is historically mestizo in both race and culture, since the nation was gradually built up from an indigenous base with the Spaniards introducing and blending in their own elements.

ORIGIN AND CUSTOMS

"Almost entirely, the Costa Ricans have descended from the Spaniards that settled in this country, following the valiant conquistadors of the sixteenth century.

At that time, Costa Rica, despite its name ('Rich Coast'), did not offer great resources to those who came to inhabit the land. Hence, of the flow of fortune seekers that headed for America, only a small number of families settled in the Central Plateau region, being attracted by an extremely pleasant climate, and fertile soil for farming. These families lived isolated from the rest of the world, isolated in the center of the country with no easy communication routes. Further, the rebellious nature of the Indians living there prevented any relations between them and the new settlers, who consequently preserved their customs and did not intermarry." (Pablo Biolley, *Costa Rica et son avenir*, Paris. 1892).

So it was that in Costa Rica an earnest, simple, moral, hard-working, robust, healthy people was formed. Despite the modern spirit that is gradually eroding the distinctive characteristics of most ethnic groups, in this country there still prevails a truly patriarchal way of life. Although the owners of coffee and banana plantations are hierarchically superior to the peasants that work on their land, they live in almost complete equality. Never have citizens of a republic been more democratic: there are practically no distinctions based on birth, fortune, or position; a man is judged by his attitudes and conduct. Moreover, respect for the established order and property has risen to its highest level. Costa Ricans, by and large, faithfully obey the laws, they do not oppose the well-constituted authority, they are peaceable, generous, fervently patriotic, and proud of their freedom.

Nonetheless, "the Costa Rican has a race defect, more accentuated in him, due probably to the enervating mildness of the climate which greatly reduces his need for initiative and resolution: he is negligent. *Mañana* (tomorrow) is an oft-repeated word, as well as, such expressions as '¿*Quién sabe?*' ('Who knows?'), '*Tal vez...*' ('Perhaps...'). He does not believe in the saying, 'Time is money.', nor does he believe that preciseness is a principle of urbanity. One can count on a Costa Rican friend's honor, loyalty, and trustworthiness, but not on his punctuality."

These people, one must admit, called to great destinies because of their democratic tradition and rich soil, also suffer from certain other vices, besides negligence, that hamper and divert them from their natural development: scant sense of order, alcoholism, drug abuse; and in the cities, pleasure-seeking and idleness, lead to a disregard for property and other individual and social rights.

"Personal dignity is a virtue that Costa Ricans must foster in their homes and schools if they are to check the spread of vices that threaten national sovereignty and individual liberties."

COSTA RICAN LANGUAGE

The official language of the country is Spanish, which the people speak with certain flaws (as far as the strict rules of the *Real Academia* are concerned) and typical provincialism, as is the case in other Latin American nations, and, indeed, even in Spain.

The few Amerindians still found in Costa Rica speak the languages of their ancestors, and live in areas so remote from the main population centers that they understand Spanish with great difficulty.

Many Costa Ricans also know English or French, since these languages are taught in the high schools and universities, as well as in a large number of commercial schools. Other languages, including German, Portuguese, Italian, are also taught in various schools and institutes. All of these languages are necessary for Costa Rica to conduct business and diplomatic relations with other countries.

Procession in Paraíso, Cartago Province. The people are devout but not fanatical.

RELIGION

The official religion of the country is Roman Catholicism, but the free practice of other denominations and religions is allowed. The people are devout but not fanatical; tolerance reigns in the country, and almost no one gets riled up about religious matters. Still, the people's religious feelings are very deep-seated, as evidenced by the large number of catholic churches: in every town there are several churches, and every village, no matter how small, has at least one church or chapel; and usually the best building is the church, built through the efforts and contributions of the parishioners.

Opposite page: San Rafael Church, Heredia.

HUMAN RIGHTS

"Human rights have been respected in Costa Rica, not because of the favor of any government or government leader, but because of the reign of the people's will, that would not settle for any other attitude. Inculcated deep in their being is a sense of love and respect for ones neighbor, manifested in many ways, such as encouraging the weakest citizens to strengthen themselves by their own efforts and initiative. Recently Costa Rica celebrated a hundred years since it incorporated into its Political Constitution an amendment providing for obligatory, free primary education, paid for by the State. It was also one hundred years ago that the death penalty was abolished in Costa Rica." (J.J. Trejos, 1985).

Youth Symphony Orchestra.

ILLITERACY

According to the last population census, the illiteracy rate in this country is 6.9% of the population over ten years of age. Among the urban population the rate is only 2%. Hence, Costa Rica has one of the lowest illiteracy rates in the world.

FOREIGNERS

There has always been a large influx of foreigners in Costa Rica, attracted by the magnificent climate that prevails in the country, and, above all, because of the undeniable protection they receive from the authorities, as well as the warm reception natives of all social classes give to these newcomers that settle here. Citizens from all seven continents are found living in this country: Central Americans, people from the Caribbean Islands, South Americans, North Americans, Europeans, Asians, Australians, and Africans. According to the 1984 national census, a total of 61,663 foreigners reside in Costa Rica. Most of these are from other Central American countries –mainly Nicaragua and El Salvador, countries currently suffering from war-related troubles. The largest groups of foreigners in the country, according to the 1984 census are distributed as follows: 42,852 Central Americans, including 30,593 Nicaraguans and 7,098 Salvadorans; 6,060 North Americans, mainly from Canada; 4,376 South Americans, mostly Colombians; and 3,227 people from the Caribbean, most of whom are Cubans.

68

8 Government and Institutions

POLITICAL CONSTITUTION

Since that memorable date of September 15, 1821, when Central America was declared independent, Costa Rica has been a representative republic. The constitution guarantees the citizens equality before the law, the right to own property, the inviolability of the home, the right to petition and assembly, freedom of speech, and the right to habeas corpus. The enjoyment of all the civil rights of the citizen applies equally to foreigners.

The functions entrusted to the State have been classified, since classical Greek antiquity into three branches of government: legislative, executive, and judicial. This "separation of powers" was refined in the Eighteen Century by the French thinker Montesquieu. He advocated the distribution of powers into several elements that would compensate one another to produce a harmonious balance, in a system of weights and counterweights, so as to ensure moderation for the benefit of the individual citizens. This concept was finally accepted by all modern constitutions, particularly in those countries that have pluralistic democracies.

FORM OF GOVERNMENT

Costa Rica, as a democratic republic, has consecrated that principle in Article 9 of the Political Constitution, which expressly establishes that the government of the republic is to be exercised through distinct powers, independent from one another: the Legislative, Executive, and Judicial powers.

Opposite page: National Monument, National Park, San José. The monument commemorates the 1856 campaign against the "filibusters".

Plaza de la Democracia (Democracy Plaza), San José.

The Court House and Tribunal of Justice buildings, San José.

The Costa Rican Magna Carta grants independence from the other powers of the State, and equal rank, to the *Tribunal Supremo de Elecciones* (Supreme Election Tribunal), without actually making this entity a fourth power, as is often stated erroneously. None of the powers can delegate to another the exercise of its functions, except in those cases expressly authorized by the Constitution, so as not to violate the principle of "separation or division of powers".

As mentioned, the separation of powers corresponds to a division of functions, usually simplified as follows: the Legislative Power legislates, i.e., it makes laws; the Executive Power executes the laws, i.e., it enforces them; the Judicial Power judges, i.e., it resolves conflicts that arise with respect to the violation or application of the laws. This arrangement is known as the formal division of powers.

It must be pointed out, however, that this division is not carried out absolutely in practice. In other words, in spite of the fact that each power has a function that characterizes or distinguishes it, as explained above, the fact is that, in addition to its main function, each power carries out other tasks that, strictly speaking, correspond to the other two powers.

Let us look at two examples: the Legislative Assembly, from the standpoint of forma division, should only legislate. But in practice it also executes and judges. Thus, when it appoints permanent or substitute magistrates, it is actually exercises an eminently executive function. Or, when it decides whether there is just cause for initiating a penal process involving the President of the Republic, its is really exercising a judicial function. The same is true of the other two powers: in actual practice the Executive Power, in addition to executing the law, sometimes legislates (when it approves a regulation) or judges (when it grants a pardon); the Judicial Power also legislates (when it approves a regulation for its employees) and executes (when it purchases vehicles).

Therefore, one must be aware of the difference between the formal definition of the separation of powers and what actually takes place.

According to Article 105 of the Constitution: "The power to legislate resides with the people, who delegate that power through suffrage, in the Legislative

Assembly." The Legislative Assembly is comprised of 57 deputies, elected by the provinces as their representatives before the nation.

The number of deputies corresponding to each province depends on the population. Deputies are elected for a four-year term and may not be re-elected immediately. A deputy candidate must be at least 21 years of age, a current citizen of Costa Rica, born a Costa Rican citizen or naturalized with 10 years of residence in the country. Deputies cannot be held responsible for the opinions they express in their capacity as deputy, either in the Assembly or outside of it, and the Constitution guarantees them, from the time they are elected until their term expires, that they shall not be deprived of their freedom (i.e., they have immunity), so that they can attend the sessions of the Legislative Assembly, for the civic welfare of the country.

Some of the most important exclusive duties of the Assembly are listed below.

a) Dictate the laws, amend them, repeal them, and give them their true interpretation, i.e., if there is any question as to their interpretation, clarify their true meaning.

b) Appoint permanent and provisional magistrates to the Supreme Court of Justice.

c) Approve or reject international agreements, public treaties, and agreements.

d) Give or withhold its consent as to the admission of foreign troops into national territory, or the docking warships or landing of planes in its ports or airports.

e) Authorize the Executive Power to declare a state of national defense, and ratify peace treaties.

f) Suspend, through a vote of at least two-thirds of all its members, the individual rights and guarantees stipulated in the Political Constitution.

g) Admit or reject accusations leveled against the President of the Republic, the Vice-Presidents, members of the Supreme Powers, and ministers.

h) Dictate the ordinary and special budgets of the nation.

i) Appoint the General Comptroller and General Deputy Comptroller of the nation.

The resolutions of the Assembly must be ratified by an absolute majority of the votes present (half plus one), except in those cases in which the Political Constitution requires a greater number of votes.

The Executive Power is exercised on behalf of the people by the President of the Republic and Ministers of Government in their capacity as committed auxiliaries.

The President of the Republic and the Vice-Presidents are elected for terms of four years. According to an amendment to the constitution that went into effect in 1969, no one may be elected to the office of president who has previously held that office. In other words, no president or former president may be elected again to the presidency. This issue has been

The Foyer, National Theater, San José.

greatly debated with valid arguments for and against it.

The requirements for President and Vice-President of the Republic are: be a Costa Rican by birth and a current citizen; be a secular citizen (i.e., not be a priest), and be at least thirty years of age.

In addition to these requirements, Article 132 of the Constitution expressly prohibits certain other public officers from being elected to these offices: the President and the Vice-Presidents, Permanent Magistrates of the Supreme Court of Justice, and the Supreme Election Tribunal, the Comptroller and Deputy Comptroller of the Republic, the Director of the Civil Registry Office and anyone who has been a Minister of the State in the 12 months prior to the date of the elections.

The President of the Republic has the following exclusive duties and functions:
1. Appoint and remove, at will, the ministers of government.
2. Represent the nation in official acts.
3. Exercise the supreme command of the National Police Force.

Hospital México, San José.

4. Submit to the Legislative Assembly, at the beginning of each year of sessions, a written message addressing the various matters related to administration, and the political state of the nation. He must, further, promote the measures he deems important for the government to run effectively and efficiently, and for the progress and well-being of the nation.
5. Request permission from the Legislative Assembly whenever he needs to leave the country, unless he plans to travel to any Central American country or Panama, and will be absent no more than 10 days at a time, in which case he is to communicate his intentions beforehand to the Legislative Assembly. This provision is compulsory while the President exercises his office and for a year after.

Beginning in 1975 this provision has been made more flexible considering that Costa Rica is now more interdependent with the rest of the world, and there are better, more rapid means of transportation, thus making it more necessary and convenient for the president to make more frequent visits to other countries.

A second set of functions of the Executive Power corresponds jointly to the President of the Republic and the Minister of Government. Some of these are summarized below:

1. Appoint and remove at will the members of the National Police Force, confidential employees and officers, and, others, that correspond to specific cases determined by the Civil Service Act.
2. Approve and promulgate laws, enforce them, execute them, and see to it that they are exactly carried out.
3. During the recesses of the Legislative Assembly, in conformity with certain requirements, decree the suspension of individual rights and guarantees,

immediately informing the Legislative Assembly of this action.

4. Promote new laws and veto those considered not to be in the best interest of the country.
5. Maintain the order and tranquility of the nation.
6. Provide for the collection and investment of the national revenue in conformity with the laws.
7. Direct the international relations of the country.

A third set of functions of the Executive Power corresponds to the Council of Government, that is, to the President of the Republic in conjunction with his ministers. As stated above, the ministers are freely appointed by the President of the Republic and are his immediate, confidential auxiliaries.

To be a minister one must be a practicing citizen, Costa Rican by birth or naturalization with 10 years of residency in the country, after becoming a citizen, be a secular citizen (not a priest), and be at least 25 years of age.

The functions of the Council of Government include:

1. Request from the Legislative Assembly a declaration concerning the national state of defense and authorization to decree military recruiting, organize an army, and negotiate for peace.
2. Exercise the right of grace in conformity with the law.
3. Appoint and remove the Diplomatic Representatives of the country.
4. Appoint the directors of the autonomous institutions whose designation corresponds to the Executive Power.
5. Resolve any other matter assigned by the President of the Republic.

Both the President of the Republic and his ministers are responsible for their use of the powers granted to them by the Political Constitution. In the case of deeds involving no crime, that

Colegio Superior de Señoritas (all girls high school), San José.

73

responsibility can be demanded of them only while in office and up to one year after.

The Judicial Power is exercised by the Supreme Court of Justice and the other courts established by the law. Only in exceptional cases do courts function outside the jurisdiction of the Judicial Power (for example, the Civil Service Tribunal and the Fiscal Administrative Tribunal).

Besides the functions specified by the Constitution, it is the duty of the Judicial Power to hear civil, penal, business, and labor-management causes, as well as all others established by the law, irrespective of the nature and role of the people involved; definitively resolve these cases and see that their resolutions are adhered to, with the assistance of the National Police Force whenever necessary (Article 152).

The Supreme Court of Justice is the highest authority of the Judicial Power; the courts, officers, and employees of the judicial branch are answerable to it.

The Political Constitution stipulates that the Supreme Court of Justice be comprised of as many Magistrates as are necessary for adequate service. Currently, there are 24 Magistrates on the Supreme Court.

The magistrates are elected by the Legislative Assembly for terms of eight years, and for the sake of the stability of the Judicial Power, they will automatically serve another term unless voted out by a two-thirds majority of the Assembly.

Magistrates must currently be citizens, Costa Ricans by birth or by naturalization with 10 years of residency in the country after becoming citizens, at least 35 years of age, a lawyer with at least 10 years as a practicing attorney or five years as a judge, and a secular citizen.

The Supreme Court of Justice is divided into four Halls; also part of the Judicial Power are other lower courts, such as The higher courts, the *juzgados* (district courts), and the city halls.

It should be pointed out that the Judicial Power in Costa Rica, enjoys well-earned prestige, and in the last few years several laws have been promulgated for the purpose of speeding up legal processes in the courts so that the goal of swift and complete justice becomes a reality.

THE SUPREME ELECTION TRIBUNAL

This tribunal is ordinarily comprised of three permanent and three special magistrates appointed by the Supreme Court of Justice ratified by the votes of at least two-thirds of all the members of this court. The members of the Supreme Election Tribunal must meet the same conditions and have the same responsibilities as the other magistrates of the Supreme Court of Justice. They also enjoy the same immunities and prerogatives corresponding to all the Supreme Powers.

One month prior to the holding of the general elections the Supreme Court of Elections must be increased to five members by hadding two special magistrates. These special magistrates serve until six months after the elections.

The magistrates on the Election Tribunal have six-year terms but may be re-elected indefinitely.

The Costa Rican electoral system, since 1949 has been continually improved. The prestige enjoyed by the Supreme Election Tribunal cause the citizens to have confidence in the integrity of their vote. In fact, so much importance has been given to this body, mostly due to the questionable events of the 1944 and 1948 elections, that the Election Tribunal even has the power to dictate to the National Police Force whatever measures are necessary to ensure that the electoral processes are carried out with the all their legal guarantees and unrestricted freedom.

SUFFRAGE

Voting is a right and duty of every Costa Rican citizen. It is a right because the essence of a democracy is the power of individual citizens, through the exercise of their vote, to choose their leaders. It is a duty because if the best people are to be chosen to hold public office, the people must voice their opinion through their vote. Voting was made mandatory in 1959 by a constitutional amendment. The vote is cast directly, universally, and secretly, using ballots on which separate columns corresponding to political parties list the candidates for the political offices of President, Vice-President, Deputies, Municipal Officials, and Trustees.

The direct vote has been practiced in Costa Rica since 1913, although already in the Constitution of 1844 there had been an unsuccessful attempt to institute it. As the term implies, the direct vote allows citizens to vote candidates directly into the respective offices rather than electing delegates who in turn make the final choice, as occurs in some countries such as the United States of America.

The fact that the vote is universal means that all citizens registered in the Civil Registry Office have the right to vote. Before the present Constitution went into effect, women were excluded from voting, and thus voting was not universal.

Since voting is secret, on the election day, at all voting centers, citizens vote in small booths in complete privacy, where they mark the ballots to indicate the candidates of their preference.

These three characteristics ensure that voting is indeed a manifestation of the people's will in Costa Rica.

Naturalized Costa Ricans are not given the right to vote immediately, but must wait twelve months after they have become citizens.

Elections are held every four years, and constitute a total renewal of the Legislative and Executive Powers, as well as the municipalities throughout the country.

The organization, direction, and overseeing of the voting activities directly correspond to Supreme Election Tribunal, which has complete independence in carrying out its functions. All the other electoral bodies are subordinate to the Election Tribunal.

ECCLESIASTICAL GOVERNMENT

Around the beginning of the Sixteenth Century the first chapel was established in our national territory, in Nicoya Vieja, the present-day town of Pueblo Viejo in the canton of Nicoya. Considered the oldest parish in Costa Rica, it was first under the jurisdiction of León and Sevilla, then Lima, Peru, and finally Guatemala. In 1921 the Vatican created the Ecclesiastical Province of Costa Rica, comprised of all the canton parishes of the country, and classified according to jurisdictions as follows: the Archdiocese of San José, Heredia, and Cartago; the Diocese of Alajuela, encompassing 18 cantons of Alajuela Province, three from Heredia, and one from San José; the El General Diocese, comprised of 12 cantons from the provinces of San José and Puntarenas; the Diocese of Tilarán, made up of 16 cantons from Guanacaste Province, two from Alajuela, and two from Puntarenas; the Apostolic Vicariate of Limón, encompassing 16 cantons from Limón Province and two from Cartago.

EDUCATIONAL DEVELOPMENT

The first schools in Costa Rica operated as extensions of the churches. During those colonial days education was viewed more as a religious mission than teaching people to use their mental and physical powers for their own benefit. Later on (Eighteenth Century) another approach to education was instituted through *escuelas de primeras letras* (primary schools) which were established in towns of at least 1000 inhabitants.

In 1818 the first permanent center of education was established: *La Casa de Enseñanza Santo Tomás*. In 1869 free, compulsory education paid for by the State was instituted. The *Escuela Normal de Costa Rica* was established in 1914, and in 1940 the University of Costa Rica was founded.

Today Costa Rica has five public higher education centers, three colleges, located in Alajuela, Cartago, and Puntarenas, 196 public high schools, both technical and academic, 18 semi-official high schools, and 3,090 public elementary schools. (*Atlas Cantonal*, 1987). In addition to these, there are a number private universities, high schools, and elementary schools.

COSTA RICAN SOCIAL SECURITY DEPARTMENT

The *Caja Costarricense de Seguro Social* (CCSS) is an autonomous institution that was founded on behalf of the manual and intellectual workers, financed by a State-imposed contribution system, in which employers and employees each pay a share in order to protect employees from the risks of sickness, invalidity, and maternity, as well as to assist them in old-age, funeral expenses, and other eventualities in life.

This institution was established in November 1941 under the supervision of the Executive Power, it was modified in 1943, at which time it became an autonomous institution, dedicated to administering mandatory social insurance and offering additional voluntary insurance. Its coverage was limited to workers 60 years old and younger.

The CCSS administers maternity, health, old-age, invalidity, and life insurance, and is financed as follows: health and maternity insurance are financed by the quotas paid by the employees and employers (4% of employees monthly salary by employees and 6.75% by the employers); self-employed workers may obtain the insurance by paying 10.75% of their average monthly income.

Invalidity, old-age, and life insurance are financed by 2.50% of employees monthly salary by employees and 4.75% by the employer; self-employed workers may obtain this insurance by paying 7.25% of their average monthly income.

The purpose of the health and maternity insurance is to provide medical, financial, and social care to insured workers and family members entitled to coverage, in the area of general and specialized medical care, hospitalization, pharmaceutical, laboratory, dental services, and financial and social benefits.

In the case of invalidity, old-age, and life insurance, the purpose is to provide the insured or his spouse (in the case of his death), with old-age or invalidity pension. The insurance also provides a pension for children under 18 years of age, or 22 years old, if they are students. If a deceased insured person has no spouse or children, the following family members in the order given are entitled to the pension: the mother, the father, the brothers and sisters, provided they have can prove that they have been depending on the insured for at least 75% of their economic support.

In the eighties the CCSS instituted the British system, i.e., a single health system, including preventive health and the extension of invalidity, old-age, and death pensions to include 100% of the population rather than the previous 60%.

With this change, all health institutions became affiliated with the CCSS, thus increasing external consultations after three o'clock in the afternoon, reducing the shortage of medicines, and providing pensions for all of the citizens.

Today the health sector has at its disposal all types of hospitals and clinical centers, both private and governmental. Most of the governmental centers are owned by the CCSS.

COSTA RICAN WATERWORKS AND SEWAGE TREATMENT

In 1961 the *Servicio Nacional de Acueductos y Alcantarillados* (National Waterworks and Sewage Service) was created. The population supplied through plumbing with easily accessible water during 1989, was 2,741,992 inhabitants, or 93.2% of the total population. The population served by sanitary sewage evacuation and treatment facilities for the same year was 2,862,581 inhabitants, or 97.3% of the population. The *Instituto Costarricense de Acueductos y Alcantarillados* (Costa Rican Waterworks and Sewage Department) during 1989 supplied water to 1,407,437 inhabitants (47.86% of the populations), with a total of 272,913 services and 251,328 domiciliary connections.

In spite of the fact that water and sewage services have exceeded the international goals established for the decade, the provision of water in many areas is intermittent and does not meet minimum requirements for human consumption, especially those services that in the hands of municipalities, since these systems are generally very old and deteriorated. In most rural waterworks systems there is no permanent, systematic control over the quality of the water. As for sewage systems, although 15 cities in the country have partial sanitary sewage networks, only eight cities offer partial treatment of water, and in most of these cases the methods used are quite inefficient.

COSTA RICAN ELECTRICAL INSTITUTE (ICE)

The *Instituto Costarricense de Electricidad* (ICE) was founded in 1949 to take care of the production of electricity for the entire country, and, in general, to resolve all matters related to national electrification. There are also a few other local electric companies, however. One of these is the *Compañía Nacional de Fuerza y Luz, S.A.* (National Power and Lighting Company), whose largest stockholder is now the ICE. This company, as well as some municipalities, generate a relatively small amount of additional electricity. The ICE produces electricity in several plants, including the hydroelectric plants of La Garita, Cachí, and Arenal, Río Macho, and Tapantí, whose production is supplemented by the thermo-electric plants of San Antonio, Colima, and Moín.

The *Sistema Nacional Interconectado* (National Inter-Connected Network) permits the transmission of electric power from La Cruz, on the Nicaraguan border, to San Isidro de El General with branching at several points to serve several important population centers. ICE's electrical production for the years 1988 and 1990 is shown below.

Origin	1988	1990
Hydroelectric	3,040 gwh	3,497 gwh
Thermal	95 gwh	47 gwh
Exchange	190 gwh	263 gwh
Total	3,325 gwh	3,707 gwh

Electrical consumption for the same period by sectors was as follows.

Sector	1988	1990
Residential	1,406 gwh	1,560 gwh
Industrial	789 gwh	921 gwh
General	678 gwh	730 gwh
Others	96 gwh	94 gwh
Total	2,969 gwh	3,305 gwh

1 gwh = one million kilowatt-hours.

The ICE also owns the telecommunications monopoly in Costa Rica (see page 223).

OTHER STATE INSTITUTIONS

The **Consejo Nacional de Producción** (National Council on Production) is an institution dedicated to regulating the supply, quality, quantity, and price of agricultural products, especially staples due to their importance in the Costa Rican diet.

The **Instituto de Desarrollo Agrario** (Institute of Agrarian Development) was established to resolve land tenancy problems. Its tasks include the control of settling virgin lands and the redistribution of existing farm lands through indemnization paid to the former owners. This institution, initially called the *Instituto de Tierras y Colonización* (ITCO = Institute of Lands and Homesteading), was founded in 1962 to resolve land tenancy problems by establishing homesteads on virgin lands, then to grant land deeds to squatters, and, since the seventies, to establish peasant settlements on lands already equipped with infrastructures, purchased from private land owners, awarding deeds to former squatters. This institute is financed in part by indirect taxes.

The *Instituto Nacional de Vivienda y Urbanización* (INVU = National Institute of Housing and Urbanization) founded in 1954 is in charge of urban planning and regulation. It has been in charge of several social housing projects involving the construction and sale of houses, but in recent years this activity has been taken over by other institutions and private enterprise, all under the coordination of the new Ministry of Housing.

The *Instituto Mixto de Ayuda Social* (IMAS = Institute of Mixed Social Assistance) was founded in 1971 for the purpose of coordinating public and private endeavors aimed at eradicating extreme poverty. During its early years this institution was also dedicated to low-cost housing construction in order to help eliminate slums. Financing for IMAS comes from a 0.5% tax on wages.

The *Instituto Nacional de Seguros* (INS = National Insurance Institute) was created in 1924 thus establishing itself as the insurance monopoly of Costa Rica. Initially it was called the *Banco Nacional de Seguros* (National Bank of Insurance). This institution handles all life, work risks, automobile, patrimonial, maritime, accident and health, livestock, crop, and diverse risks insurance. The Fire Fighting Department of Costa Rica is managed by INS.

Asignaciones Familiares (Family Allotments) was created mainly to provide food for children of low-income families through school lunch programs. It is financed by five percent tax on wages.

The *Refinadora Costarricense de Petróleo, S.A.* (RECOPE = Costa Rican Oil Refinery Company) was originally founded by private businesses for the purpose of setting up an oil refinery in Costa Rica. This enterprise in 1963 signed a contract-law with the Government of Costa Rica in order to implement the project. That contract awarded to the government 15% of RECOPE's stock. During 1973 and 1974 the government purchases the rest of the shares. In 1975 RECOPE was nationalized and put in charge of all the fuel distribution in country. It also took over all the storage tank complexes, that various foreign companies owned in the country: El Alto, Cocal de Puntarenas, Caldera, and Golfito. Services stations, according to the contract, cannot be operated by RECOPE, and many of these today are privately owned. Technically speaking, private business may import petroleum fuels, but due to the high duty charged, it is practically impossible to do so. RECOPE sales for 1989 were 7,280,000 barrels of fuel, of which 1,690,000 were gasoline, 2,790,000 diesel fuel, 1,409,000 bunker, and various other fuels. The value of petroleum imports was US$147,068,000, purchased at an average of US$20.08. The principle suppliers have been Mexico and Venezuela.

The *Registro Nacional* (National Registry Office) encompasses the Public Registry Office, the Industrial Property Registry Office, the Credit Registry Office, the National Land Registry Office, and the Motorized Vehicle Registry Office. The Public Registry Office has been in existence since 1865 and includes the Immovable Property and Mortgage Registry offices. The National Registry Office is under the jurisdiction of the Ministry of Justice.

The registration of people is done through the Civil Registry Office, a department of the Supreme Election Tribunal, and is divided into departments, including the electoral and civil departments.

The *Junta de Protección Social* (Board of Social Protection) is a public entity in charge of administering the national lotteries. Most of the income from lotteries is received by this board and turned over to the CCSS in order to finance part of its hospital expenses. The board also contributes funds for education, elderly homes, and other service and social assistance agencies.

This institution was founded in 1845 under the name of *Junta de Caridad del Hospital San Juan de Dios* (Board of Charity of the San Juan de Dios Hospital).

Guaria Morada (Catleya skinneri-orchidaceae), the national flower (common orchid in Costa Rica).

Legislative Assembly building, San José.

79

9 Political and Administrative Organization

The territory of Costa Rica is divided into seven provinces: San José, Alajuela, Cartago, Heredia, Guanacaste, Puntarenas, and Limón. The provinces, in turn, are divided into cantons. In each canton there is a municipality or municipal corporation whose members are elected by the people to administer the community's interests. The cantons are subdivided into districts, and these into barrios, and *caseríos* (townships).

According the Executive Decree No. 15772-6, of October 9, 1984, with respect to administrative territorial division, is comprised of seven provinces, 80 cantons, and 421 districts.

SAN JOSE PROVINCE

The provinces of San José is the most important in the country due to it population, resources, and industrial activity. Its mean geographical coordinates are 9°38'15" north latitude and 84°00'39" west longitude, and its maximum breadth is 143 kilometers. It is bounded on the north by the provinces of Alajuela and Heredia, on the east by Cartago and Limón, and on the south and west by Puntarenas.

In pre-Colombian times the territory corresponding to the modern province of San José, was inhabited by the Huetar and Brunca Indians.

The city of San José was founded on May 21, 1737 under the name Abra de la Boca del Monte. During that same year the first chapel was dedicated to the church father, San José, around which lived only a handful of settlers. The town was made the capital of the State on May 16, 1823, and since August 31, 1848 it

Opposite page: View of downtown San José.

The National Stadium, San José.

*La Sabana
Metropolitan Park,
San José.*

has been the capital of the Republic of Costa Rica.

The province is drained both by rivers that empty into the Caribbean Sea and by those that empty into the Pacific Ocean.

On the Caribbean side is the watershed of the Chirripó River, whose main tributaries are the rivers Blanco, Cascajal, and Honduras (called Zurquí at its source). On the Pacific side is the watershed of the Térraba River (which sometimes overflows and floods Palmar Norte, Palmar Sur, Balsar), the watershed of the Pirrís River, which passes through Parrita, that of the Grande de Tárcoles, into which flow the principle rivers that drain greater San José (making it one of the most polluted rivers in the country). Other rivers that drain San José Province are the Savegre, the Tusubres, and the Barú.

At the confluence of the rivers Virilla and the Tiribí is the Electriona Electric Plant. Other electric plants are located in the cantons of Goicoechea, Santa Ana, and Tarrazú. These plants, providing electric power for practically the whole province, are owned and managed by the *Compañía Nacional de Fuerza y Luz* (National Power and Lighting Company),

and the *Instituto Costarricense de Electricidad* (ICE = Costa Rican Electrical Institute), and the *Cooperativa de Electrificación Rural los Santos R.L.* (Los Santos Rural Electrification Cooperative).

Geologically the province of San José is formed mainly of sedimentary rocks from the Tertiary Period. There are also some outcrops from the Cretaceous Period in the cantons of Puriscal, Aserrí, Acosta, Turrubares, and León Castro, and materials from the Quaternary period are also found in almost all the cantons, but to a lesser degree than those of the Tertiary. This variety of materials probably owes itself to the great diversity of geomorphological units running through the province, namely, those of tectonic and erosive origin (Cordillera de Talamanca), volcanic origin (Sierra Volcánica), alluvial sedimentation (the plains), denudation (Cerros de Alajuela), intrusive action (Cerros de Escazú), massive movement (Cerros de Puriscal), glacial action (Mount Chirripó area), and those of structural origin (Cerro Caraigres and the Pangolín and Alfombra faults).

The soil in certain sections of this province has limitations for some crops and activities. For example, the cantons of Puriscal, Atenas, Acosta, and Mora have an annual of over 5000 mm and very steep slopes making these lands highly vulnerable to erosion. These areas should be protected as watersheds and admired for their natural beauty. Other areas, however, such as the cantons of San José, Goicoechea, Tibás, Moravia and Montes de Oca are suitable for any use. (*Atlas Cantonal*, 1987).

The climate of San José Province, in general, is moderate; only in the low parts of the valley of the Grande de Tárcoles River are the temperatures relatively hot, but they seldom reach 30°C.

The crops produced on the soils are quite varied: a great deal of coffee, sugarcane, and legumes, as well as a wide variety of fruit, vegetables, and flowers. The population of the province is 890,434, with a population density of 180 inhabitants per km² (1984 Census). The land are constitutes 9.7% of the national territory.

Politically, the province of San José is divided into 20 cantons (see Map No.

10), 13 of which are belong to the greater metropolitan area, an urban concentration which has continued to expand out from the center of San José and now touches the provinces of Alajuela, Cartago, and Heredia. It encompasses 31 cantons and 147 districts.

This province has the greatest number of socially, culturally, and scientifically interesting places: recreational parks, zoos, sports and tourist centers; the National Museum and museums of history, anthropology, jade, contemporary Costa Rican art, Indian crafts of ceramic, stone, and gold; parks such as La Sabana recreational park, Simón Bolívar National Park, Plaza Víquez recreational park; theaters such as the National Theater, the Melico Salazar Theater, and several smaller theaters that present live plays every night of the week except Mondays; and a host of other culturally interesting spots.

In San José are also located the headquarters for most of the major higher learning centers in the country: the University of Costa Rica; the *Universidad Estatal a Distancia* (State Extension University), the Autonomous University of Central America, the Latin American University of Science and Technology, the Academic Center of the Technological University of Costa Rica, and others.

The city also has all sorts of private and public health centers, hospitals and clinics, most of which are connected with the *Caja Costarricense de Seguro Social* (CCSS = Costa Rican Department of Social Security), such as the San Juan de Dios Hospital, the Calderón Guardia Hospital, Hospital México, the Children's Hospital, and the Cervantes Blanco Hospital.

San José province also has the most important highways and roads leading to other parts of the country.

The following sections describe the main characteristics of the cantons of San José Province.

San José Canton

In this the principal canton of the province is San José City, its governmental seat, and also the capital of the nation. The canton is divided into 11 districts: Zapote, San Francisco de Dos Ríos, La Uruca, Pavas, Hatillo, San Sebastián, El Carmen, Merced, Hospital, Catedral, and Mata Redonda. The land of the canton is flat, and is drained by the rivers Tiribí, Torres, María Aguilar, Ocloro, and other minor ones, all sub-tributaries of the river Grande de Tárcoles. These fertile soils are produce a variety of crops with abundant harvests. The climate is moderate due to the elevation –average

Paseo Colón (continuation of Avenida Central on the western side of town), San José.

Avenida Central,
San José

1,150 meters above sea level. The temperature varies between 12 and 27.5°C, with the lowest temperatures occurring in December and January, and the highest in June and July.

The maximum length of this canton is 16 kilometers going from northeast to southeast. At first the canton was called Boca del Monte, then La Villita, then Villa Nueva, and finally San José.

The canton of San José has an area of 44.7 kms² and a population density of 5,391 inhabitants per square kilometer. It has 241,464 inhabitants, or nine percent of the total population of the country, according to the 1984 census.

The major industrial zones in the canton are: La Uruca, Cementerio, and Pavas Oeste.

Elaborate communication systems and good roads, including some freeways, railroads to the most important ports, bus services, both interurban and lines linking the canton to the rest of the country. Located in this canton are the main health centers of the country, as well as the most important national heritages and places of cultural interest, many recreational areas, the studios of the *Sistema National de Radio y Televisión* (SINART = National

Radio and Television System), and the headquarters for the *Instituto National de Aprendizaje* (INA = National Education Institute).

The main agricultural product is coffee, grown in certain sectors of the canton.

San José City

San José City is the capital of San José Province as well as the capital of the nation, the headquarters of the principal Powers of State and the most important center of political, cultural, economic, and social activity in the country. Also, in the Pavas District is the Tobías Bolaños Airport for small aircraft.

Around San José has grown up a large metropolitan area which takes in 13 of the 20 cantons of the province; that is, 65% of the cantons are within this urban concentration.

The most important transportation links are land routes such as freeways, highways, and secondary roads concentrated in the metropolitan area and extending to many different parts of the country.

The streets in the center of the city, all straight, curbed, and made of asphalt-covered concrete. They classified as *calles* (streets), which run north and south, and *avenidas*, which run east and west. All are numbered, but few Costa Ricans pay much attention to the numbers, preferring to give directions in terms of well-known landmarks.

The numbering system for the streets of San José works as follows: *Calle Central* and *Avenida Central* (both numbered zero) cross in the heart of the city; going north from *Avenida Central* the *avenidas* have odd numbers ascending from *Primera* (First) –*Primera, Tercera, Cuarta, Quinta* (First, Third, Fourth, Fifth), etc.; going south from *Avenida Central* the *avenidas* have even numbers ascending from *Segunda* (Second) –*Segunda, Cuarta, Sexta* (Second, Fourth, Sixth), etc. In a fashion similar to that of the avenues, going east from *Calle Central* the *calles* have odd numbers ascending from *Primera*, and going west they have even numbers ascending from *Segunda*. Hence going north and east from the heart of the city the numbers are odd, and going south

and west the numbers are even. The numbering of the buildings follows an analogous system: if a building is located on an avenue, the first digit of its number indicates the street after which it is found; if it is on a street, the first digit indicates the avenue after which it is found. The main plazas of San José are: the National Park, a beautiful garden 14,000 square meters, in the center of which is a monument that commemorates the 1856 campaign against the "filibusters",

85

in which five women representing the five republics of Central America symbolize Central American unity against the invader; Parque Morazán, irregularly shaped and divided in the middle by *Avenida Central* and *Calle Sétima* with a monument in the intersection called *El Templo de la Música*. The *Plaza de España*, as short distance away, is situated between *Parque Morazán* and *Parque National* (on the north side of *Avenida Tercera*). *Parque National* has an artistic terrace with well-kept plants, comfortable benches, good lighting at night —one of the most pleasant spots in the city. Nearby is *Parque National Simón Bolívar* (containing a zoo) extends picturesquely over both sides of the Torres River. Around these parks and plazas are lovely homes. The first three mentioned are all on the *Paseo de las Damas* (another name for Third Avenue). The *Plaza Central* or *Parque Central* is also a lovely garden located in front of the *Catedral Metropolitana* in the very center of the city. This park has a unique musical pavilion with an underground hall which today is the Carmen Lyra Children's Library (Carmen Lyra a famous Costa Rican writer famous for her tales for children).

There are also some small plazas such as the *Plaza Carrillo* (also called *Parque de la Merced*) in front of the post office building; *Plazoleta Juan Mora Porras*; *Plaza de la Cultura* located alongside the National Theater; *Plaza de la Democracia* in front of the National Museum, and others that contain national monuments.

The city also has several important recreational areas, for example, near the its southern limit, the Cleto González Víquez Sports Complex behind the *Liceo de Costa Rica* (one can get there from *Avenida Central* by following *Paseo de los Estudiantes* (*Calle Novena*) south; and the *Polideportivo de San Francisco de Dos Ríos*. One of the largest parks is *Parque Metropolitano La Sabana Padre Chapuí*, with installations for many sports, as well as picnic areas and spacious meadows and wooded areas. This park is linked with the city by *Paseo Colón*, a continuation of *Avenida Central* going west. In this sector of the city there are magnificent homes and broad sidewalks.

On *Avenida Primera* between *Calle Cuarta* and *Calle Sexta* there is boulevard, built in 1989. The *Parque National de Diversiones*, (National Amusement Park), located in La Uruca, has mechanical rides, both out in the open, and indoors; the *Parque de la Paz* (Peace Park, similar to La Sabana Park) to the south of San José City was created in 1989 as a place for play, and picnicking.

Some outstanding places of cultural interest include the National Theater, the Melico Popular Theater, the *Plaza de la Cultura*, under which are located the museums of pre-Colombian gold artifacts, and the Numismática of the Central Bank of Costa Rica. In the Plaza de la Cultura itself there are temporary arts and crafts exhibits, as well as other cultural and artistic exhibits. The National Museum specializes in archeology, history, and natural sciences. The Jade Museum in the *Instituto National de Seguros* (INS = National Insurance Institute) has pre-Colombian objects, especially those made of jade. The *Museo de Arte Contemporáneo Costarricense* (Costa Rican Contemporary Museum), as well as several theaters and art galleries, specialize in the works from the Nineteenth and Twentieth centuries.

Almost all public buildings are of modern architecture and well decorated. Some examples are the Metropolitan Cathedral, the *Palacio Episcopal*; the Postal-Telegraph Building; the *Banco Central*, the *Banco de Costa Rica*, the *Banco National*, the *Instituto National de Seguros* (INS = National Insurance Institute); schools named after Latin American countries: México, Chile, Argentina, Nicaragua, and others named after famous people: Juan Rafael Mora and Ricardo Jiménez, for example; the National Library; and many others build more recently.

There are also many national heritage sites such as the National Theater, the dome and the entrance to the old Chapuí Psychiatric Hospital, the *Casa Amarilla* (Yellow House), the *Castillo Azul* (Blue Castle), the National Museum, and the residence of the former president of the nation, Rafael Calderón Guardia; as well as buildings and monuments of historical architectural interest such as the *Edificio*

Metálico (Metal Building), the Caribbean Railway Station, the *Colegio de Señoritas* (all girls high school), the old Central Penitentiary, and the Barrio Grande Chapel. There are also buildings of historic-architectural interest such as the *Liceo de Costa Rica* and the Post Office Building. Other are of historic-cultural interest such as the Variedades Theater and the historic remains of the old main customs building.

The Government Palace, today the Legislative Assembly headquarters, in a prominent spot in the center of San José, has a very notable Moorish style. The present *Palacio de Justicia* (Hall of Justice) and the Supreme Court of Justice buildings (three in all) are large modern buildings on the east side of downtown San José. The Merced Church is a large, splendid, well-decorated Gothic-style building.

On the eastern side of the city there is the Santa Teresita Sanctuary (Catholic Church), a relatively small building, but well-delineated in its architectural details.

As mentioned, the principal health centers of the country are found here, including the hospitals México, San Juan de Dios, Doctor Rafael Calderón Guardia, National Gerontology, Doctor Raúl Blanco Cervantes, National Children's, Carlos Sáenz Herrera, National Manuel Antonio Chapuí Psychiatric, the National Rehabilitation Center, Doctor Humberto Araya Rojas, and the *Instituto Materno Infantil Carit* (Mother-Child Maternal Institute), as well as clinics such as the Doctor Moreno Cañas (in Barrio Cuba), Doctor Solón Núñez Frutos (in Hatillo Centro), and the Doctor Carlos Durán clinic (in Barrio Córdoba), and many others in the governmental seats of each canton.

Also located in San José City is the headquarters for the Autonomous University of Central America, and the Latin American University of Science and Technology, as well as a branch of the Technological Institute of Costa Rica.

The General Cemetery is worth seeing, especially during November 1 and 2, when practically everyone in the city goes there to leave flowers at the tombs of their relatives. It has magnificent mausoleums of elegant Italian design.

The buildings of the banking institutions mentioned earlier, and many private buildings of two stories or more are admirable for their solid construction and fine architectural excellence.

Most residential dwellings are low, build either of cement block or wood, with roofs of galvanized corrugated tin.

The city is in a constant state growth, and has extended in all directions, but most rapidly toward the west. The level land here favors urbanization. Moreover, many important barrios and *caseríos* (townships) have formed. On the north side are the barrios Amón, Otoya, and Escalante; on the east, Los Yoses, La Granja, and Peralta are distinguished neighborhoods due to the elegance and variety of styles in numerous private homes. In addition, there are new modest neighborhoods on the southwest such as Hatillo, San Sebastián, and Zapote.

The communities surrounding the center –Guadalupe, San Pedro, San Vicente, and San Juan de Tibás– are today practically extensions of San José City. Many people from San José of diverse economic standings have built their homes in these suburbs.

In these neighboring cantons there are barrios with large estates with picturesque walls, as well as modest homes and a budding commerce that has extended throughout the greater metropolitan area –book stores, clothing and shoe stores, publishing houses, automobile dealers, appliance stores, and big industries.

Private or cooperative bus services transport passengers across the city from east to west, linking the center with La Sabana and San Pedro, and north and south, from Guadalupe, Moravia, San Juan and other nearby towns. These buses, along with many other vehicles, constantly transporting people and goods in and around the city make for heavy traffic in the capital city, especially during working days.

There are moving companies, contractors, transportation services, and mortuaries for all economic levels. In department stores, shops, restaurants, and hotels, customers are served with the greatest care and finesse, pleasing even the most exacting customers.

Many fine hotels are available for tourists and business people: locally owned hotels such as the Europa, Costa Rica, Balmoral, the new Hotel San José-Palacio, as well as, two owned by international firms –the Holiday-Inn and the Corobicí with over 150 rooms, convention centers, private suites for practically any activity.

As for industry, there are foundries, soap and detergent factories, candles, canned goods, biscuits, candies, cigarettes and cigars, matches, packaging, glassware, stockings and other clothing, beer, wines, soft drinks, perfumes, cosmetics, all kinds of furniture, and construction materials and equipment. Also there is a growing contract labor industry (*maquila*) in which local enterprises provide part of the labor in the production of certain articles (e.g., clothing, jewelry, radios, television) and, now, even computer software. In the pharmaceutical industry, including several companies with very elaborate modern laboratories, has been experiencing phenomenal growth.

Several banks, and credit establishments, both state-owned and private, as well as credit unions, and international banks have their headquarters in San José.

The National Library is a popular institution offering excellent service in all its departments. It owns around 100,000 volumes which it offers to the public with few restrictions.

Another noteworthy establishment is the National Museum, which despite its modest offering of antiquities and curios, has impressive archeological collections, as well as specimens of practically all the animal species native to the country, and a beautiful garden containing many examples of Costa Rican plant species.

The press has in the country has reached a high level of sophistication. The newspapers of the capital, with a format similar to those of the best in the world, attest to the fact that journalism in Costa Rica is a vital force in the nation's intellectual progress. There are several big morning and evening newspapers, specialized weekly newspapers, and colorfully illustrated magazines. Radio and television also has very modern studios, equipment, and staff trained in the latest technology. Thus, it is no exaggeration to say that Costa Rican journalism is among the best in Latin America.

After enumerating so many positive features of the city, it must be recognized that the inner city of San José little by little, as many cities of the world, has been losing its identity, and becoming an indiscriminate mass of people, buildings, and streets. The sidewalks are too narrow and many in need of repair, for the easy passing of pedestrians, and the streets cannot sufficiently accommodate the hoards of vehicles passing through at all hours of the day.

As the center of the city has deteriorated, large commercial firms are moving to the outlying areas. And as this process of decentralization occurs, sizable parcels of fertile land have been sacrificed, with little planning, to business and great expanses of concrete and asphalt. What this unbalanced urbanization has meant to the "lungs" of the people of San José has been, for all practical purposes, chaos. The green borders of coffee plantations that once encircled the city are being mercilessly replaced. (Jorge Borbón Z., 1988).

Some citizens, however, are aware of these problems and are taking action. The Costa Rican government has also begun to implement some measures to regulate vehicle traffic. Still, much remains to be done.

A farm near San Antonio, Escazú

Escazú Canton

This canton is bounded on the north by San José Canton, on the east by Alajuelita, on the south by Acosta, and on the west by Santa Ana. Its area of the canton is 34.39 kms², with a maximum length of 13 kilometers. It is picturesquely situated on the northern slopes of the Hills of Escazú with many recreational villas built there.

The soil of in some areas of this canton presents some rigid limitations with respect to its use. For example, from the *Cerro Coyote* to the southeast part of San Antonio there are limitations inhibiting their use for permanent crops, semi-forest, livestock, or even rational uses of the forest resources. Also, 22% of the southern region of the canton, on Mount Pico Blanco, near the town of Jaular, and at the confluence of the rivers Tiribí and Torres their are severe limitations, such as high susceptibility to erosion because of the steep slopes. (*Atlas Cantonal.* 1987).

During the pre-Colombian era this was a rest spot for Indian travellers headed for Pacaca (modern-day Ciudad Colón) –hence its name Escazú, which is derived from the Indian word *Itzkazú* meaning "rest" (*Atlas Cantonal*, 1987). In 1848 it became the second canton of San José Province.

The canton is drained by the rivers Agres, Chiquero, Cruz, and Convento, all tributaries of the Tiribí River. It produces good quality coffee, vegetables and fruits, and livestock. Its districts are the Escazú, San Antonio, and San Rafael. It has a population of 33,101 inhabitants with a population density of 960 inhabitants per square kilometer. This canton is part of the greater metropolitan area of San José. Guachipelín to the north of this canton has been proposed as an industrial zone.

The town of Escazú is situated at the foot of Mount Piedra Blanca, an immense calcareous mass covering over 10 hectares. Some of its streets are gravel, but most are now paved. Its colonial-style houses and church are a unique attraction for visitors. The public buildings include the town hall, postal-telegraph office. This town, as well as Santa Ana, is linked to the capital by excellent highway and roads. It has magnificent school buildings, including Country Day School, a school mostly for foreigners in which most of the classes are given in English, and the *Liceo de Escazú*, established as a high school in 1970. Beautiful homes of well-to-do Costa Ricans and foreigners enhances this delightful canton a stones throw from the nation's capital. Its average temperature is a pleasant 20°C (68°F).

The District of Escazú, with a population of 10,505 inhabitants, covers an area of 3.78 kms²; San Antonio, with 12,338 inhabitants covers 11.60 km²; and San Rafael with 10,258 inhabitants covers 18.02 kms². (1984 Census).

Casa de Cultura Joaquín García Monge (formerly a school)

Desamparados Canton

Desamparados, named after the first chapel dedicated to Our Lady of Desamparados in 1821, was established

Catholic Church in Desamparados. It was the first chapel built in honor of Our Lady of Desamparados in 1821 that lent its name to the Desamparados Canton established in 1848.

as a canton in 1848. (*Atlas Cantonal*, 1987).

It is bounded on the north by San José Canton, on the east by Cartago Province, on the south by Tarrazú Canton, and on the west by Aserrí Canton. Its topography is irregular, partly resting on a ravine corresponding to the Central Tectonic Depression and partly on the Hills of Candelaria.

The fluvial system of this canton belongs to the Pacific versant, specifically to the watershed of the Pirrís and Grande de Tárcoles rivers. The principal tributaries of the Pirrís are the Tarrazú and the Alumbre, which join to form the Grande de Candelaria River.

The Grande de Tárcoles watershed encompasses the rivers Jorco, Damas and Cañas and others that originate in the canton and carry the wastes of the entire canton.

This canton is also part of the greater metropolitan area, except for the districts of Frailes, San Cristóbal, and Rosario.

Its main agricultural products are coffee and livestock, as well as some fruits and vegetables. It has an area of 117.36 kms² and a population of 108,824 inhabitants.

Its 11 districts are: Desamparados, San Miguel, San Juan de Dios, San Rafael, Arriba San Antonio, Los Frailes, Patarrá, San Cristóbal, El Rosario, Damas, and San Rafael Abajo. In the San Antonio District there are hot springs and a clay mine, and San Miguel has a coal mine.

The town of Desamparados, the head of the governmental seat of the canton has 43.352 inhabitants. it is situated at 1,161 meters above sea level five kilometers from San José City, at the southern end of the central region.

Its proximity to the capital and its quaintness make this town very attractive; many families from the capital have settled there and built lovely homes. There are, in fact, great concentrations of relatively new houses due to the numerous housing projects of recent years.

The canton has some important buildings, such as the modern Doctor Marcial Fallas Clinic, in the Desamparados District, the elegant Catholic Church, worthy of any modern city, and other buildings of historical and architectural interest, such as the colonial-style first school of Desamparados, the Barrio Salitral Mansion and the *Casa de Cultura Joaquín García Monge* (a cultural center which was formerly a school).

Puriscal Canton

This canton extends northward to the Grande de Tárcoles River. It is bounded on the south by Parrita Canton, the Picagres River (tributary of the Río Grande) separates it from Mora Canton on the east, and it is bounded on the west by Turrubares Canton. Located on the high Hills of Puriscal, the terrain of the whole canton is very uneven, but the soil is fertile. The climate is cool and pleasantly dry. In some areas water is scarce. Farmers here produce most of the products produced in the rest of the country —mainly coffee, tobacco, and beef cattle. Unfortunately, it is one of the areas most affected by deforestation, which has exacerbated the problems of massive landslides, the washing away of topsoil, and others. Adding to this region's troubles, a recent earthquake and a series of earth tremors resulted in heavy damage to many houses.

A good highway links Puriscal to the capital city, making it possible to travel between the two points in less than an hour. Formerly the highway between Puriscal and Puerto Quepos was the only access route to the Central Pacific Zone, but it became much less important when the Costanera Sur Highway was constructed. The old highway is still, however, the only road linking the districts of this canton.

Puriscal has 23,123 inhabitants living on a total land area of 553.21 kms². Its districts are: Santiago, Mercedes Sur, Barbacoas, Grifo Alto, San Rafael, Candelarita, Desamparaditos, San Antonio, y Chirres.

The governmental seat of the canton is Santiago, located 35 kilometers from San José City, at 1,105 meters above sea level. Its population is 7,843 inhabitants. The town consists of twelve square blocks. The public buildings include: the Catholic Church; the *Palacio Municipal*, which contains the office of the *Instituto Costarricense de Electricidad* (ICE = Costa Rican Electrical Institute), a post office, a *Ministerio de Agricultura y Ganadería* (MAG = Ministry of Agriculture) office, and others; two academic centers –the *Liceo Académico* (Academic High School) and the *Instituto Agropecuario* (Agricultural Institute); the regional center for the *Universidad Estatal a Distancia* (UNED = State Extension University); a public library, and a Social Security clinic.

Business in the town is very active: it has several department stores, small grocery stores, and some small industries, including a cigar-making cooperative.

Settlement of the canton began around 1815. The first chapel was built there in 1858, and in 1871 the present church was built in honor of Santiago de Gales. This church was recently damaged by a wave of earth tremors that hit the canton. The Darío Flores School is in a new building was founded in 1900, and in 1945 it was made an auxiliary school in secondary education. It 1953 it was in inaugurated as the *Liceo Académico de Puriscal*.

Formerly the region today known as Puriscal was called Cola de Pavo. Its present name evolved from the word *purisco* which refers to the time the beans begin to blossom.

Tarrazú Canton

Situated in the Dota Mountains, its terrain is generally rough, although between the mountains there are beautiful, fertile valleys, with an excellent climate of temperatures ranging from 14 to 25°C. The area is drained by many small streams that originate in the watershed of the Pirrís, the Naranjo, and the Damas rivers, all of which have numerous tributaries.

Although the absence of good roads to the interior of the country has hampered the agricultural development of this canton, there are well-kept cattle

ranches, coffee, various kinds of fruit, and *achiote* (a seed used to make red food coloring) of very good quality are produced. Also avocado, apples, *granadilla* (a tropical fruit similar to pomegranate in form but yellow in color), peaches, and citrus fruits are grown with good results. Coffee growing is the most important activity followed by cattle raising.

The total land area of the canton is 237.23 km², and it has a population of 8,845 inhabitants. Its three districts are: San Marcos, San Lorenzo, and San Carlos.

The governmental seat of the canton, San Marcos (population of 5,381) is situated on a high hill between the Parrita River and one of its tributaries that run down from the Mount Trinidad, 35 kilometers southwest of San José City, at 1,429 meters above sea level. Its main buildings include: the Catholic Church, the Parsonage, the *Palacio Municipal*, the Health Center, the National Bank, the Continental Hotel, the Zacatecas Hotel, the *Edificio Cristal*, and the offices of three cooperatives: COOPETARRAZU, COOPESANTOS, and COOPESANMARCOS. There is only one park containing a monument, with no apparent structure. The streets are asphalt-covered and in good condition.

Public services include: the telephone office, Social Security office, Health Center, State Extension University Center, a branch of the National Bank, and the *Banco Anglo*, the Coffee Growers Savings and Loan Credit Union, and the electric office. There is a good bus service between this town and the capital city.

This canton is linked to San José City by a good highway that intersects with the Pan-American Highway and another highway that goes through the city of Desamparados. Another good road leads to the Pacific coast.

Four hundred meters from the Catholic Church there is an interesting bridge over the Parrita River on whose banks, near the villa there is a hot spring frequented because of its health properties.

The climate here, as in the rest of the canton, is moderate, and even chilly at times —even to the point that frost occasionally forms on the ground at night.

The first access route into the area was an ox-cart road built in 1872. The first school was inaugurated in 1884, destroyed in an earthquake in 1919, and was rebuilt in 1935. The *Instituto Agropecuaria de Tarrazú* (Agricultural Institute), opened in 1963, is now called the *Liceo de Tarrazú*.

The first official name of the canton, established in 1862, was Hato de Dota. Its present name is of Indian origin, which according to historians evolved from the word *atarrazú*, meaning "rocky ground at the mouth of the mountain".

Aserrí Canton

Located on the northern slopes of Hills of Candelaria, its climate is moderate. It is bounded on the north and the east by Desamparados and Alajuelita, on the south by Parrita Canton, on the southeast by the cantons of Tarrazú and León Cortés Castro, and on the west by Acosta Canton. The total area of the canton is 168 kms² and a total population of 30,588 inhabitants, giving a population density of 182 inhabitants per square kilometer. It is comprised of the districts: Aserrí, Tarbaca, Vuelta de Jorco, San Gabriel, La Legua, and Monte Rey (where there are excellent coffee processing plants).

A town began to form in this area in the Eighteenth Century, and in 1862 the canton was established. It was originally named after the Indian Chief Aczarrí who governed the region when the first Spanish settlers arrived. The present name has evolved from the name of the Indian Chief.

The first official school was set up in a small adobe house. Later the present school building was constructed and began operating in 1897 during the first term of President Rafael Yglesias Castro. The school is named after Manuel Hidalgo Mora. The *Liceo de Aserrí*, opened in March 1970 while José Joaquín Trejos Fernández was President of Costa Rica.

The terrain of almost the whole canton is hilly. It is drained by the rivers Pirrís and the Grande de Tárcoles. The principal crop grown here is coffee, but sugarcane, corn, and beans are also grown. Some farmers are also engaged in beef cattle raising.

In this canton are the Protected Zones of Caraigres and the Cerros of Escazú.

La Piedra de Aserrí (Rock of Aserrí) in the background is 30 meters long. At the foot of the rock there is a small cave which has inspired many superstitions.

Photo of Ciudad Colón at a distance, taken from the Universidad de la Paz Highway.

The first covers 13% of territory. South of the Aserrí District is a mineralization zone which occupies 32% of the area of the canton.

The town of Aserrí, with 20,968 inhabitants is at an altitude of 1,308 meters above sea level. It has a rubblework church, a school, an attractive municipal building, and a postoffice. A good highway links this town with San José, 12 kilometers away. A short distance southwest, a huge rock, nearly 30 meters long, appears to be precariously suspended in place so that it could come crashing into the town at any moment. At the foot of this rock is a cave which has inspired many superstitions that date back to the first inhabitants of the land. Tradition has it that in this cave lived the witch, Ña Zárate, who would frequently walk the slopes of the mountain guarding the treasures she had hidden there. The scenic location and splendid panoramic view of this lovely high valley surrounded by mountains make this a favorite tourist attraction.

Mora Canton

This canton is situated between the cantons of Santa Ana and Puriscal on the northwest and west; it is bounded on the north by the cantons of Antenas and Alajuela, and on the southeast by Acosta Canton at 850 meters above sea level. It covers a total land area of 162.09 kms² and has 12,584 inhabitants.

The five districts comprising the canton are: Ciudad Colón, Guayabo, Tabarcia, Piedras Negras, and Picagres.

This zone was discovered by Juan de Cavallón in 1560. At the end of that same century the village of Pacaca was established. That town became the modern-day Ciudad Colón.

In 1883 the canton of Pacaca came into being. The name was changed to Mora as an expression of national gratitude, and in honor of the former presidents of Costa Rica, Juan Rafael Mora-Fernández and Juan Mora-Porras. In 1883 during the term of President Próspero Fernández-Oreamuno, the title "Villa" was added to the village of Pacaca, and that same century, during the government of Alfredo Gonzáiez-Flores (1916) the name Villa Pacaca was changed to Villa Colón, in memory of the discoverer of America. Today the town is known as Ciudad Colón.

Since most of the land area of the canton sits on the northern slopes of the Hills of Puriscal, the terrain is mountainous and rough. Its fluvial system of this canton pertains to the Pacific Versant; it is drained by the rivers Pacacua, Jaris y Picagres, Quebrada Muerte, Grande y Quebrada Honda, Chucás, Tabarcia, Negro, Cañas, Quebrada Ruinas, Jorco, Viejo, and Claras.

It produces coffee, sugarcane, citrus fruits, and beef. Its climate is moderate in most places, but quite warm on the banks of the Virilla River.

Ciudad Colón, population 7,361, is the principle town of the canton. Its six *caseríos* (townships) are: El Pito, Ticufres, Quebrada Honda, Hacienda El Rodeo, Cedra y Jaris. The people here are hard-working and well-mannered. Situated in a high valley surrounded by the hills of Caliente, Tigres, and La Estrella, the landscape is picturesque, and the climate very pleasant. This town, still called by its old name, Pacaca, before the arrival of the Spanish explorers, had been the village of and Indian tribe, whose descendants are now scattered all throughout the surrounding hills.

It has a well-developed, urban section of 40 square blocks through which passes from east to west the highway that leads to Puriscal Canton. The main public buildings include the Catholic Church, simple but spacious, the *Palacio Municipal* (Town Hall), the school, the Telegraph and Post Office, and the Sanitation Department building.

Located 25 kilometers from San José, it is linked to that city by the highway that leads to Puriscal, passing through Escazú, Santa Ana, and Piedades (the old route). Today there is another, much quicker, route –the Próspero Fernández Highway.

Goicoechea Canton

This is the eighth canton of the province with respect to administrative order. It is located on a long, narrow strip of land the runs between the cantons of Moravia, Vázquez de Coronado, Montes de Oca, San José, and Cartago.

The early settlers made their homes in what is known today as Calle Blancos, the first street or road in the area. The street got its name from the great number of people with the family name Blanco, who lived there. From here the settlement grew toward the east, forming what today is the center of the canton.

This canton is drained by the river Torres and other streams, as well as the rivers Purral, Tiribí, Ipís, and Durazno, and the Mozotal, Cangrejos, Patalillos,

San Francisco de Goicoechea Church, now declared a national monument.

Patal, Barreal streams. All of these, except the Torres River, originate in the canton on the western slopes of Mount Cabeza de Vaca.

The terrain is relatively flat. The climate is temperate, and quite pleasant. Farmers in this canton produce coffee, fruits and vegetables, beans, corn, and, to a lesser extent, beef cattle. Demographic growth in recent years has centered mostly around coffee growing, although the main crop of the early farmers was tobacco.

In 1891 Goicoechea became a canton, with Guadalupe designated as the governmental seat.

The canton, named after the distinguished Franciscan priest Friar José Antonio de Liendo y Goicoechea, has a population of 79,931 and is comprised of six districts: Guadalupe, San Francisco, Calle Blancos, Mata de Plátano, Ipís, and Rancho Redondo.

Near the capital city, Guadalupe, the center of the canton, is commercially the most active and affluent town. It is, in fact, totally dedicated to business and industry. This district has an area of 2.48 kms² and a population of 25,506.

The district of San Francisco, population 3,138 with and area of a half a square kilometer, is mostly residential.

The Catholic Church there has been declared a national monument due to its unique architecture.

Calle Blancos, with an abundant source of manpower, has the greatest concentration of industry in San José Canton. Located in this district are prestigious companies such as Cofala, Coca-Cola, Cofesa. The district has 16,155 inhabitants and a land area of 2.39 kms².

Mata de Plátano, a district of 7,490 inhabitants living on a total land area of 7.85 kms² has traditionally been a farming community, mostly dedicated to coffee growing, but recently housing projects have begun to change that.

Ipís has the greatest population density in the canton –26,151 inhabitants on 5.76 kms² of land– due to numerous housing projects in the last few years: La Facio, La Mora, Zetillal, etc.

The district of Rancho Redondo, entirely rural, is dedicated mostly to cattle raising and dairy farming. The population is 1,491 inhabitants, and the land area is 12.52 kms².

The town of Guadalupe, the governmental seat of Goicoechea Canton, is scenically situated on the eastern side of San José, three kilometers from the country's capital, and extends as a finger toward the northeast. At an elevation of 1,204 meters above sea level, it has an annual mean temperature of 21°C.

In 1844 the first chapel, was dedicated to the patron saint, San José. Six years later it was rededicated to the Virgin of Guadalupe. In 1855 the construction of the first church was begun at the site of the present church, which was built and inaugurated many years later.

The first school in the town was built in 1883 in what is now the central park, across from the church. Subsequently Carlos Gagini School was built, and in 1939 the first educational center, called *Escuela Pilar Jiménez Solís*, was inaugurated. Then, in 1955 during the presidential term of José Figueres Ferrer, the *Liceo Napoleón Quesada* opened.

Goicoechea Canton, part of the greater metropolitan area, has in its jurisdiction the Calle Blancos industrial zone and another one under development –Ipís. It also has the Doctor Ricardo Jiménez Núñez Clinic, the Avance Hydroelectric Plant, the historical and architectural landmark, the Women's Reformatory, the lookout point, Rancho Redondo, and even the Cordillera Volcánica Central Forest Reserve.

Guadalupe has a good philharmonic orchestra, a nice park in front of the church, reliable, modern electrification, waterworks, and sewage disposal systems, as well as efficient postal and other services.

Santa Ana Canton

This canton is situated in the Central Tectonic Depression, at the foot of the Hills of Escazú and Puriscal. Its climate is warm and dry and quite comfortable.

It has 19,605 inhabitants and covers an area of 61.42 kms². It includes the districts of Santa Ana, Salitral, Los Pozos, Uruca, Piedades, and Brasil.

Santa Ana was settled in the Sixteenth Century. In 1850 the first Catholic chapel was built in honor of Saint Ann. In 1873 the Central Elementary School of Santa Ana was established, and in 1972, the *Liceo* began its activities. Probably the canton got its name from the first landowner, Jerónimo de Retes, who in 1658 named his land Santa Ana in honor of Saint Ann. It officially became a canton in 1927.

Santa Ana is drained by the rivers Uruca and Corrogres, the Lajas and Rodríguez streams, and the rivers Navajas, Pilas, Canca, La Cruz, San Marcos, and Muerte, which originate on the Hills of Escazú and are tributaries of the Virilla River.

The canton of Santa Ana has public elementary schools in the centers of each of its districts, an others in its largest townships. There are also several private elementary schools and a kindergarten. It has one high school –*Colegio de Santa Ana*. The main roads are generally in good condition except for the one going to Salitral and another going to Uruca-Piedades. The bus service,

considered adequate, is owned and operated by the cooperative METROCOOP, R.L.

Tourist attractions in the canton include the Simón Bolívar Park in the Uruca District, a mineral spring with excellent health properties in the Salitral District, and the green mountains offer many beautiful sights everywhere. In the district of El Brasil on the Virilla River there is a scenic waterfall called *Catarata del Brasil* frequented by many tourists. Also, the Catholic Church in Brasil is historically and architecturally interesting. Public services are modern and efficient. Electric power is distributed by the *Compañía Nacional de Fuerza y Luz* (National Power and Lighting Company). Most of the canton enjoys this service. The water system is municipal; during the dry season water must be rationed as supplies diminish. As for telephone service, there are many public telephones throughout the canton.

This canton is primarily dedicated to farming, it chief products being onions and beef cattle, but it also grows other vegetables and fruits, all of high quality. These farms are concentrated primarily in the Salitral District. Coffee is also an important crop to Santa Ana's economy.

Santuario Nacional del Santo Cristo de Esquipulas, Alajuelita.

The industry here consists, for the most part, of pottery made by individual families from clay taken from Costa Rican soil. There is also the Kan Lung Shoe Factory, the *Industria National de Acero* (INASA = National Steel Industry), contract labor assembly shops, and other small industries of various sorts. The canton, part of the greater metropolitan area, has two hydroelectric plants (Belén and Brasil) and has proposed an industrial zone.

The town of Santa Ana, the governmental seat of the canton, is located 10 kilometers from San José City, to which it is linked by the same highway that passes through Puriscal, Ciudad Colón, and Escazú. Today, however, the Próspero Fernández Freeway facilitates access to the center of the country, thereby avoiding the need to pass through Santa Ana.

The town has no park. Its most important historical buildings include a Spanish-style Catholic Church (which celebrated its centennial in 1986) and the former residence of General Jorge Volio. And, although it is not considered historical, the Andrés Bello Elementary School is over 100 years old. A prominent monument here is a statue of General Jorge Volio, that stands in front of the Municipal Building.

Santa Ana is scenic, the climate pleasant, especially in the dry season (December to May). It has 6,200 inhabitants, and what was once a small township has been grown into a well-defined town. It has a Spanish-style church, a town hall, and excellent urban services that keep it neat and clean. It also has bank branches of the *Banco National* and the *Banco de Costa Rica*, a Health Center, a Rural Guard building, and a mayor's office.

Alajuelita Canton

Alajuelita is bounded on the northeast by San José canton, on the southeast by Aserrí, on the southwest by Acosta, on the east by Desamparados, and on the west by Escazú.

Its population of 31,390 inhabitants live on a total land area of 21.17 kms².

The annual mean temperature is 21°C. Its chief products are coffee and beef cattle. The districts of this canton are Alajuelita, San Josecito, San Antonio, Concepción, and San Felipe.

The first settlers began to arrive in 1650, and the first chapel was built of adobe blocks in 1835. In 1906 the present church was consecrated and dedicated to the Holy Christ of Esquipulas. It was declared a national sanctuary on January 15, 1907.

The first school was built in 1855; in 1925 a new one was built, first called Napoleón Quesada, and then Abraham Lincoln; then in 1972 the *Liceo de Alajuelita* began its classes.

The present name of the canton has evolved since 1800 when it was called Lajuelita. Since 1806 it has been called Alajuelita. There are two versions as to the origin of the name. One states that it is derived from the river today called Alajuelita, which got its name from the fact that the whole river bed is covered with a stone called *laja* in Spanish (shoal in English). The other version states that most of the dwellers here originally came from Lajuela, the modern Alajuela. It became a canton in June of 1909.

Distinguished citizens have settled in Alajuelita. Father Manuel Alvarado, President of the Government Junta in 1823, was one of the owners of the Hacienda La Verbana, in the San Felipe District —one of the first haciendas of the canton. Several famous people in national life —Saturnino Tinoco, Federico Tinoco Yglesias, Federico Tinoco-Granados, Fabián Esquivel, and others— were all owners of Hacienda La Verbana.

An interesting detail often mentioned is that when the first coup d'etat occurred on May 27, 1838 to put Braulio Carrillo in power, he himself was on his farm in Concepción de Alajuelita "planting beans".

Today Alajuelita is a quiet community, with many family operated cottage industries, and a flourishing agricultural development in the districts of San Antonio, San Josecito, and part of San

Felipe, where magnificent coffee (the chief crop) and vegetables are grown.

As far as industry is concerned, Alajuelita Canton has been limited in its development due to the stipulations of the National Urban Development Plan, which offers no facilities for industry. Hence, most of the people here must commute to the capital or other nearby industrial centers to work.

The canton is situated in a favored spot in the Central Region, that affords visitors to *Cerro La Cruz*, the San Antonio District, and part of San Josecito panoramic views of practically the whole of San José. There is an excellent asphalt road leading up to San Jose, where tourists can enjoy splendid sights from two different lookout points.

The canton is drained by the rivers Rojo, Tiribí, Cañas, Quebrada Común, Río Limón and its tributaries, Quebradas Guacamayo, Chinchilla, Coche, Poás and its tributaries, as well as the Río Lajas, and Río Agres.

This canton, also comprising part of the greater metropolitan area, offers as special attractions to visitors the *Santuario de Esquipulas*, Mount San Miguel, where there is a huge iron cross, 26 meters high,

built in 1933, inaugurated as a national monument in 1934, and in 1984 lighting was installed, making it visible at night a great distance away.

The canton is surrounded by mountains and urban sectors consisting mostly of the dwellings of very poor people.

The city of Alajuelita has 8,280 inhabitants. It is four kilometers from the capital city to which it is linked by a good road.

In the Catholic Church the parishioners pay homage to a statue of the *Santo Cristo de Esquipulas* (the Holy Christ of Esquipulas), to which traditional annual pilgrimages bring many devout followers every January 15. There are good municipal services and others such as the Red Cross, and a bank branch.

Public services include six elementary and pre-kinder schools, a postal-telegraph office, a branch of the National Bank of Costa Rica, the Civil and Penal Court, a modest soccer stadium, basketball, volleyball, and mini-soccer courts, the Town Hall, a health and nutrition center, a Cultural House and five Catholic Churches, and around 25 churches of other non-Catholic Christian faiths, and two new shopping centers (one of which includes a *Palí*, a discount grocery store).

The rate of deforestation in the mountainous zone over the last few years has been alarming. Moreover, there is a great need for adequate housing, sources of employment, playgrounds, health centers and specialized trade schools, as well as sewers, water systems to provide suitable drinking water, and recreational facilities, especially for children and young people.

Some traditional crafts have survived until today: pottery making, ceramics, and other typical activities. The area is still relatively peaceful, although some delinquency, characteristic of urban zones has been gradually creeping in.

Most people living in Alajuelita Canton are of the working class, second in numbers are farmers and farm laborers, and there are only a small percentage of professionals.

Today a good system of roads makes travel easy; electric power and public and private telephone service covers the entire canton.

Several drinks and dishes are typical in this canton. The drinks (lightly fermented) include *chicha* (made of corn, pineapple juice, and molasses), *chinchiví* (made of sugarcane juice), and *guarapo* (also based on sugarcane juice). Among the typical dishes *picadillo de arracache* (a hash made of a wild root, potatoes, and sausage) is the most well-known. These dishes and drinks are customarily sold during festivals in honor of saints.

The canton of Alajuelita offers three main tourist attractions: the *Cruz de Alajuelita* (Cross of Alajuelita), situated in the San Antonio District, the lookouts San José and Imperial, located in the same district, the *Santuario Nacional del Santo Cristo de Esquipulas* (National Sanctuary of the Holy Christ of Esquipulas), in the canton seat.

Vázquez de Coronado Canton

Situated on the western slopes of the Hills of General and Bella Vista and the foothills of the Irazú on the northeast end of San José Province, Vázquez de Coronado has 24,514 inhabitants, and a total land area of 222.20 kms². It is comprised of the districts, San Isidro, San Rafael, Jesús, and Patalillo.

Its uneven terrain is drained by the rivers Durazno, Macho, Desarrumbo, Cascaja, and Blanco (the latter two being tributaries of the Río Sucio), the Honduras (called Zurquí at its source), the Virilla, the Varela Stream, the rivers, Ipís and Agra, which originate in the canton.

The canton produces coffee, fruits and vegetables, and ornamental plants, but because of its rich pasture lands, it produces excellent beef and milk. In fact, it sends more milk each day to the capital than any other canton. It has now also become famous for its fine apples and peaches.

The region was explored and conquered by Juan Vázquez de Coronado, who considered it one of the choicest spots in the Spanish Kingdom. In 1864 it was given the name San Isidro de la Arenilla, as first settler had brought with him a wooden statue of San Isidro Labrador. Since that time, it has been the patron saint of the area. The name Arenilla has to do with the sandy lands caused by flooding that occurred in what today is the center of San Isidro.

In November 1910 the canton was established under the name of Vázquez de Coronado in honor of the conquistador and governor, Juan Vázquez de Coronado.

The first chapel was erected in 1864, and in 1878 the parish church was built. By 1886 construction of a brick church was started, and by 1928 the present Catholic church building began to be built. Tourists from all over come just to see this gothic construction.

The first elementary school was built in 1886, in 1961 the present one was built, and in 1970 the high school was inaugurated.

The town of San Isidro (population 9,154) sits on a plain, 1,385 meters above sea level, nine kilometers from San José

City. Its climate is pleasantly cool –an average of 18°C. Both for its climate and scenery, San Isidro is frequented in the dry months by families from the capital, who want to a way for a picnic outing in the country.

In this canton are the headquarters for the Inter-American Institute of Cooperation on Agriculture (IICA) and the Clodomiro Picado Snake Zoo, which has a laboratory for producing snake-bite serum.

But what characterizes this town more than anything else is its church, with its beautiful, bold architecture, one of the finest works in the nation, whose elegance is matched by its sacred images and embellishments –a work of art any capital city could be proud of.

Acosta Canton

This canton is situated in the territory of the Hills of Bustamante, on which the cantons of Puriscal and Aserrí are also located. Acosta is bounded on the northeast and the north by the cantons of Mora, Escazú, and Alajuelita; and on the south by Parrita Canton.

The canton has an area of 342.24 kms² and 14,853 inhabitants. Its principal farm crops are coffee, itabo, macadamia, citrus fruit, corn, beans, and beef. There are two ornamental plant processing cooperatives in San Luis (a town in the canton). Because of the great demand, these cooperatives are exporting large quantities of ornamental plants, itabos, and macadamia to the United States of America and Canada, thus providing jobs for many young people in the canton. There is also a citrus processing cooperative in Barrio María Auxiliadora. This cooperative prepares and sells orange juice to the Dos Pinos and Coronado dairy cooperatives. Another cooperative processes coffee and also exports some of its products to other countries.

In the San Luis District another industry owned by a women's association makes jams and preserves and sells them in the capital.

Regarding tourism, one tourist center, is the Balneario El Valle, a swimming resort located some 10 minutes from the center of San Ignacio. This resort has recreational areas, swimming pools and meadows all designed to give visitors a delightful day in the country. It should also be noted that the municipality has purposed to do everything possible to get the national government to declare the Acosta Route (Bijagual-Parrita) a national highway, since it is quite a short route to Parrita.

Acosta Canton has a relatively cool climate. Although this is a mountainous zone, the soil is very fertile. It is located 29 kilometers from the capital city along a paved road. Its districts are San Ignacio, Guaitil, Palmichal, Cangrejal, and Sabanillas.

This canton was first settled by people who had migrated from Desamparados, Aserrí, Alajuelita, and San Francisco de Dos Ríos, between 1874 and 1875.

The first chapel was built in 1878, and in 1899 a parish church was built in 1899. The elementary school at first used the house of one of the early settlers; in 1944 construction was begun on a new building. The *Liceo de Acosta* (high school) opened its doors for classes in 1966, and in 1976 it was converted to technical school, and its named was changed to *Colegio Técnico Profesional Agropecuario de Acosta* (Agricultural Technical School of Acosta).

The most important buildings of Acosta include a branch of the *Banco Nacional de Costa Rica*, a Social Security office, an extension office of the Ministry of Agriculture and Livestock, the Mayor's Office, the elementary school, the Agricultural School, the Canton Delegation, the Health Center, the Post Office, and the Monseñor Sanabria Park in San Ignacio.

The principal streets are asphalt, and the country roads are gravel but in very good condition.

As for public services, practically the whole canton has the basic ones, and even the smallest, most remote villages have electric power.

The districts have supervised public telephones, and in the center of San

Ignacio there are public coin-operated phones, two of which are in the central park, and two more in the *Delegación Cantonal* (Canton Delegation). Bus service is provided by a cooperative –COOPECARAIGRES R.L.– located in Barrio María Auxiliadora in San Ignacio in a comfortable building where there is also a filling station.

Currently, the *Caja Costarricense de Seguro Social* (CCSS = Costa Rican Social Security Department) is negotiating the construction of a clinic in Sabanillas that would provide service to the neighboring towns of Caspirola, Teruel, Colorado, Bijagual and Breñon. This much needed project is close to being approved.

The whole area comprising the district of Sabanillas is beautiful with its gorgeous mountains and rivers over which passes the highway to Parrita. Since this road also comes very close to San José, proposals are being made to the Costa Rican Institute of Tourism (ICT) to build a tourist center in the area.

In this canton there is an archeological monument that was discovered on the Pozo Azul Farm in Bijagual de Acosta, owned by Mr. Sergio Rojas. It was uncovered by specialists from the National Museum, which has a great deal of data on the area. After a thorough investigation, the museum agreed to present the case to the National Archeological Commission, and the commission issued a decree to conserve the site, given the importance of the find. One can get to this farm on a wide gravel road. (As stated, in 1987 a proposal was made to the Ministry of Public Works and Transportation (MOPT) to make that road a national highway, and now there is much more reason to do so.) The archeological remains are found dispersed over a broad terrace, located at the confluence of the rivers Candelaria and Parrita (also called Pirrís). Around the farm house many boulders have been observed, some of them seem to be lined up in rows. The mounds found have several forms –some circular, others elongated that measure from two to five meters wide by 10 to 25 meters long. The circular ones could

have been a sort of plaza. Three rectangular tombs that were uncovered have boulder walls and lids. Inside of them were found earthenware pots, ceramic dishes, statuettes, and stones, as well as some gold figurines. There once lived in this region a large Indian population. The municipality has requested that this whole farm be declared a municipal, regional and national archeological site.

The canton was named after Tomás de Acosta, the governor of the province of Costa Rica before it was a colony (1797-1810).

The town of San Ignacio, with 5,036 inhabitants, is located on the skirts of the Hills of Escazú, some 10 kilometers from the town of Aserrí, to which it is linked by good asphalt road.

Tibás Canton

Located between the cantons of San José, Goicoechea, Moravia, and Santo Domingo, it has a total land area of 8.15 kms^2 and a population of 57,683, i.e., 7,079 inhabitants per square kilometer. The principle agricultural activity is coffee growing, but only in small sectors. On the west side of the canton, in Barrio Colima, is an industrial zone in a state of development, with various kinds of industry dispersed throughout the area.

In terms of area, this is one of San José's smallest cantons, but it is also one of the most populous. It comprises the districts of San Juan, Cinco Esquinas, and Anselmo Llorente.

The first settlers of the this canton arrived during the Sixteenth Century, and until the Eighteenth Century the descendants of one of those Spanish settlers, Cristóbal Chaves, were still known to be living in the territory.

In 1835 the construction of the first chapel was begun, and in 1865 a parish church was built and named after John the Baptist (*San Juan Bautista*).

In 1886 the first elementary school was built (Miguel Obregón Lizano Elementary School), and in 1958 the *Liceo Mauro Fernández* (a high school) opened for classes.

Tibás officially became a canton in July of 1914. Its name is of native Indian origin and means "hot" or "beautiful river".

The canton is drained by very few rivers: the Rivera Stream, and the rivers Virilla and the Torres, which are canton limits. The governmental seat of the canton is San Juan, with 22,415 inhabitants, located two kilometers north of the capital city of San José, on a high plain. Since there are few water sources here, it was necessary to install a costly pipeline to bring in sufficient suitable water from the mountains to serve the needs of the people. It is a lively town surrounded by coffee plantations and gardens, with straight, wide streets, well-lighted at night, and telephone and telegraph services that cover the whole town. The schools are spacious and well-equipped; the church is elegant and aesthetically decorated in its interior. Most of the canton is very close to the capital.

The city covers a wide area, as it was established in 1835 (then called El Murciélago) as the capital of the nation. The whole area is divided into lots to form a perfectly symmetrical and rectangular center.

The canton has fine shopping centers and very good public services fitting for any modern city.

Moravia Canton

Barrio La Guaria, Moravia

Situated among the cantons of Tibás, Santo Domingo, San Isidro, Vázquez de Coronado, and Goicoechea, is Moravia, with 33,038 inhabitants living in three districts: San Vicente, San Jerónimo, and Trinidad.

The terrain is uneven, but the soil is fertile and watered by the rivers Ipís and San Francisco, tributaries of the Virilla. It produces magnificent coffee, beans, fruits and vegetables, as well as milk from its fine dairy cows.

Moravia acquired its name when it became the fourteenth canton of the province, by decree No. 55 of August 1, 1914, just sixty days into the term of President Alfredo González Flores.

The population of Moravia emerged out of a nameless forest area during the early part of the Eighteenth Century. History records that in 1736 when San José was founded, there were already numerous dwellers north of the Río Torres. It began with around 15 settlers, all poor farmers, probably descendants of the Spanish conquistadors, but not famous ones.

Since then the population has continually grown, never losing its homogeneity, and always with the spontaneity of numerous families from the interior of the country, who have made their homes here, most owning their own property.

San Jerónimo covers the most extensive area: 18.58 kms². La Trinidad has 4.67 km² and San Vicente 5.37 kms². The total area, then is 28.62 kms². The canton stretches from southeast to northeast. The whole canton is fertile, but in recent years its agricultural use is more and more being sacrificed for progress in other realms, especially urban growth.

Large areas are devoted to schools that teach sciences and arts, as well as new residential zones, all of which have led to a decline in farm production, especially in San Vicente. The La Trinidad District, also heading in that direction, still reserves a good portion of its soil for growing coffee and fruits and vegetables, but it is, slowly but surely, becoming an extension of the capital district as well.

In San Jerónimo agricultural activities still predominate, with a substantial dairy production. Important people from San José already have sizable land holdings here, and farming continues to give way to greater an greater urban development.

Within the Moravia District is part of the Cordillera Central Forest Preserve, located in La Hondura, which has been a national preserve since 1888, by a decree of President Bernardo Soto. Further, a substantial portion of the Braulio Carrillo National Park stretches from southeast to northeast over the entire canton of Moravia. It must be remembered that the road to Carrillo (located at the confluence of the rivers Sucio and Honduras) was Costa Rica's artery of communication with the Old World, created out of the need to get the coffee raised in the interior to Puerto Limón for export to European markets. Through this route, too, passed the Bishop, Dr. Augusto Thiel into exile on July 18, 1884. (*Atlas Cantonal*, 1987).

With respect to education, Moravia has several kindergartens, many elementary schools, and a good number of high schools, both public and private, such as the *Liceo Laboratorio* (Laboratory School) of the University of Costa Rica. Some are staffed by nuns and priests (Catholic), and following a bilingual curriculum and method of study, English-Spanish, except for the Japanese School of Costa Rica.

Regarding employment, hundreds of people from Moravia lend their services to industry and commerce in other parts of the country, while others work right in the canton. Moreover, many men and women come to Moravia each day from neighboring cantons to work there –in various large and medium-sized industries, as well as in different types of stores. Because of the excellent manufacture of leather goods some years ago, Moravia was acclaimed by an Executive Decree, which declared it the "Leather Industry Canton", just as Sarchí had been decreed the "Typical Ox Cart Making Canton".

The name Moravia was promoted in Congress by Deputy Leonidas Briceño (from Guanacaste), in honor of Juan Rafael Mora. And although the proposal was not backed by the general consensus of the citizens of the new canton, it was accepted by the group. But since there was already a canton called Mora, the name was modified to Moravia.

San Vicente, the canton seat, is located four kilometers northeast of downtown San José. At an elevation of 1,231 meters above sea level, its has an average annual temperature of 21°C. It has a considerable populated area with splendid private schools and a town hall. Of its 24,661 inhabitants many work in the capital city.

This is one of the most attractive towns in San José Province, both for its climate and its tranquility. Is Catholic Church, large and well-kept; it has a beautiful altar made of limestone, unique in the country, as a marvelous work of sculpture.

The town is linked to Guadalupe by a short stretch of paved road, and to San Juan of Tibás by a good asphalt road. It is also close to the capital, and good, regular bus services carry passengers both ways several times an hour.

Montes de Oca Canton

This canton is bounded on the north by Goicoechea, on the south by the cantons of Curridabat and La Unión, on the east by Cartago Canton, and on the west by the canton of San José. Its maximum breadth is 16 kilometers.

Around the year 1700 the town now called San Pedro, Montes de Oca was known as Santiago de la Granadilla. The name was later changed to Villa de San Pedro del Mojón, in reference to the geographic landmark (*mojón*) that marked the limit between this district and San José (*Atlas Cantonal*, 1987).

The present name is in honor of Faustino Montes de Oca, a distinguished citizen that diligently sought the progress of the community. In 1881 the first parish church was erected, and the current Catholic Church was consecrated in 1958.

This canton has several high schools: *Liceo José Joaquín Vargas Calvo*, *Liceo de Monterrey*, and *Colegio Calasanz*.

The canton was created in 1915 with four districts: San Pedro, Sabanilla, Mercedes, and San Rafael. Today it

The University of Costa Rica in San Pedro, the governmental seat of Montes de Oca Canton.

occupies an area of 15.16 kms² and has a population of 39,065. The rivers that drain the canton include the Torres and its tributary streams –the Patal, Salitrillos, and Negritos–, the Río Ocloro, and the Poró Stream.

The town of San Pedro, the governmental seat of the canton sits at an elevation of 1,205 meters above sea level. It has very good public services and transportation. This, the most populous district of the canton with its 24,519 inhabitants, covers a land area of 4.82 kms². It makes up part of the greater metropolitan area. In it is located the main facilities of the largest university in the country, *Ciudad Universitaria Rodrigo Facio* of the University of Costa Rica. Other universities whose headquarters are here are the Autonomous University of Central America, and a fairly new one, the University of Puerto Rico.

At the eastern end of the canton is one of the most frequented parks in the country, *Parque del Este.*

Agriculturally it produces mainly coffee, fruits and vegetables, ornamental plants, and milk.

This fifteenth canton of San José province is touches the east of San José City. San Pedro (the town closest to San José) has grown so much in the last few years that it has overflowed its jurisdictional limits to become yet another extension of the capital city.

Turrubares Canton

Turrubares, the sixteenth canton of San José Province, is comprised of the following districts: San Pablo, San Pedro, San Juan de Mata, and San Luis. It is bounded on the north by the Río Grande de Tárcoles, on the south and west by Puntarenas Province, and on the east by Puriscal Canton.

On a total land area of 415.69 kms² live 4,417 inhabitants, dispersed throughout the canton. This agricultural community produces abundant corn, beans, rice, sugarcane, and beef cattle. These products are sold at the markets in Orotina and San José. The climate here is, for the most part, mildly warm, but cool in some high spots –the heights of Poró, Nasas, and Turrubares, which belong to the *Cerros de Puriscal.*

The first settlers to these parts arrived during the second half of the Eighteenth Century from neighboring zones.

The first chapel was built in 1879, and in 1897 the present Catholic Church was built and dedicated to San Pablo. The first elementary school (San Pablo) was erected in 1942. The Technical Agricultural High School of Turrubares began its activities in 1974.

It is believed that the name of the canton was derived from the Indian word *Turruraba* which evolved into *Turrubara*, corresponding to the chief that ruled the region. Or perhaps, the canton got its name from the Turrubares River that crosses it.

The canton seat is San Pablo with a population of 755. The main road is the one that goes from Santiago de Puriscal to Orotina. There is a telegraph service; mail is carried to and from the capital city by the *Ferrocarril al Pacífico* (Pacific Railway). The San Juan District, with 2,648 inhabitants, is considerably bigger than the head of the canton. The canton overlaps the Turrubares Protected Zone and also covers most of the Carara Biological Reserve.

Dota Canton

This seventeenth canton of San José Province has 4,934 inhabitants. In accordance with the decree of October 23, 1931, it includes the following districts: Santa María, Jardín, and Copey. It is bounded on the north by Desamparados Canton, on the south by Pérez Zeledón Canton, on the east by Cartago Province, and on the west by Tarrazú Canton.

Santa María is the governmental seat of the canton, which along with its townships –San Rafael, Higueronal, Cedral, La Guaria, San Lucas, San Joaquín, and Naranjo– has a total population of 3,324. Dota Canton produces excellent coffee, coveted for its aroma, and unmatched quality. Its also produces citrus fruit and beef cattle. It has easy access to the interior of the country by means of the *Carretera Interamericana* (Inter-American Highway), which goes through the eastern side of canton. The rest of the canton is linked to this highway by the road to Tarrazú.

The area was first settled in 1864 and then was given the name Santa María in

1867. In 1870 the parish church, called Santa María de la Cueva Santa, was built. In 1893 the present church was built. In 1885 the existing school, *Escuela República de Bolivia* was built, and in 1972 the *Colegio Técnico Profesional Daniel Flores* (Daniel Flores Technical High School) opened for classes.

There is also a Social Security Office, the Health Center, an office of the Ministry of Agriculture, a chapter of the Red Cross, a Ministry of Public Works and Transportation Office, a Rural Assistance Guard Unit, a branch of the National Bank of Costa Rica, the Municipal Building, the Santa María de Dota Park (the only one in the canton), and several historical buildings, including three adobe houses and a monument to the fallen in battle from both sides of the Civil War of 1948.

The community has electric power, public water service, telephones, a postal-telegraph office, and buses, that include very good service to and from the capital city.

According to a popular account, the canton got its name from the journeys made by the Chief Ota of the Quepos Indians. Adding a d to the name, it became Dota. (*Atlas Cantonal* 1987).

The canton is drained by several major rivers: the Savegre, which is joined by the Río Brujo and its tributaries, the Roncador, and the streams Ojo de Agua Seca and Jaboncillo. In addition, there

Another view of the University of Costa Rica, Rodrigo Facio Campus in San Pedro, Montes de Oca.

is the Naranjo also joined by the Río Brujo, and the streams Llano Grande y Salitrillo, the rivers San Joaquín and San Lucas, and the tributary streams Pirranga and Guaria. Other rivers include the Pirrís, Pedregoso, San Rafael and tributary streams Palmital, Loaiza, Chontal, and Rivas, and the Parrita River with the Yugo stream, all of which originate right in the canton.

Seventy-eight percent of the canton's area is taken up in forest reserve (Los Santos) and five percent in buffer zone (Cerro Nara).

Curridabat Canton

According to political-administrative order, this is the eighteenth canton in the province. It is one of the closest to the capital, but the next to the last to establish its own government as a canton. Until 1929, it had been a district of San José Canton.

It is bounded on the north by the canton of Montes de Oca, on the east and south by Desamparados Canton, and on the west by San José. Its four districts are the town of Curridabat, Granadilla, Sánchez, and Tirrases. The population is 31,954.

The town of Curridabat, today with 19,821 inhabitants, is one of the oldest in Costa Rica. In the sixteenth century under the Spanish government it had been an important political unit, but when Costa Rica became an independent republic, it remained a mere district of San José Canton. But finally, in 1929 it regained its status as *villa*, and was made the governmental seat of the canton. It wasn't until 1970 that its category of *ciudad* (town or city) was confirmed.

It has a beautiful Catholic Church, a public elementary school, and a populous central zone. It is drained by the rivers Puruses and María Aguilar. Unfortunately, those rivers also serve as sewers for a large quantity of industrial and human wastes.

Coffee and livestock are the only agricultural products of Curridabat. The land of the canton, covering an area of 15.95 kms², is mostly flat, well irrigated, and fertile. Its average elevation of 1,000 meters above sea level makes for normal temperatures that vary from 20 to 25°C.

The current parish church was built in 1905. The first school was established in 1860; the present one, Juan Santamaría School, was built in 1965. The *Liceo de Curridabat* (high school) began its activities in 1972.

The name Curridabat evolved from the name of the Indian Chief Conirana, who ruled the region when the first Spaniards arrived. (*Altlas Cantonal* 1987).

The canton is drained by the rivers María Aguilar y Tiribí, Pio, Piuses, Chagüite, and Ocloro, as well as the Poró, Minas, Granadilla, and Zopilote streams.

Curridabat forms part of the greater metropolitan area. Located within it is an developing industrial zone covering 11% of the area of the canton. This industrial zone extends along the main road between San Pedro de Montes de Oca and the capital.

Pérez Zeledón Canton

Pérez de Zeledón was the second to the last to become a canton in San José Province. It is bounded on the north by the cantons of Dota and Paraíso, on the east by the cantons of Turrialba, Talamanca, and Buenos Aires, on the south by Buenos Aires Canton, and on the west by Osa and Aguirre cantons.

It has a population of 82,970 inhabitants. It produces coffee, vegetables, and beef cattle. It encompasses the districts of Ureña (or San Isidro), El General, Daniel Flores, Rivas, San Pedro, Platanares, Pejibaye, Cajón, Barú, Río Nuevo, and El Páramo. With a total land area of 19,905.51 kms², it has the largest areas of all of the cantons in San José Province.

The canton is drained by the watershed of the Río Grande de Térraba, including the Río General, Pacuar, Limón, Pejibaye, Peje, and Convento; and the watershed of the rivers Savegre and Barú, both of which originate right in the canton.

The zone occupied by this canton was inhabited by Brunca Indians when the first Spaniards arrived in 1600.

The first chapel was built in 1850, and in 1967 the present one was inaugurated. Since 1902 there has been an elementary school in the canton, since 1953 there has been a high school, today called the *Liceo UNESCO*, and since 1973 a regional branch of the National University has operated here.

Pérez de Zeledón became a canton in 1931, named in honor of Pedro Pérez Zeledón, a distinguished Costa Rican. (*Atlas Cantonal*, 1987). Its territory constitutes an immense reserve of wealth for the future of the nation, and it is linked to the interior of the country by the Inter-American Highway.

San Isidro, the governmental seat of the canton with 28,261 inhabitants, is a driving force toward advancing development. In a few short years a very active commerce has emerged, directly linked to San José. It has a wide variety of stores and commercial establishments, and excellent services of electric power, water and sewage treatment, and air transport that links it with the rest of the country. It geographic position greatly favors it, as it sits in a fertile and picturesque valley called *Valle de El General* with a magnificent climate, has made this region just as important agriculturally as the valleys of Cartago and San José.

Notable institutions and facilities in this town include the *Instituto Nacional de Aprendizaje* (National Learning Institute), the Dr. Fernando Escalante-Pradilla Hospital, the *Casa del Refugio* (a national monument) located in the village of Ojo de Agua, and a multi-sports arena. This town also has a beautiful Catholic Cathedral, having formerly been an episcopal diocese of this region.

Its principle agricultural activities involve coffee, beans, corn, tobacco, and fruit trees, as well as livestock raising. The main attractions for tourists are centered around the foothills of the Cordillera de Talamanca, especially the Cerro de la Muerte (Buena Vista), and the Chirripó National Park.

León Cortés Castro Canton

This canton came into being by Law No. 12 of June 12, 1962. It is bounded on the north by Desamparados Canton and partly by Aserrí Canton, on the east by Dota Canton, on the south also by Dota Canton and Tarrazú, and on the west by Aserrí Canton.

It is comprised of five districts and their townships: 1) San Pablo, the canton seat (townships are Loma de Angostura, Montes de Oro, Rosario, Carrizales, La Cuesta San Antonio, and Granadilla); 2) San Andrés (townships are Higuerón, Rastrójales, Llano Grande, and Bajo Gamboa); 3) Llano Bonito (townships are Santa Juana, Bajo Mora, San Rafael Abajo, Santa Rosa, San Francisco, and San Rafael Arriba; 4) San Isidro, and; 5) Santa Cruz (townships are Cedral and La Lucha).

The canton has a population of 8,087 inhabitants, including 2,532 in the governmental seat. The main products are coffee, hemp, and beef.

This canton, which during pre-Colombian times was completed inhabited by Indians, was not settled until the second half of the last century.

The present canton seat was named after Saint Paul (*San Pablo*) and the father of the first citizen that arrived. The first chapel was built in 1879, and in 1972 the current parish chapel was erected. The first school of the canton was established in 1880, and the present school was inaugurated in 1921, and named after Manuel Castro Blanco, the first settler. Since 1973 the *Colegio Técnico Profesional Industrial León Cortés Castro* (technical industrial high school) has been operating.

In 1962 León Cortés Castro officially became a canton (canton number 23 of San José Province). It was named after and in gratitude for the Costa Rican President León Cortés Castro, due to the many services he rendered on behalf of this canton. (*Atlas Cantonal*, 1987).

Note: the three cantons, Dota, Tarrazú, and León Cortés, for their proximity and similarity are commonly called "Los Santos" ("The Saints") (Saint Mary, Saint Mark, and Saint Paul).

ALAJUELA PROVINCE

Alajuela Province is bounded on the north by the country of Nicaragua, on the east by Heredia Province, on the south by San José Province, and on the west by the provinces of Puntarenas and Guanacaste.

In terms of population and administrative order, this is the second province in the nation. It has an area of 9,752.8 kms², making it the third largest in land area (after Puntarenas and Guanacaste).

Politically it is divided into 15 cantons and has a total population of 427,962 inhabitants. (See Map No. 11).

The three last cantons, Upala, Los Chiles, and Guatuso (previously districts of Grecia Canton), all became cantons in March of 1970.

In the northern part of Alajuela Province are the plains of San Carlos and Guatuso, a rich store of agricultural wealth. And, over the last few years the construction of new roads that cross these zones have facilitated the explotation of this wealth.

Every variety of climate found in Costa Rica is found in this province: from chilly in the northern parts of the central cantons, San Ramón and Alfaro Ruiz, to hot in the northern cantons, as well as in Orotina and San Mateo cantons.

The province is drained by a multitude of rivers, some of which empty into the Río Grande de Tárcoles, the artery that empties into the Pacific Ocean. Other rivers empty into the San Carlos and Río Frío rivers on the northern versant of the country.

The mountains of Aguacate on the west and San Carlos on the north, as well as the Poás Volcano and some of its ramifications, are the most prominent peaks in the province.

For many years agroindustry was the main occupation of Alajuelans, but with the industrial development initiated when Costa Rica signed the first bilateral free trade treaties, and later when Costa Rica joined the Central American Common Market, various industries have been emerging, that range from the production of canned goods to large-scale machinery manufacture.

This development, however, has not hindered, but rather has benefitted agriculture and livestock raising. In fact, today San Carlos produces the best quality milk in the nation. Coffee, sugarcane, vegetables, strawberries, peaches, mangos, and cashews are all crops whose production has been greatly expanded. All of these are now exported on a large scale. Other significant agricultural exports include flowers, various tubers, *caña india* (used in making incense), ornamental plants, tobacco, beef, and poultry.

The first europeans to arrive settled between the rivers Toro and Tres Amigos. Then in 1574, east of the middle of the Jesús María River an Indian settlement, called Santa Catalina, was established. After the Eighteenth Century other settlers began to farm the areas between the rivers Alajuela, Targuás, Ciruelas, and Río Grande. It was in the village of Alajuela that the first chapel was built, and from which the modern city and province of Alajuela grew.

Today, this province is one of the most properous in the country. Moreover, it has very good schools at all levels: the Western Branch of the University of Costa Rica (since 1968) located in San Ramón, a branch of the Technological Institute of Costa Rica in Santa Clara, San Carlos (since 1975), the *Colegio Universitario de Alajuela* (Alajuela College), the *Escuela Centroamericana de Ganadería* (Central American Livestock School) in Balsa de Atenas, and others.

In terms of land area, this province is the third largest, after Puntarenas and Guanacaste, and in terms of population, it is the second largest, after San José. It has a population density of 44 inhabitants per square kilometer. The illiteracy rate is 7.9%. The unemployement rate is 6.3%, with 47.4% of the population economically active. Most of the population works in agriculture (43%), while 29.3% is engaged in other activities (1984 Census).

Opposite page: Monument to the National Hero Juan Santa María, in Juan Santa María Park, Alajuela City.

Central Park, actually named Plaza del Benemérito General Tomás Guardia, Alajuela City.

In this province are seven operating hidroelectric plants, two electric power cooperatives, and the reservoir of the La Garita Dam, the International Airport of Juan Santamaría, and the Itiquís Irrigation Project, whose purpose is to improve the socio-economic development of the region.

Alajuela Canton

This canton includes the western end of the Central Depression and the first slopes and foothills of the Barva and Poás volcanoes. It is drained by the rivers Poás, Alajuela (also called Maravilla), Ciruelas,

La Agonía Church, Alajuela City.

Itiqués, Río Segundo, El Tambor, Tizate, Cororado, and other smaller ones, all tributaries of the Río Grande de Tárcoles.

The canton seat is Alajuela City, also the capital of the province. Its districts are: San José, La Guácima (also called Santiago Oeste), Río Segundo (also called Santiago Este), Sabanilla, San Isidro, Carrizal, Sarapiquí, La Garita, Desamparados, San Antonio, Turrúcares, San Rafael de Ojo de Agua, and Tambor.

In La Garita is the La Garita Hidroelectric Plant, owned and operated by the *Instituto Costarricense de Electricidad* (ICE = Costa Rican Electrical Institute), the first one built by this governmental enterprise. In San Antonio is the largest slautering house in the country, Montecillos, and also Flour Milling Cooperative of Costa Rica, which produces virtually all of the wheat flour in the country.

Because of their diverse climates, each of Alajuela's districts is distinguished for different agricultural or livestock products. For example, San Isidro and Sabanilla are chilly most of the time, while Guácima and Turrúcares are quite hot.

The population of Alajuela Canton was 127,472 at the 1984 census, 56,972 more than in had been 38 years before.

110

The Cathedral and its dome in Alajuela City is over 100 years old.

Alajuela City

The village of Alajuela was established on October 12, 1782 between the rivers Alajuela (Maravilla) and Ciruelas, as the population center then called La Lajuela was formed from the inhabitants of this community and those of Poás, Río Grande, Targuases, and Ciruelas. This was a stupendous choice: it was the best location in the Barva Valley, and at an elevation of 952 meters it has an ideal climate with and average temperature of 23°C.

As the country developed this town became linked, first by railroad and then by highway, with the ports of Limón on the Caribbean side, and Puntarenas and, recently, Caldera on the Pacific side.

Here, too, is the Juan Santamaría International Airport (the largest in the country), 21 kilometers from San José along the General Cañas Freeway, and 21.5 kilometers on a National Highway from Heredia.

Alajuela has 15 avenues running east and west and 11 streets running north and south, all perfectly straight. Circling the city is *Calle Ancha*, which joins the National Highway. It is the only street in the country that circles a whole town.

The park commonly known as *Parque Central* is actually Plaza del Benemérito General Tomás Guardia, named for this illustrious past president. In this park there is a water fountain, and a kiosco, where the local band frequently gives concerts. There is also a bust of the famous historian Efraín Arroyo Blanco, in recognition of his struggles on behalf of the city.

Another park is the *Parque Juan Santamaría*, in which stands the statue, *Héroe Nacional* (National Hero), honoring the national hero who give his life in a sublime sacrifice, at the Battle of Rivas

Palmares Park, and in the background, San Rafael Hospital, Alajuela City.

on April 11, 1856. There is also the *Monumento de los Héroes Caídos* honoring the fallen in battle in the national campaign against the "filibusters"; General Próspero Fernández Oreamuno Park (also called *Parque del Cementerio*); Palmares Park, named after the canton with the same name, *Parque de Niños* (Children's Park); and the Estercita Castro Children's Library; as well as several sports plazas in Barrio de El Carmen.

Some of the most important public buildings are the Town Hall, the Civic Center, the Juan Santamaría Cultural-Historical Museum, the *Colegio Universitario de Alajuela* Building, the Institute of Alajuela, the San Rafael Clinic, the Marcial Rodríguez Conejo Clinic, branch buildings of the banks –*Nacional de Costa Rica, Anglo, Crédito Agrícola de Cartago*, and the *Mutual de Vivienda*; and soon there will be a Municipal Theater. There are magnificent private business buildings and many beautiful residences as well.

The cathedral and its dome, over a century old, are symbols Alajuelans hold dear as though they were part of their own heart. Inside the cathedral lie the remains of the former presidents, General Tomás Guardia and León Cortés Castro. The *Templo del Santo Cristo de Esquipulas* (Temple of the Holy Christ of Esquipulas), also called *La Agonía*, is one of the most impressive churches in the republic, both for its architectural proportions and for its artistic structure.

Other Catholic church buildings in the city are those of La Concepción, El Llano, El Carmen, Corazón de Jesús, and the Chapel of María Auxiliadora.

There are also churches of other denominations, such as the Baptists, Methodists, Seventh Day Adventists, Mormons, and others. Alajuela is definitely an exemplary liberal city in this respect.

Interesting tourists sites include the Fraijanes Lagoon in San Isidro and several recreational centers.

During the last few years the city has been rapidly growing out of what had been known as its city limits. Now clustered around the original center are the barrios of Villa Hermosa, Ciruelas, San Luis, El Arroyo, and La Agonía –the oldest ones– as well as the most recent, Casas Baratas, Lotes Murillo, Lotes Llobet, Cristo Rey, Paso Flores Cementerio, El Brasil, Pueblo Nuevo, El Retiro, Guadalupe, Meza Tropicana Uno, Tropicana Dos, El Cafetal, Aguilar Soto, Miraflores El Erizo, and Los Higuerones.

The city and its suberbs have excellent services of public lighting, electric power for houses and business, and drinking water from the city's own water sources and facilities owned by the Municipality (this service is in the process of improvement right now). There are also factories that make clothing, process many kinds of foods, bottle soft drinks, make different kinds syrups and sweets; and first quality shops and department stores, magnificent restaurants, many variety stores and pharmacies. In short, Alajuela offers the best of the provinces (after the capital) in most everything.

Because Alajuela has been the cradle of many distinguished people in our public and scientific life, it holds a prominent place in the history of Costa Rica.

It is linked to the rest of the country by very good roads, including one of the most modern freeways in the nation, and excellent telephone, mail, telegraph, telex, and fax services.

San Ramón Canton

This canton is situated to the extreme northeast of the Central Tectonic Depression on hills that jut off from the Aguacate Mountains and merge into the foothills of the Poás Volcano in the center of the canton.

Its terrain is generally hilly. The climate is cool (between 19 and 21°C). It is drained by the rivers Barranca and Río Grande de Tárcoles.

It produces excellent coffee, corn, beans, potatoes, tobacco, sugarcane, vegetables, *caña india*, and beef.

It also produces other economically less important crops such as flowers and tree fruits. These are distributed in various parts of the country.

The parish church in the town of San Ramón, beautiful and majestic, built of steel manufactured in Germany.

As for farming and land use, it is mostly extensive, making use mostly of manual systems with very limited use of farm machinery. It has greatly improved its cattle raising methods, and the quality of the animals and better care for the farms is now rendering better returns on the investments made.

In this canton there is considerable forest coverage: an estimated area of around 200 kms². It has, in fact, one of the richest reserves in Costa Rica, but since it is also an important watershed, it is imperative that the proper technical and protective measures be taken to preserve it.

The forest zone is located in the northwest sector of the canton along the ridge of the *Sierra Volcánica Central*, on either side of the continental divide, but with more on the Caribbean side.

Today, thanks to bank credits and capital from the canton itself, industry in San Ramón is experiencing a phenomenal economic growth, thus giving jobs to hundreds of citizens in the canton. There are furniture factories, mechanical shops, and gate and grating factories. There has also been extraordinary development with respect to small clothing factories of all sorts, generally family-owned and operated, and other larger clothing factories, which now employ a total of some 800 people, and pay substantial wages.

In the districts of San Rafael and Santiago, primarily, there are some areas that lend themselves to the extraction of raw materials to be used in the manufacture of ceramic goods. Hence, in this town there are factories that make articles to be sold in the capital and neighboring cantons. The arrival of these industries has also helped to meet compelling economical needs in the community.

Alberto M. Brenes Park, San Ramón.

The population was at the 1984 census 39,963, living on a total land area of 990.63 kms², for a population density of 40 inhabitants per square kilometer. This canton has experienced an increase of approximately 11,063 inhabitants in 35 years, based on the 1950 census of 28,900.

San Ramón Canton is divided into the following districts: San Ramón, Santiago Sur, San Juan, Piedades, San Rafael, San Isidro, Los Angeles, Alfaro, Volio, Concepción, Zapotal, and Peñas Blancas (which in 1970 was the last one to become a canton).

The town of San Ramón, the canton seat, is located northwest of the Central Tectonic Depression, at 1,052 meters above sea level, which makes for an average temperature of 21.2°C. It has 9,524 inhabitants.

The community has good public services: waterworks, electricity, several public buildings, health care, pharmacy, daily mail deliveries to San José, telegraph, urban telephone, good roads connecting it with the other towns and villages of the Central Depresion and other districts in the canton.

The hotels here and restaurants in various parts of the city offer very good service to their customers. There are also tailor shops, shoe shops, auto repair shops, cabinet makers, traditional ox cart factories, soft drink factories, broom makers, gasoline stations, taxicab services, movie houses, libraries, social clubs, branches of the National Bank of Costa Rica, the Bank of Costa Rica, and the *Banco Popular*, elementary schools, high schools, churches, department stores, jewelry stores, watch repairers, sports fields, and a branch of the University of Costa Rica.

The central urban area of San Ramón clearly follows the precolonial Spanish arrangement: "blocks of 100 yards divided into lots 50 x 50 yards and streets spaced 20 yards apart".

The main public buildings in the town are the Town Hall, George Washington Elementary School, Patriarca San José High School, Laboratory School, Dr.

Carlos Luis Valverde V. Hospital, the Central Market, the public library, a branch of the National Bank of Costa Rica, the Canton Delegation of the Rural Guard, the Postal-Telegraph Office, the Social Security Office, the building occupied by a branch of the University of Costa Rica, the Waterworks and Sewage Treatment Building, the La Sabana School, the Santitation Unit, a chapter of the Costa Rican Red Cross, the Agricultural Extension Agency, the Traffic Delgation, and the Tremedal Church.

The parish church building, beautiful and majestic, and one of the finest in Costa Rica with respect to architecture (concrete formed over a steel structure built by Krupp of Germany), is the spiritual gathering place of the people of San Ramón and a shining reflection of the their faith.

There are also modern private buildings and offices used for business as well as residential apartments.

An attractive well-kept part in the city, called *Parque Alberto M. Brenes*, in memory of the renown Costa Rican botanist, is a peaceful place where people go to rest and chat, especially the young people, and a place of many happy memories for adults, who have discussed so many topics here under these shady trees (including plans for national political changes).

The most important historical building here is the old *Palacio Municipal* (Town Hall), just north of the park, which before the 1929 earthquake had two stories, constructed entirely of stone. In 1924 it was partially destroyed; its second floor was lost, and only the first floor was rebuilt.

When the Western Regional University Center was created, the property was donated by the Municipality of the canton to the University of Costa Rica. There are now plans to install in this building a historical museum and exhibit rooms.

The town has wide, well delineated streets, most of them asphalt. Some of them are in the process of being repaired.

The Catholic Church in Grecia, built of iron imported from Belgium in 1897; the altar is made of solid marble.

Noteworthy of the people of this canton, is their community concern that motivates them to join forces in resolving problems and improve their standard of living. For this reason, there are several development associations at the canton level.

"The people of San Ramón must be admired for their cultural and intellectual dedication. Moreover, their artistic values have always caused their country to shine. This attitude is in part explained by the fact that, in the last century, prominent political figures sought exile in San Ramón and contributed much to its development, both materially and intellectually."

Its principal roads include the highways to Atenas, and Naranjo, which links San Ramón with the towns of Grecia and Alajuela, and the Inter-American Highway that passes through the canton connecting it with Puntarenas and San José.

Grecia Canton

Grecia is situated in the center of the populated region of the province, among the cantons of Naranjo, Sarapiquí, Alajuela, Poás, and Valverde Vega. Valverde Vega Canton divides this canton into two parts. Grecia's terrain, as its climate, is quite varied but always pleasant. The land is drained by the rivers Sarchí, Agualote, Poró, Rosales, and other minor ones, all of which descend from the massif of the Poás Volcano. The canton produces coffee, corn, beans, and a lot of vegetables, but its preferred crop is sugarcane, whose proceeds have contributed greatly to the growing prosperity of this rich region of the country.

The canton has a population of 38,361 inhabitants living in the districts of Grecia City, the canton seat, San Isidro, San José, San Roque, Tacares, Río Cuarto,

View of the Forest Reserve in Grecia.

Puente de Piedra, and Bolívar. Its population as compared to the 1950 census has diminished by 10,651 inhabitants, primarily due to the separation from it of several towns, including Upala, Los Chiles, and Guatus, which became cantons of Alajuela Province after 1970.

The town of Grecia, with 11,374 inhabitants is positioned in a fertile and heavily farmed valley, formed from the folds of the foothills of the Poás Volcano. It has a typical central sector with its market, theater, as well as all the comforts of a modern, progressive city: a town hall and good schools placed in settings conducive to learning. The Catholic Church, made of iron imported from Belgium, is the only one of its kind, and in it are some paintings worthy of mention.

The climate here, with an average temperture of 24°C is very healthy. It is 18 kilometers from Alajuela and is connected to it and the cantons of San Ramón, Naranjo, and Atenas by good paved roads. It has electric power, plumbing, telegraph, daily postal service, a charity hospital called San Francisco de Asís, and an extension office of the Western Regional Center of the University of Costa Rica in Villa Tacares. Since 1981 it has also had the National Liquor Factory located in Rincón de Salas.

The town of Grecia was settled by people from Alajuela, San José, and Heredia, who began to arrive in 1828. The present church is remarkable, in that it was constructed of iron imported from Belgium in 1897, and the altar is made of solid marble. The high school, *Liceo León Cortés Castro*, opened for classes in 1953. Grecia Canton covers a land area of 395.73 kms² and has a population density of 97 people per square kilometer. Its largest district is Río Cuarto, with 254.20 kms², and the smallest is Grecia with only 6.82 kms². The population density of the canton is 1,658 inhabitants per kms². It has promising potential with respect to tourism, primarily due to its uniquely beautiful church, its customs, and because within it there are several recreational resorts, as well as the Juan Castro Blanco Forest Preserve.

San Mateo Canton

The canton of San Mateo, the fourth in the province, is bounded on the north by San Ramón Canton, on the south by Orotina Canton, on the east with Orotina, and on the west with Esparza. The terrain of this canton is for the most part hilly, especially in the northern sector. Its climate is quite warm, averaging 26 to 27°C, but not overly humid and, hence, generally healthy.

The fertile soil of this canton produces rice, corn, beans, sugarcane, and abundant and exquisite fruit of many kinds, for which their is much demand in capital and the rest of the country. From the forests here fine woods used in construction and cabinet making, such as cedar, *pochote*, *guachipelín*, *madera-negra*, and others, have been extracted, but due to the absence of controls with respect to use, these forests have been all but stripped away.

The ground here also holds rich veins of gold, primarily in the northwest part of the canton, where the Aguacate Mine is located, but which consumes large sums of money to operate.

The canton is drained by the rivers Machuca, Aguagria, Surubres, and Jesús María.

The districts of the San Mateo Canton are San Mateo, Jesús María, and Desmonte with the villages of Ramadas, Maderal, Dulce Nombre, and several other townships. The total population is 3,783 inhabitants —only 133 more than that recorded by the census of 35 years ago. According to the 1950 census, almost all of them lived in the Villa de San Mateo (population 3,100), today the canton seat.

The town of San Mateo, with 1988 inhabitants is situated at the foot of the the Aguacate Mountains, 40 kilometers from Alajuela City, at an altitude of 254 meters above sea level. It has a handsome church, a town hall that contains the main public offices, and a market, buzzing with buyers and sellers, and where one can find the products of most of the canton's suppliers. The town has plumbing in perfect condition, public lighting, telegraph, and daily mail delivery. It is linked to the San Ramón, Orotina, and Esparza cantons by good roads, and it is only five kilometers from the Orotina railway station along the railroad to the Pacific.

San Mateo owns its origin to the construcction of a road, around the year 1700, between Cartago, through Esparza, to Caldera. Its name, San Mateo, comes from the chapel built there in 1859.

Its greatest development was propelled by the construction of an ox cart trail between San José and Puntarenas, which enabled it to become a canton in 1867.

San Mateo covers a land area of 125.90 kms², and has a population density of 30 inhabitants per square kilometer. Although it is one of the least populated cantons in the country, it does not lag in development, since it is mainly comprised of small haciendas owned by people who live in the capital. Its Damas Bridge over the Río Jesús María near Esparza is considered a historical landmark.

Atenas Canton

The canton of Antenas is bounded on the north by the cantons of Palmares and Naranjo, on the east by those of Grecia and Alajuela, on the south by those of Turrubares and Mora, and on the west by those of Orotina, San Mateo, and San Ramón. In this canton live 15,011 people –3,011 more than the population at the census taken 35 years ago.

It is divided into the districts of Atenas, Jesús, Mercedes, San Isidro, Concepción, San José, and Santa Eulalia (the smallest in population).

The terrain, quite irregular east of Alajuela Canton, pruduces coffee, sugarcane, beans, corn, vegetables, and beef.

Atenas, the governmental seat of canton, situated on a cliff of the Aguacate Mountains at an elevation of 698 meters, has 4,451 inhabitants –1,251 more than 25 years ago. The canton was first inhabited by Indians and then since 1750, by citizens who came from Alajuela, Heredia, San José, and Cartago. They called this first settlement Sabana Larga. The zone owes its development to an ox

Bridge over the Río Grande, Atenas, Alajuela Province.

cart trail made in 1843, the construction of the Pacific Railway, and the opening of the Costanera Highway, which has made Atenas a rest spot for travellers going between the capital and the Pacific, since this new highway is now the main access route between San José and Quepos. En route to Quepos it passes through La Garita, Alajuela, Orotina, and Parrita.

Atenas officially became a canton in 1862, and today it has four districts: Atenas, Mercedes, Jesús, and Concepción. It forms part of the greater metropolitan

Escuela Centroamericana de Ganadería (Central American Livestock School), in Atenas Canton. Graduates of this school receive a para-university degree.

area. Located in this canton is the *Escuela Centroamericana de Ganadería* (a university-level school specializing in husbandry).

The average temperature of the canton is 24.5°C, a pleasant, healthy climate, especially for people who suffer from arthritis. It is scenically situated over rocky terrain surrounded by peacefully green hills of countless nuances.

It has a lovely church, built in 1910, two good school buildings, a town hall, a postal-telegraph office, and adequate plumbing, and it has had public electric power since 1915. It is 21 kilometers from Alajuela, and six kilometers from the Pacific Railway Station in Atenas. It is drained by the Río Grande, which around Garita has a dam that generates electricity. Near the district of Jesús the Río Grande becomes the Río Grande de Tárcoles. A bridge over the Río Grande, part of the Alajuela-Atenas Highway, is considered a historical landmark.

Atenas Canton has a veterinary clinic, a health center, magnificent shopping centers, and a protected forest zone in the Jesús District. In addition, there are many stands alongside the road that sell

Cerro Espíritu Santo, Naranjo, Alajuela Province.

products made right in the canton —candied grapefruit rinds, corn products, roasted cashews, *gallos* (like a taco made with a soft tortilla), empanadas, and other typical foods.

Naranjo Canton

On the slopes of the Poás Volcano, among the cantons of Grecia, San Ramón, Alfaro Ruiz, Atenas, Palmares, and Valverde Vega is Naranjo Canton. Its terrain is irregular but very fertile. The climate is pleasant with an average temperature of 20 to 21.6°C.

Most of the canton is cultivated, but there still remain a few forested areas with timbers such as *danto*, oak, *quizarrá*, *ira*, *guachipelín*, *madera-negra*. There are also rock quarries under construction. In the southwestern sectors of the canton are the Río Grande and Chayote protected forest zones. The chief agricultural products are coffee, tapioca, plantain bananas, corn, beans, rice, sugarcane, and tobacco. Also, cattle raising has been gaining in importance.

The districts of Naranjo are San Miguel, San Juan, San José, Cirrí Sur, San Jerónimo, and Rosario. The total population is 23,588 (5,088 inhabitants more than 35 years ago). With a total land area of 126.62 kms², the population density is 186 inhabitants per square kilometer. Most of the population, however, is concentrated in the canton seat.

Naranjo was first settled in 1830, and the first services began to emerge in 1885 when the first chapel was built. Then in 1886 the first school was erected. Plumbing was installed in 1925 and public lighting 10 years later.

The town of Naranjo (population 11,600), the governmental seat of the canton, is located at the foot of the Espíritu Santo Hills, at an elevation of 1,036 meters above sea level, 28 kilometers from Alajuela City. It has a beautiful Catholic Church, a town hall, and two schools. Its streets are wide and straight, and the town is generally pleasing to look at because of its tasteful ornamentation and cleanliness. The plaza has a beautiful fountain in the center (supplied by public water), and trees and other plants in the plaza give it the appearance of a lovely garden. This is one of the most properous towns in the province, with telegraph, daily mail service, excellent electrical power, and a hospital. There are also several inns and hotels, and a good variety of commercial establishments, as well as some small industries and shops. Every year in Naranjo the people hold a big festival in honor of the *Virgen de Lourdes*, which brings many pilgrims from all over the country.

The town is linked to San Ramón, Grecia, Palmares, and Atenas by very good roads; the national highway to San Carlos also passes through Naranjo. On Mount Espíritu Santo the people from Naranjo have erected a splendid monument to *Cristo Rey* (Christ the King).

The town is drained by the San Lucas Stream and the Pilas River. The name of the town (meaning orange grove) was given because of the large number of orange trees the early settlers found here. At first it was called Los Naranjos, but the name was eventually shortened to Naranjo.

Today this canton is undergoing rapid development, which has afforded it many public services, including a fine stadium, a clinic, a regional center of the *Instituto*

Nacional de Aprendizaje (INA = National Institute of Education) and a lookout point on Mount Espíritu Santo for tourists. Naranjo also offers gorgeous views because of the topography of the canton.

Palmares Canton

This canton is situated in the valley formed by the foothills of the Aguacate Mountains, among the cantons of San

The town of Palmares, in the center of the canton, is 35 kilometers from Alajuela City.

The church in Palmares is made entirely of cut rock.

Ramón to the west, Atenas to the south, and Naranjo to the east. It has a population of 17,815. Its districts are Palmares, Zaragoza, Buenos Aires, Santiago, Candelaria, Esquipulas, and La Granja. The most heavily populated districts are Zaragoza and Buenos Aires –respectively 4,136 and 3,096 inhabitants. The district of Zaragoza is actually bigger than the canton seat, Palmares, whose population is 3,766, the reason being that Palmares has a land area of only 1.09 kms².

Palmares Canton has grown by 4,315 inhabitants in 35 years. It covers a land area of 38.06 kms², the largest districts in it being Zaragoza and Santiago with 8.05 kms² each.

The principle wealth of Palmares is coffee, grown on a large scale and of very good quality. It also produces beef cattle, tobacco, and *caña india*. The small town of Palmares is 35 kilometers from Alajuela City, in an elevated position in the center of the canton.

It has one of the most beautiful churches in the country, made completely of cut stone. It also has a small but well-staffed hospital, a school, a town hall, and a postal-telegraph office with daily mail delivery. The citizens of Palmares are very devout in their religion and, at the same time, progressive. The name of the town (meaning "palm grove") comes from the many royal palm trees that were there when the area was first settled. Later the same name was given to the canton.

The main tourist attraction in Poás Canton is the Poás Volcano.

The canton has had public high school since 1958, electric power since 1913, and plumbing since 1896.

Poás Canton

This canton is situated on the southern slopes of the Poás Volcano. It is bounded on the south and the east by Alajuela Canton, on the west by Grecia, and on the north by Valverde Vega. This canton consists of a 22-kilometer strip of land running northeast to southeast from the crater of the Poás Volcano to the confluence of the rivers Poás and Prendas.

The terrain is very irregular; the climate is moderate and pleasant. The principle wealth of the canton is the sugarcane it grows, but it also produces coffee, beans and corn, tapioca, ornamental plants, and livestock –mostly dairy cattle.

The name of the canton comes from the name the settlers gave the area –Púas (barbs, or thorns)– because of the thorns of the many blackberry bushes found growning there.

The population of the canton grew by 4,989 inhabitants in 35 years, based on the 1950 census. Today the canton has 13,939 inhabitants, and it is divided into the districts of San Pedro, San Juan, San Rafael Carrillos, and Sabana Redonda.

San Pedro de la Calabaza, now the canton seat, was the first village established. It has 5,060 inhabitants, 1,500 more than it has 35 years ago. It is located 10 kilometers from Alajuela City, at 1,148 meters above sea level, and has a chilly average temperature of 11.5°C.

It has a good Catholic Church, an elementary school, a postal-telegraph office, a municipal slaughtering house, a high school since 1969, plumbing since 1911, and electric power since 1914. It also has a clinic, a hydroelectric plant (in Carrillo), good restaurants, and the Carachas Poás Lookout Point.

The most frequented tourist attractions here are the Poás Volcano and the Grecia Forest Reserve.

Orotina Canton

This canton, created in 1908, is bounded on the north by San Mateo, on the east by Atenas, on the west by Esparza, on the southwest by Garabito, and on the northeast by Turrubares. The Pacific Railway (since 1902) crosses the canton from east to west, which has contributed greatly to its progress. The districts of the canton are Orotina, Mastate, Hacienda Vieja, El Coyolar, and La Ceiba. It has a population of 18,894 inhabitants (2,594 more than 35 years ago) and covers a land area of 141.92 kms².

The development of the canton really began with the opening of the *Camino de Carretas* (Ox Cart Trail) in 1843 and continued with the working of the mines beginning in 1862, the lumber industry, and cattle raising, attracting the greatest number of settlers (including foreigners). Because this canton sits on alluvial terraces, its soils are extremely fertile.

The town of Orotina, with 6,539 inhabitants, is crossed by the *Ferrocarril Eléctrico al Pacífico* (Pacific Electric Railway) at 66 kilometers from San José City, at an altitude of 229 meters above sea level. Its climate is hot, and it receives a relative small amount of rainfall.

It has an ordinary Catholic Church (83 years old), good local schools, and a postal-telegraph office. The Agricultural Institute began its activities there in 1962. It also has good shopping centers, stores, restaurants, hotels, and many other commercial enterprises, as well as a clinic in very good condition.

It produces beans, corn, and fruit, and from its forests fine woods are constantly being extracted.

The canton sustains itself economically primarily from citrus fruit, as well as gold and kaolin mining.

San Carlos Canton

This northernmost canton of Alajuela Province is bounded on the north by the country of Nicaragua, at the San Juan River; on the northeast by Los Chiles Canton, on the south by the last foothills of the *Sierra Volcánica Central*, and the cantons of Alfaro Ruiz, Valverde Vega, and San Ramón; on the east by the cantons of Sarapiquí; and on the west by the cantos of Tilarán, and Guatuso. The land here is relatively flat and is drained by the rivers San Carlos and Río Frío and their tributaries (many of which are navegable).

The climatic periods are not so well defined as those of other parts of the country, and rarely does a week pass without a heavy rain shower. From February to the beginning of May, however, it rains a little less.

The climate here is influenced by the climatic conditions of both the Caribbean and the *Sierra Volcánica Central*. Annual rainfall reaches 4,500 millimeters or more, although toward the north and west rainfall tends to diminish, and there the dry spell is longer. Thus, for example, Los Chiles has three dry months and Cuatro Bocas has four.

The area of San Carlos Canton was discovered by the Spaniards in 1640; they called it San Jerónimo de los Votos. Later it was settled by a group from the Quesada family that came from San Ramón, and who contributed greatly to the development of the region. At that time a village was formed, then known as La Unión, and today called Ciudad Quesada. By 1963, 42,300 people were living there. But rapid demographic growth has caused the settlement to expand outward. Today, although the canton still has many land reserves, the population has grown by 33,276 over the last 30 years. This growth has been possible for the improvement in the communication systems.

At first, colonization was centered around La Unión (today Ciudad Quesada), then it was Florencia, then Sarapiquí. Thus, settlement spontaneously advanced from the centers toward the lowlands.

Ramón Quesada worked for over a half a century on behalf of the progress of this rich region. His greatest effort went into forming a company to open a railroad from the center of the country to these lands. Now, two highways serve this purpose: a 28-kilometer highway to Los Chiles de Aguas Zarcas and an

18-kilometer one to La Vieja (finished before 1967). Moreover, most of the districts of the canton are interlinked by good alphalt roads, all of which connect with the center of the canton. The only cantons that are not linked in this way are Pocosol, Cutris (the plains of San Carlos), and Pital, which for the most part, have only dirt roads, that are practically impassible during the rainy season.

San Carlos Canton is politically divided into the districts of Quesada (the governmental seat of the canton), Florencia, Buena Vista, Aguas Zarcas, Venecia, Pital, La Fortuna, Tigra, Palmera, Venado, Cutris, Monterrey, And Pocosol. Ciudad Quesada, with 21,696 inhabitants is the business center of the canton; it has been the canton seat since 1911, and has been classified as a *ciudad* (city or town) since 1953. From the standpoint of urban structure, it has become, for all practical purposes, the hierarchial center of the entire northern region.

Observing the actively economic population of this canton, it is noted that 56.8% work in the primary sector, only 11.3% in the secondary, and 24% in the terciary.

In terms of land use, most of the land is taken up in pasture land, since most of the canton is dedicated to extensive livestock raising. Other farm products include beans and corn, sugarcane, coffee, cacao, plantain bananas, *caña india*, tubers, and various kinds of fruit.

Productivity, economic impetus, and modern transportation facilities have all contributed to this canton of 3,370.98 kms² being transformed into one of the most developed in the country, with the greatest development achieved in Ciudad Quesada. It has all types of services, including a hospital. In the town of Santa Clara there is a regional branch of the Technological Institute of Costa Rica, and an electrical power cooperative. But despite the fact that this one of the most developed cantons, a most annoying problem is its lack of roads that are passable all year round, since during much of the year only the southern part remains constantly open to travel to the capital of the country, or with downtown Ciudad Quesada –by means of the Heredia-Puerto Viejo-Río Cuarto route or the Naranjo-Ciudad Quesada route. The northern sector only has reliable roads up to Tilarán Canton and parts of the Pocosol and Pital districts. In the Cutris District the roads are passible only during certain periods of the year.

The lack of adequate roads also has repercussions in other services such a health and technical assistence in agriculture, as well as in some areas of education.

The canton has the first lands to become plains, today called the *Llanuras de San Carlos* (Plains of San Carlos), a name also given to the canton in 1911 stemming from the popular notion that the plains came into being by the washing of the San Carlos River.

Alfaro Ruiz Canton

This the eleventh canton of Alajuela Province, officially became a canton on June 21, 1915.

The governmental seat is Zarcero, located 22 kilometers north of Alajuela City, on the Tigre Hills, foothills of the Poás Volcano. This town, whose population is now over 2,000, has been undergoing notable development. Its hard-working people are distinguished by their progressive spirit and their hospitality.

Virtually the whole canton is comprised of professing members of the Roman Catholic Church, who with great devotion gather in their temple, admired for its splendid beauty. It was built and decorated by local citizens. The excellent decor of the church is the work of the self-taught artist, Misael Solís.

One of the greatest tourist attractions, both locally and abroad, is the magnificent park, whose fame has spread to other American countries and to Europe. Proof of this fame is the large number of trophies, certificates, and medals that have been awarded by various embassies from around the world, especially to the craftsman, a humble resident named Evangelista Blanco Brenes.

Regarding education, Alfaro Ruiz has elementary schools in each of its districts. The secondary school for the canton is the *Instituto Técnico Profesional Agroindustrial* (Agro-Industrial Technical School), founded int 1969.

Tourists can visit any district of this zone at any time of the year, since its system of highways and local roads is in perfect condition. Most of these roads are paved.

It is also linked with San Carlos and Naranjo by a fine highway. Both Zarcero and the other districts have excellent public services including electric power, telephones, mail, plumbing, garbage pick-up, cooperatives, a chapter of the Red Cross, bus services, and a fire fighting department, as well as stores and other businesses.

The population of 7,005 inhabitants has excellent health services. In Zarcero is the Health Center that has branch health stations in each of the districts. There is also a Social Security clinic, but the most serious health cases are sent to the hospitals of San Carlos, San Ramón, and Grecia through the local Red Cross service.

The people of Alfaro Ruiz work mostly in agriculture and dairy farming. Agricultural products include cabbage, broccoli, cauliflower, beets, potatoes, lettuce, peaches, strawberries, and flowers. Most of the milk produced is sold to the Dos Pinos Dairy Cooperative. This canton is also famous for its delicious cheeses and *natilla* (sour cream).

It is said that the natural beauty of Zarcero is so prodigious that anyone who comes here, will return. The name this town is derived from the sarsaparilla plant, that grows in this region. The canton is named in honor of Juan Alfaro Ruiz, a national hero.

The canton has six districts: Tapezco with 1,714 inhabitants, Guadalupe with

417, Palmira with 767, Zapote with 635, Laguna with 955, and Zarcero with 2,517.

The canton is considered by the Costa Rican Tourist Institute (ICT) to be a tourist center particularly because of its crafts and its parks.

Valverde Vega Canton

On October 26, 1949, by Decree No. 766 Valverde Vega Canton was founded. Subsequently, on September 18, 1963 Decree No 3,200 made Sarchí Norte the governmental seat of the canton.

Sarchí Norte, at 970 meters above sea level, covers an area of 15.11 kms². As of the 1984 census the town had 4,336 inhabitants.

Among the main buildings are the Town Hall, a branch of the National Bank of Costa Rica, the *Banco Anglo Costarricense*, the Canton Delegation of the Rural Guard, the Fire Fighters Station, a chapter of the Red Cross, the Catholic Church, and several cooperative offices: Coopesarchí, Coopevalverde Vega R.L., Coopearsa, and Coopenessa, mainly

One of the tourist attractions in Alfaro Ruiz Canton is its magnificent park.

The arts and crafts of Valverde Vega have become famous, not only nationally, but also internationally.

dedicated to the the processing of coffee and ornamental plants.

In front of the Catholic Church there is a lovely, well-kept park with a fountain and a monument to the ox cart.

The town is located alongside an asphalt national highway, and all of the town's streets are asphalt as well.

Throughout the canton there is adequate drinking water service, administered by the Municipality, electrical power supplied by the Costa Rican Electrical Institute (ICE), and four public telephones at different spots in town.

Agriculturally, the canton grows much of the produce consumed by the population, but more important to the economy, are coffee and sugarcane. There are also coffee processing plants and a sugar mill.

The arts and crafts of this canton have become famous, not only nationally, but also internationally. Here one can find handmade articles from the smallest to furniture and fine, colorfully painted ox carts, which are the pride of Costa Rica. Sixty percent of the population works in this vocation.

Tourism here has been phenomenal: hundreds of tourists arrive each day, even including movie and television stars, who often come just to buy the handmade wooden articles.

As for health care, there are good health centers providing adequateql

service (through the *Clínica Seguro*) and a Hygiene Center. It has a beautiful elementary school accomodating 560 pupils, and a technical high school. In addition, each district has its own elementary school.

The town of Sarchí is considered to be a tourist center for its arts and crafts. Within its jurisdiction are the forest preserves, Juan Castro Blanco, and Grecia, as well as the Poas Volcano National Park.

The canton of Sarchí has 10,716 inhabitants distributed in five districts: Sarchí Norte, the canton seat with 4,336; Sarchí Sur with 2,743; Toro Amarillo with 273; San Pedro with 1,833, and Los Rodríguez with 1,531.

Upala Canton

Upala touches the Nicaraguan border, as well as the cantons of La Cruz, Liberia, Bagaces, Cañas, Guatuso, and Los Chiles. It has 26,061 inhabitants living in seven districts: Upala, the canton seat, has 7,008 inhabitants, Aguas Claras has 4,426 (and contains the Rincón de la Vieja National Park); San José with 4,819; Bijagua with 2,701 (part of the Cordillera Volcánica de Guanacaste Forest Reserve is located here); Delicias with 2,540; Dos Ríos with 1,839; and Yolillal with 2,728. Most of the population (81.6%) works in agriculture: cacao, beans, corn, rice, tubers, and livestock.

In Upala, the canton seat, is a hospital, an elementary school, and a high school. It has had plumbing since 1976 and electrical power since 1978. It also has all kinds of businesses and services.

The first settlers, arriving from Nicaragua, Cañas, and Bagaces, cleared the trees and planted traditional crops such as cacao, brought from Nicaragua. They also changed the name of the place from Zapote to Upala, a native Indian name.

Having become a canton in 1970, this is one of the most recent cantons in the province of Alajuela.

Los Chiles Canton

This canton is bounded on the northeast by the country of Nicaragua, on the west and south by Upala and Guatuso, and on the southeast by San Carlos. Los Chiles is located some 210 kilometers from the capital. It has 11,404 inhabitants distributed among four districts: Los Chiles, the canton seat with 5,154; Caño Negro with 1,231; El Amparo wityh 2,509, and San Jorge with 2,510.

This canton has elementary schools (built in 1970), a technical agricultural high school, a parish church, an airport, a cementary, a park, a hospital, a bank branch, and several community organizations, and many businesses and services.

The people make their living by raising beans, rice, cacao, corn, cattle for milk and beef; cutting and selling timber; and, on a lesser scale, growing cassava and other tubers.

In the district of Caño Negro is located the Caño Negro Wildlife Refuge.

Los Chiles Canton has a network of local roads totalling approximatesly 1,200 kilometers. Most of these are dirt roads in dreadful condition, and completely impassible during much of the rainy season. The canton is linked with San Carlos by a good road.

Guatuso Canton

This canton, number 15 in Alajuela Province, came into being in March 1970. It is bounded on the north by Los Chiles Canton, on the west by Upala, on the south and southwest by Tilarán and Cañas, and on the southeast by San Carlos Canton. It has 6,774 inhabitants who make their living mostly from raising corn, beans, various tubers, cacao, rice and livestock.

There are three districts: San Rafael, the canton seat with 3,689 inhabitants; Buena Vista with 2,107, and Cote with 978.

The canton has good services, especially in the governmental seat: elementary schools, a technical agricultural high school, a Catholic Church, a learning center, and electrical power since 1979.

Perhaps the most pressing problem of the canton is the lack of adequate roads. It does have an aspalt road that goes from San Carlos Canton to San Rafael District, but to the other districts there are only gravel roads, impassible during the rainy season.

The fluvial system of the cantons of Upala, Los Chiles, and Guatuso is comprised by the Río Frío, whose watershed, along with the rivers Pocosol, Zapote, Medio Queso, and others, drains this region.

125

CARTAGO PROVINCE

The entire province of Cartago is situated on the eastern versant of the country, distinguishing it from the provinces of San José, Heredia, and Alajuela with respect to climate, seasons, and farming. Most of the province pertains to the Reventazón River watershed. The terrain is generally irregular, because of ramifications of the *Cordillera de Talamanca* and the mountain masses of the Irazú and Turrialba volcanoes, that run through the province. Among all of these mountains is Cartago Valley, which is part of the province.

The ramifications of the mountains mentioned divide the Cartago Valley into smaller valleys such as El Guarco, a sandy area covered with granite stones from the Irazú Volcano. It is over this valley floor that the Cartago City is built. To the northeast is the valley of Turrialba, with rich pasture lands and large farms. There is also the Tucurrique Valley, noteworthy because of its picturesque topographical

position and wonderful climate, the plains of Tuis and the valleys of Orosi, Pejibaye, and Ujarrás, all of which have very rich soils. In general, the province has a moderate climate, with some chilly zones.

The chief products of the province are: coffee (of especially good quality from the valleys of Orosi) Tucurrique, and Cachí, sugarcane, corn, beans, potatoes, and magnificent vegetables. Also, because its excellent grazing lands, it raises top-grade dairy cattle that produces some of the finest cheeses and butter in the nation. It also grows peaches, quince, and many other kinds of fruit. Some areas are even quite suitable for vineyards. Besides these agricultural products, gold, copper, mercury, and coal are known to exist there, but thus far they not been mined.

The province of Cartago has eight cantons (see map No. 12). Its total population is 271,671 inhabitants, who live on a total land area of 3,124.67 kms². It is the third most populated province in the country.

Opposite page: Inside the Basílica de Nuestra Señora de los Angeles (Our Lady of the Angels), whose appearance is celebrated every August 2, with a famous pilgrimage.

Outside the Basílica de Nuestra Señora de los Angeles, Cartago City.

Cartago became a province in December of 1948; its name goes back to 1563 when Juan Vázquez de Coronado chose this site in El Guarco Valley to relocate the town of Garimuñoz. That town was in the region of the modern Santa Ana Canton.

The first vicarage was erected in 1565 in Orosi Valley, and in 1753 it was declared a Basilica.

In 1782 the first school was established, and in 1869 San Luis Gonzaga Secondary School was opened for classes. In 1971 the *Instituto Tecnológico de Costa Rica* (ITCR = Technological Institute of Costa Rica) was created, and August of that same year the Atlantic Central Regional Branch of the University of Costa Rica was opened (in Turrialba). In 1980 the *Colegio Universitario de Cartago* (Cartago College) was established.

Also worthy of mention is the township of Ujarrás, since it had been the seat of a very important town during the colonial era. There are the remains of the church, built at the end of the Seventeenth Century by Governor Miguel Gómez de Lara as an expression of thanksgiving to the *Virgen de Concepción* for having frustrated the filibuster incursion of Mansfield Morgan.

Cartago Canton

This canton is bounded on the north by La Unión Canton and the province of San José, on the east by Oreamuno and Paraíso cantons, on the south by San José Province, and on the west by El Guarco Canton. It has very good grazing lands that produce fine quality livestock. It also grows various kinds of fruit that thrive in cooler climates, and coffee.

Its eleven districts are: 1) East Cartago, with 2.39 kms² and 14,428 inhabitants; 2) West Cartago, with 1.99 kms² and 9,500 inhabitants; 3) El Carmen with 4.22 kms² and 11,997 inhabitants; 4) San Nicolás with 28.23 kms² and 14,675 inhabitants; 5) San Francisco with 104.15 kms² (the largest in land area), and a population of 8,963; 6) Guadalupe with 13.24 kms² and 8,066 inhabitants; 7) Corralillo with 33.09 kms² and 6,538

inhabitants; 8) Tierra Blanca with 9.53 kms² and 3,527 inhabitants; 9) Dulce Nombre with 39.15 kms² and 4.783 inhabitants; 11) Quebradilla with 18.71 kms² and 2,410 inhabitants. Thus, the canton covers a total land area of 284.51 kms² and a has total population of 87,125 inhabitants. The canton is part of the greater metropolitan area, except for the Corralillo District and parts of the San Francisco and Dulce Nombre districts. (*Atlas Cantonal*, 1987).

Within the canton there are several national heritages declared historical landmarks: the ruins of what was to be the Apóstol Santiago Parish Church known as the "*Ruinas de la Parroquia*" ("Parish Ruins"), the Barracks of Cartago, and the house in which the former president, Jesús Jiménez Zamora was born.

The terrain in this canton is, for the most part, flat, although in some areas it is quite uneven. It has fertile valleys that produce especially good coffee and sugarcane. There are also coffee processing yards, and sugar mills. In addition, good vegetables, including chayotes and potatoes are grown, and there are beautiful cattle ranches.

Cartago City

Cartago is the capital of the province with the same name. It was founded by Spaniards in 1563 at the foot of the Irazú Volcano in the El Guarco Valley (altitude 1,435 meters above sea level). It is one of the oldest towns in the country, having been a Costa Rican metropolis throughout the colonial era. Its climate is very pleasant and healthful, with the temperature varying between 16 and 19°C, depending on the time of year.

Is streets are wide; the buildings are relatively new and comfortable, solidly built to resist earthquakes, since the city was totally destroyed by an earthquake in 1910. It has good drinking water and sewage removal and treatment services, electrical power, telephones, and mail service. It has several Catholic churches. One of these in the west sector, El Carmen, is distinctly gothic in style. On the east side is the Basilica of Los Angeles, where people revere an old statue of *Nuestra Señora de los Angeles* (Our Lady of the Angels). This devotion has spread throughout the country, notable especially on August 2, when the appearance of the Virgin is celebrated with a famous pilgrimage, a day when people from all over Costa Rica come, many of them walking all the way from San José, or ever farther.

In recent years Cartago has progressed considerably, as the metropolitan area has extended outward new buildings and adornments have contributed to making this city now one of the most attractive in the country.

Commerce here is well developed with fine grocery, clothing, department and other stores, pharmacies, hardware stores, some food processing factories, sawmills, and workshops. There are also bars and restaurants comparable to those of the capital, hotels and inns with good service, and taxicab and bus services that provide constant service in the city and to neighboring towns, including fast bus service every ten minutes to San José. It also has a main theater and several movie theaters; three charity institutions: the *Asilo de la Vejez* (a home for the elderly),

the Max Peralta Hospital, and the Children's Hospital; two public schools, six high schools: *Colegio San Luis Gonzaga*, the oldest educational institution in the country, *Liceo Sagrado Corazón de Jesús, Colegio Vicente Lachner Sandoval, Colegio Seráfico San Francisco, Colegio Vocacional de Artes y Oficios de Cartago* (Vocational Arts and Trades High School of Cartago); *Instituto Profesional Feminino Arabela Jiménez de Volio* (girls' professional institute); two higher learning institutions: the *Instituto Tecnológico de Costa Rica* (Technological Institute of Costa Rica) and the *Colegio Universitario de Cartago* (Cartago College); and the Capuchinos Fathers Convent, which also manages a small publishing house.

Cartago is a quiet city, with a certain patriarchal air, reflected in the sobriety of the people's customs. Its climate is pleasant and healthy, and the comforts here offered to visitors keeps tourists coming in all year round. It has three parks: Central Park, Jesús Jiménez, and Los Angeles; four historical buildings: the Pirie Building, Colegio de San Luis Gonzaga, the Municipal Market, and the *Ruinas de la Parroquia* (Church Ruins); and three monuments: one dedicated to Jesús Jiménez Zamora (located in the

Ruinas de la Parroquia (church ruins), Cartago City.

129

park, on the north side of the Municipal Market), one dedicated to Melico Salazar Zúñiga (Central Park), and another dedicated to Ricardo Jiménez Oreamuno (in front of the INS Building); some forest reserves, such as the Río Sombrero Watershed, in the San Francisco District, the Bosque de Quercua, with potable freshwater springs, in the San Nicolás District. There is also the Prusia National Park, in the Tierra Blanca District, and the majestic Irazú Volcano, which attracts thousands of tourists each year.

Several public service institutions operate in Cartago Canton: the *Junta Administrativa del Servicio Eléctrico* (JASEC = Administrative Electrical Service Board), the Municipality of Cartago, a branch of ICE (the Costa Rican Electrical Institute), and a branch office of the CCSS (Costa Rican Social Security).

The electrical power service is administered by the JASEC. Waterworks, sewage treatment, trash pick-up, and street cleaning are all handled by the Municipality of Cartago; telephone service is supplied by ICE.

The Atlantic Railway passes through Cartago City. Moreover, it is linked with the capital, 21 kilometers away, by an excellent freeway.

Paraíso Canton

Southeast of Cartago Canton is Paraíso Canton, which is comprised of the districts Paraíso, Santiago, Orosi, and Cachí. It has a total population of 27,823 inhabitants and covers a total land area of 411.91 kms², according to the 1984 census.

The town of Paraíso is six kilometers from Cartago and is linked to that city by the Atlantic Railway and a good highway. It has 14,800 inhabitant. The average temperature is 19°C. It has good public services, a clinic, and a developing industrial zone.

This canton, established in 1848, now belongs to the greater metropolitan area, except for the southern part of the Orosi District. It is drained by the rivers Reventazón, Cuericí, Villegas, Dos Amigos, Qurí, Purisil, Macho, and Palomo. There are also a numerous streams that, as they receive waters from their tributaries, grow into sizable rivers.

Within this canton is the reservoir formed by the Cachí Dam, the hydroelectric plants, Río Macho, Birrís Uno, and Birrís Dos, as well as several public interest sites: the ruins of Ujarrás, the lookout points at Orosi and Ujarrás, the lake resorts at Charrarra and Laguna

Doña Anacleta Lagoon or Parque de la Expresión, Paraíso Canton, Cartago Province.

The colonial church at Orosi is a national landmark. It was built of adobe brick by Franciscan missionaries.

de Doña Anacleta (also called *Parque de la Expresión*), the Lankaster Gardens, and the Orosi Church (now a colonial museum), and a fine high school built in 1968 during the presidential term of Joaquín Trejos Fernández (*Atlas Cantonal*, 1987).

The town of Paraíso was called the *Pueblo de Ujarrás* (Ujarrás Village) from 1562 to 1832. In 1832 to the people were getting ready to move the village, due to the instability of the land and the constant danger of flooding from nearby rivers, and because of diseases that were assailing the area. But it continued there under a new name, Villa de Paraíso, which was eventually shortened to Paraíso.

The first chapel was built between the years 1561 and 1569; it was made of straw. In 1575 another was built of adobe, and by 1693 a rubblework church building was erected, and for the first time there a church was dedicated to the Virgin Mary. In 1920 the building was declared a national monument, and in 1965 construction was begun on the present Catholic Church, which by 1981, was declared the national sanctuary of the *Señora de la Limpia Concepción del Rescate de Ujarrás* (Lady of the Pure Conception of the Recovery of Ujarrás)

The second district, Santiago is the most fully dedicated to farming in the canton. It produces sugarcane, coffee, fruit and vegetables, legumes, bananas, and several types of livestock. Vegetation thrives in this area, making for a vivid contrast against surrounding areas that are practically bare and void of plant life, due to severe erosion. In this district there is a Catholic Church, a delegation of the Rural Guard, a soccer field, an elementary school, a post office, and a railway station for the railway that leads to the Caribbean.

The third district, Cachí, is also heavily involved in agriculture, particularly in coffee growing. This is an important district since located in it is the Cachí Hydroelectric Project. Part of this project consists of an outstanding engineering feat, the Cachí Dam, which forms a large artificial lake. Another appealing feature this area has is the scenic winding route, full of magnificent views, which is the only route to Cachí.

The fourth district of Paraíso is Orosi, also largely dedicated to farming and cattle raising for milk and beef. It is a tourist zone *par excellence* and even has several swimming resorts such as Los Martínez, Los Patios, and Hotel Río, all of which use naturally heated water that

The Cachí Dam of the Cachí Hydroelectric Project and the large artificial lake it has formed.

are coffee, sugarcane, chayote, tomato, vegetables, legumes, and flowers. Both dairy and beef cattle are raised, as well. It is worth mentioning that the chayote and other crops (non-perishables), as well as flowers are exported, and over the last few years the amount exported has been steadily on the rise.

Industry in the canton includes machine shops, manufacture of knives and machetes, production of asbestus cement, meat processing, and clothing and other manufacture (mainly for export).

With respect to tourism, in the last two years there has been a need to broaden this area's capacity to accommodate tourists. Hence, the canton has been planning in coordination with the Cartago Chamber of Tourism, possible ways to develop the tourist industry in Paraíso, which appears to have promising potential due to the many interesting and scenic spots there.

Among the principle buildings in the canton are the Santuario Nuestra Señora de Ujarrás, the Paraíso Municipal Building, the Delegation of the Rural Guard, the Mayor's Office, the Liceo de Paraíso (high school); the elementary school buildings: José de Liendo y Goicoechea, Eugenio Corrales Bianchini,

comes from a fracture in the earth's crust, originating around Patarrá. Also in Orosi is the old Catholic Church, now a Colonial Museum, the El Llano Reservoir, from which 1,800 liters per second are drawn to supply the greater San José metropolitan area. Other points of interest are the Río Macho Hydroelectric Project, the Río Macho Forest Reserve, and the Tapantí National Wildlife Refuge. It also has a district delegation of the Rural Guard, a Social Security clinic, a soccer field, and several business services.

Farming is the most important activity in Paraíso Canton. The principle crops

The Paradero Lacustre Charrarra (lake resort) in Ujarrás, Paraíso Canton, Cartago Province.

Ruins of the church at Ujarrás. In Ujarrás township was born the famous Costa Rican clergyman, Florencio del Castillo.

Llanos de Santa Lucía; the Public Library, a Clinic of the CCSS (Costa Rican Social Security), a Health Center, nutrition centers, a chapter of the Costa Rican Red Cross, the Fire Fighters' Station, the *Centro Bilingüe Villa Paraíso* (Villa Paraíso Bilingual Center), the postal-telegraph office; branch buildings of the Nacional and Crédito Agrícola banks; a telephone switching station; and the Municipal Market. It has three parks: Central Park (República de México), Expresión Laguna de Doña Ana, Municipal Sports and Recreation Park. It also has town historical landmarks: the Ruins of Ujarrás and the Orosi Colonial Church.

The Orosi Colonial Church, built during the colonial period, is well-preserved and has been declared a national landmark. The walls were built of adobe bricks and the roof of tile, by Franciscan missionaries. It is admired not only for its beauty, but also for the fact that it has endured frequent earth tremors and earthquakes for over three centuries. The church contains much-esteemed images, particularly a painting of the Immaculate One, a work of great merit. Also in the sacristy are several relics from the colonial period, ornaments and priestly garments, prayer books, and missals, and other articles.

Several projects could greatly benefit the canton: harnessing water from the Guzmán Springs, separation of city streets, and repair of local roads.

Ujarrás

Although the township of Ujarrás belongs to the district of Paraíso, it warrants its own section since it is a flourishing tourist zone, and is actively involved in the agricultural production of non-traditional items exported to European and United States markets. Ujarrás is also distinguished for having been the first town to build a church dedicated to the Virgin Mary. Moreover, here was born the famous clergyman, Father Florencio del Castillo, and here is the *Balneario Las Ruinas* (swimming resort), the *Paradero Lacustre Charrarra* (lake resort), which has grassy areas, a restaurant, sports fields, water sport facilities, ferryboat rides, and wooded areas with picnic and recreational facilities. Nevertheless, what has made this place famous, more than anything else, is its religious customs and devotion.

La Unión Canton

Part of this canton is on the western slopes of the Central Tectonic Depression, and part on the eastern slopes. The terrain is somewhat hilly. In the canton are the La Carpintera Hills, where many streams that drain San José Province originate, Mount El Alto, and the Hills of Ochomogo. The climate here is cool and healthful. The main farm products of these fertile lands are coffee and sugarcane. On the side of the Cartago Valley cattle are raised on lush pasture lands.

La Unión comprises the following districts: Tres Ríos, San Diego, San Juan, San Rafael, Concepción, Dulce Nombre, San Ramón, and Río Azul.

The population of 41,005 inhabitant live on a total land area of 44.83 kms² (according to the 1984 census).

Settlement of this canton dates back to the Eighteenth Century with the establishment of the first village, Valle de los Tres Ríos. The first chapel was built in 1751 but was destroyed by an earthquake in 1841. Then construction of a new one was begun in 1855, and in 1869 the parish church was erected and dedicated to Our Lady of Pilar.

In 1877 the first school was built. The school still exists, but the building was replaced in 1942. In 1967 the *Liceo de La Unión* (high school) was inaugurated.

La Unión was classified as a canton in 1848. Two versions purport to explain the origin of the name. One states that it comes from a "union" of missionaries formed in the canton. The other alleges that the name comes from the union of three rivers, today called the Tiribí, Chiquito, and the Fierro. (*Atlas Cantonal*, 1987).

The canton seat, Tres Ríos, is situated 10 kilometers west of Cartago City and about 11 kilometers east of San José, at the foot of Carpintera Hills. The average temperature is a pleasantly, healthy 19°C. Its principle buildings are the Catholic Church, a lovely school, the Municipal Building, and two elegant pavilions, built for the Sanitation Unit and the Children's Clinic. There are many, varied commercial establishments, some workshops, and bakeries. Its downtown area, not very spacious, is, nevertheless, quite populous, and preserves much of its colonial air.

The cemetery is especially attractive. It is well-kept and arranged symmetrically in a very picturesque setting, with immaculate mausoleums. It is artistically decorated with assorted plants and flowers.

Tres Ríos is one of the spots most frequented in the dry season by families from the capital. Many of these families own recreational cottages in the area. The town has 8,661 inhabitants. A small municipal band livens up the central park every weekend. This canton is part of the greater metropolitan area. It has a hospital, two hydroelectric plants, the national monument, Arbol del Centenario, a good multi-sports center, offices of the Ministry of Agriculture, the *Instituto Costarricense de Investigación y Enseñanza de Nutrición y Salud* (Costa Rican Institute of Nutrition and Health Research, 10 years old), the Post Office, the Rural and Civil Guards, the Fire Fighters' Station, and a chapter of the Costa Rican Red Cross. It also has good restaurants, for the most part located on the road to Cartago.

Until a short time ago the canton had difficulty in maintaining an adequate water supply, but the problem was resolved when water sources were given back (Padre Carazo, Chigüite, and Pizote). It has also had problems with its streets, but a contract was signed to asphalt the city streets that access the districts, and now the work is almost completed.

The canton has several schools: Mario Quirós Sasso, specializing in accounting and secretarial skills, the *Liceo Franco Costarricense* (a private high school where classes are given in French), located in Concepción, Tres Ríos, and the *Liceo Nocturno La Unión* (night high school). It has several industries that provide employment for most of the local population as well as commuters from other cantons: Ycatica, Irex, Jobonería Colima, and Textilera Tres Ríos, for example. It also has some development associations and cooperatives of various types. Some of its tourist attractions include the protected zones of Río Tiribí and the Carpintera Hills.

Jiménez Canton

This canton is bounded on the northeast by Alvarado Canton, on the south by the Reventazón River, on the east by Turrialba Canton, and on the west by Paraíso Canton. It has a population of 11,861 living on a total land area of 283.53 kms².

The terrain here is very uneven, with many high areas and low valleys making for an extremely varied climate. The advantage of this is that there are many virgin lands, or lands with very few years of cultivation. Today the principal activities of the canton are livestock raising and sugarcane growing. It also has splendid coffee plantations, and produces fine vegetables, tubers, and legumes. There is a sugar mill right in the canton. The Atlantic Railway crossing Jiménez is the main factor that has contributed to its rapid development.

The districts of Jiménez Canton are Juan Viñas, Tucurrique, and Pejibaye.

The canton was first settled during the second half of the Nineteenth Century. The first village, today Juan Viñas, used to be called El Naranjo.

The first chapel was built in 1880, and in 1939 it was given the name Cecilio Lindo Morales. The high school, *Liceo Juan Viñas* opened during the second presidential administration of José Figueres.

Jiménez be a canton in 1903 and was named in honer of the former Costa Rican president, Jesús Jiménez Zamora.

The canton is drained by many tributaries of the Reventazón River, than run all through it. In this region are the Río Macho and Tapantí Forest Reserves, and a swimming resort that attracts many tourists.

The town of Juan Viñas, the canton seat, has an average temperature of 20°C. Surrounding the town are coffee and sugarcane plantations and cattle ranches. One of the most picturesque areas in the country, it is situated in a beautiful valley three kilometers from the railroad accessible by a good road that winds through the mountains. It is also linked to the capital of the province by a good road that passes through the town of Paraíso. In its central area there are comfortable and elegant homes, a good church and magnificent school buildings. It has a population of 5,543

inhabitants. The canton has good public services, a Social Security clinic, offices of the Supreme Court of Justice, a branch office of the *Banco Crédito Agrícola de Cartago* (Farm Credit Bank of Cartago), the National Production Council, and a high school. It also has a branch office of the Ministry of Agriculture, the Cachí Hydroelectric Plant, shopping centers, and the El Jardín Restaurant.

Among the most pressing problems of the canton figure the irregular water supply, the lack of employment sources, forcing people to commute to the Cartago Industrial Park of San José (the only employers are the sugar mill and the La Hacienda coffee processing plant, providing employment and housing, but, unfortunately when a worker losses his job he also is left without a place to live). These conditions have given rise to illegal settlements.

The canton is also hampered by a lack of adequate local roads and effective sewage removal, since the municipality has no machinery to address the problem. This situation is now in the process of being resolved, however, by a project that will bring a number of benefits to the canton.

Turrialba Canton

This canton is comprised of the following districts: Turrialba, La Suiza, Peralta, Santa Cruz, Santa Teresita, Tuis, Tayutic, Santa Rosa, and Pavones, and has a total population of 50,567 inhabitants. This easternmost canton in Cartago

Juan Viñas, Jiménez Canton, Cartago Province.

The Monumento Nacional Guayabo (Guayabo National Landmark Park) in Turrialba Canton at the foot of the Turrialba Volcano.

Province, is situated between the cantons of Jiménez Alvarado, and Paraíso, and Limón Province. The terrain is irregular, with valleys and hilly areas, all with a pleasantly warm climate. The fertile soil is used for extensive coffee plantations, sugarcane, corn, pejibaye, macadamia nuts, tree fruits, and tubers. There are also rich pastures that support outstanding cattle ranches. Large sugar mills here process the sugarcane right in the canton. All of these activities benefit from the Caribbean railway that crosses the canton.

Within this canton are the Indian communities of Bajo Chirripó and Chirripó (or Alto Chirripó).

The region was first settled by indigenous peoples from the Huetar Kingdom east of here, and then by the Spaniards. In 1842 this area was designated as a confinement zone for people accused of minor infractions of the law. Due to the invasion and settlement, the people of this town have had to pull up stakes and move three times.

The first school (private) was built in 1889. In 1902 the first public school was established, and in the 1908 improvements were made to the building. In 1944 the public high school was established, today called the *Instituto Clodomira Picado Twight*.

The canton has had a Catholic Church since 1575. Reconstructed several times, it became a parish church in 1906. The canton came into being in 1903. Its name, according to Carlos Gagini is derived from that of the Turriraba River, which was eventually transformed by the Spaniards into Turrialba (*Atlas Cantonal*, 1987).

The town of Turrialba is one of the most important in the region from Cartago to Puerto Limón, because of its commercial activity. It is surrounded by large coffee and sugarcane plantations and cattle ranches. At 646 meters above sea level, its average temperature of 28°C is healthier than the hotter climates of the lowlands on the Caribbean Coast.

It has a population of 23,705 inhabitants. Turrialba has experienced phenomenal growth over the past few years. Its location about midway between

Limón and San José is the primary cause of this progress, evidenced by all of the activities of its urban and business life: prosperous businesses, new meeting centers, important public buildings, and emerging industries are all indicators of its advance. Further, it is linked to San José and Limón by good highways. Close to downtown Turrialba is the *Instituto Interamericano de Ciencias Agrícolas* (CATIE = Tropical Agricultural Research and Training Center). In 1971 the Atlantic Regional Center of the University of Costa Rica and the Dr. William Allen Hospital were established, and the archeological site at Guayabo was declared a national historical landmark.

Turrialba, however, has been affected with respect to business movement by the opening of a new highway to Guápiles, that provided a quicker route between Limón and San José.

Alvarado Canton

This canton extends over the southern slopes of the Irazú and Turrialba volcanoes and is situated between the cantons of Oreamuno, Paraíso, Jiménez, and Turrialba. It has a total population of 8,338 inhabitants and is comprised by the following districts: Pacayas, Cervantes, and Capellades. Its climate is cool, and even chilly in some spots. The soil is fertile. This canton was inhabited by indigenous peoples in pre-Colombian eras, and at the onset of the Nineteenth Century the first white settlers arrived from San Pedro (the modern canton of Montes de Oca). In 1902 the first school was built, and in 1972 the *Colegio Técnico Profesional de Pacayas* (Pacayas Technical High School) opened for classes.

The canton, created in 1908, was named in honor of Father José Joaquín Alvarado, the first parish priest of Pacayas.

The town of Pacayas, the canton seat, with 3,760 inhabitants, is located 17 kilometers northeast of Cartago City accessible by a good highway. Its average temperature is 18°C. In the region surrounding this town there are fine cattle ranches, as well as farms where potatoes, beans, corn, vegetables, coffee and sugarcane are grown. Also here are the hydroelectric plants Birrís No. 3 and No. 4. This canton, too, is part of the greater metropolitan area. It has electrical power, bank branch offices, a post office, good transportation provided by Copee-Baire, a few stores, no market, a Ministry of Agriculture office, a chapter of the Costa Rican Red Cross, the Fire Fighters' Station, dance halls, a soccer field under construction, a gymnasium, a sports academe, a multi-sports center project underway, several kindergartens, a Social Security clinic, nine elementary schools distributed throughout the canton, a high school, a health station, and a nutrition center.

There is a potato chip factory in the canton, the *Industria de Papas Tostadas Riquis*, but most people here make their living from farming, and most of the women who are employed work in Cartago.

Several spots in the canton are popular tourist attractions: the Irazú Volcano National Park, the Cordillera Volcánica Central Forest Reserve, the El Salto Waterfall, a house near the Irazú Volcano over 100 years old, and the old Santa Teresa Church.

There is a project under way to connect the Irazú-Turrialba Highway to complete what is referred to as the Cartago Tourist Ring. This will bring to the canton many benefits, including tourists as the access route will be considerably shortened.

Pacayas, Alvarado Canton, Cartago Province.

137

The hills surrounding Pacayas, Alvarado.

Two problems are currently hampering the canton: the poor condition of the local roads due to insufficient budget, and the absence of a rubbish dump, which indirectly causes pollution of the rivers as garbage is deposited in them.

Oreamuno Canton

This canton extends northeast of Cartago City, partly over the El Guarco Valley and partly over the slopes of the Irazú Volcano, giving it a varied climate with temperatures ranging between 14°C and 19°C. Its hilly and fertile land is used mainly to grow potatoes, vegetables, and coffee, and for pastures.

It comprises the districts of San Rafael, Cot, Potrero Cerrado, Cipreses, and Santa Rosa, and has a total population of 24,145 inhabitants. It was created in 1914 and was named after a former Costa Rican president, Francisco María Oreamuno-Badilla.

The town from which the canton grew was established first in Cot, at first by the aborigines, and in 1561 the Spaniards visited the place, calling it San Antonio de Padua (the saint of that day). The first chapel was built in 1854 in what is now the town of San Rafael, and in 1981 a parish church was erected. The current elementary school was inaugurated in 1970, and the *Colegio Técnico Profesional Agropecuario de Oreamuno* (agricultural high school) began its classes in 1973.

San Rafael, the governmental seat of the canton, has 14,824 inhabitants and is located two kilometers from Cartago. It has a good Catholic church, two schools, and a town hall. Some of its streets are made of cobblestone.

The district of Cot, located on a side of the Irazú Volcano, five kilometers from Cartago, has a population of 4,595 inhabitants. The people are of indigenous origin. It has two elementary schools, a Catholic church, and a public plaza. Its narrow streets form square blocks. The climate is chilly and very healthy. The land is used mostly for large-scale corn growing. On the outskirts of Cot there was a sanitorium. The new highway going up the Irazú Volcano passes through this district. It has available the usual public services: a municipal building, post office, public library, Rural Guard unit, an elementary school in each district, and agricultural high school, a supply cooperative, two restaurants, and a hotel.

In this canton there is an old chapel where lie the remains of Monsignor Sanabria. There is also a monument to the former Costa Rican president, Braulio Carrillo. One of the most pressing problems of this canton is the inadequate drinking water supply, since the plumbing is old and of insufficient capacity for the growing population. There are plans, however, to install a new system. Another problem facing the canton is the lack of jobs, but it should be resolved soon with the opening of a dairy products factory just built, and a textile industry soon to be opened by a Korean company.

El Guarco Canton

The eighth canton of Cartago Province is divided into four districts: 1) El Tejar, the governmental seat of the canton; 2) San Isidro, with the townships of La Cangreja, Palmital, Estrella, Vara de Roble, Empalme, Bajo Florida, Cañón, Macho Gaff, Tres de Junio, Salsipuedes, and Ojo de Agua; 3) Tobosi, with the townships of Purires and Tablón; and 4) Patio de Agua, with the township of Caragral. The canton has a total population of 20,807 inhabitants living on a total land area of 167.69 kms² (according to the 1984 National Census). El Guarco Canton is bounded on the north and east by the central canton of Cartago; on the south by Dota Canton, and on the west by Desamparados. The climate is similar to that of Cartago City, three kilometers away. Its terrain is flat. The town of Cartago was originally founded here, but today most of the area is dedicated to farms and beautiful grazing lands.

The principle crops are coffee, corn, potatoes, beans, and many kinds of vegetables. Tejar (meaning to weave) gets its name from the weaving industry there. There are also brick factories and large charcoal factories that supply most of the country. Pottery making is the preferred industry of the canton, but rope is also made of hemp grown right alongside the cattle pastures.

The first chapel in the canton was built in 1570, and in 1914 a parish church was erected in honor of the Immaculate Conception. In 1985 the El Guarco Parish Church was elevated to the rank of Basilica. The first school in the canton was built in 1894. The Elías Leiva Quirós High School opened in 1970. El Guarco officially became a canton in 1939 and was named in memory of the Huetar chief who once lived in this region.

The town of Tejar, the canton seat, with 11,158 inhabitants has a lovely, spacious school that bears the name of the renowned former president of Costa Rica, Ricardo Jiménez. The Catholic Church here is true work of art, whose interior is one of the most beautiful in Cartago Province. The canton has its own waterworks and plumbing system but it does not deliver enough water to meet the needs of the population. Electric power is provided by the same system that provides power to the rest of the province. The people make their living from farming, industry, and commerce (many important businesses are located here).

El Guarco is undoubtedly one of the cantons that has given most to country through it citizens who have contributed to the fields of education, law, politics, and commerce. In this canton are grocery stores, a branch office of the National Bank, a post office, an office of the National Production Council, a sanitation unit, and a dental clinic. Also located here is the San Isidro National Horse Racetrack, where every weekend national tournaments are held, alluring many tourists. Plans are also underway to make a recreational park at the original site of the "muddy city" (Cartago).

The San Isidro National Racetracks in El Guarco Canton, Cartago Province.

139

HEREDIA PROVINCE

This province occupies a strip of land that stretches north to south in the middle of the country. It is bounded on the north by the San Juan River, on the east by the Limón Province and part of San José, on the south by San José, and on the west by Alajuela Province. Part of this province (the smallest of the seven in land area) is formed partly by the Barva Mountains, and the rest extends over the plains of the north. The climate is generally moderate. The agricultural products of this province are the same as those of the other central provinces. It grows a lot of coffee; in fact, some cantons are devoted completely to that crop. The land here, without exception is the best in the country. The major river here is the Sarapiquí; the small rivers that drain the province are tributaries either of the Virilla River, the Río Grande de Tárcoles, or the Sarapiquí. The province has a population of 197,575 inhabitants who live on a total land area of 2,656.66 kms², divided into 10 cantons. (See Map No. 13.)

Heredia became a province in December of 1848. Its name dates back to the petition made by its citizens in 1700 to the President of the *Real Audiencia de Guatemala*, Captain General Alonzo Fernández de Heredia, that he grant the title of "Villa" to the region. This he did calling it Villa de Heredia. (*Atlas Cantonal*, 1987).

The territory of this province was first settled by Huetar Indians from the Western Kingdom, then by the Spaniards who came to the Barva area in 1568. In 1706 other settlers arrived from Cartago.

The first chapel was built in the village of Barva in 1575, and in 1736 a parish church was erected. In 1751 the first school was founded, and by 1843 there were university professors from the *Universidad de Santo Tomás* living in the province. In 1875 secondary education was initiated, in 1915, the *Escuela Normal de Costa Rica* (a teachers' college) was

Opposite page: Antiguo Fortín (old fort), Heredia City.

The parish church of Heredia City, located alongside the central park, is a historical landmark from the colonial period; its construction dates back to the Eighteenth Century.

Another view of the Heredia Parish Church.

begun, and in 1973 the *Universidad Nacional*, whose headquarters are known as the Omar Dengo Campus, was created.

The province of Heredia, which grew up from the original town of the Immaculate Conception of Cubujuquí, has a hydroelectric plant and a developing industrial area in the southern part of the province called La Valencia, Barreal and La Ribera in the cantons of Belén, Santo Domingo, and Heredia.

Heredia Canton

Heredia, the first canton of the province, is made up of the districts of Heredia, Mercedes, San Francisco, Ulloa, and Varablanca. It is situated in the central part of the province, on the foothills of

Government-Postal-Telegraph Building in Heredia City, declared a historical-architectural landmark.

142

the Barva Mountains. The terrain is somewhat mountainous and the climate moderate. The southern part of canton produces a great deal of coffee and beef cattle. The canton has a total population of 154,896 inhabitants.

Heredia Canton was created in 1848. It has always placed a great emphasis on education, and in its first school of music founded in 1831, studied Manuel María Gutiérrez, the composer of the National Anthem of Costa Rica, as well as other important Costa Ricans. It was also in this canton that the second secondary school in the country was founded. (*Atlas Cantonal*, 1987).

This canton, except for the Varablanca District, belongs to the greater metropolitan area. It has two industrial zones (Barreal and La Valencia), the National Food Distribution Center (CENADA), the San Vicente Hospital and a Social Security clinic, the central campus and headquarters of the National University, and a branch of the Autonomous University of Central America. Here too, is an old fort and the house of Alfredo González Flores, a former president of Costa Rica; the *Liceo de Heredia*, historical-cultural landmark; and the Government-Postal-Telegraph

Building, classified as a building of historical and architectural interest. In this canton also is the Braulio Carrillo National Park, the Cordillera Volcánica Central Forest Reserve, as well as the volcanic sulfur mineralization zone.

Heredia City

The city of Heredia is the capital of the province and The governmental seat of Heredia Canton. It is 10 kilometers from the national capital San José to which is linked by the Atlantic Railway and by fine paved highways. As of the 1984 census, it had a population of 21,440 inhabitants living within the confines of the city alone.

The city is situated among the low-lying slopes of Mount Zurquí and the Barva Mountain Mass. It is surrounded by coffee plantations and permanently green grasslands. At 1,150 meters above sea level, it has an average temperature of 20.2°. Its downtown area of slightly over a square kilometer is neat and orderly with square blocks and straight streets that run northeast to southeast.

It has three Catholic Churches: the Parroquial (Parish Church), built in the Eighteenth Century and reminiscent of the colonial period; the Carmen and the

Liceo de Heredia in Heredia City, a historical-cultural landmark.

143

Parroquia de los Angeles. It has four high schools, several good elementary schools, a handy market, a Municipal Hall, two schools of higher learning, theaters, and some public buildings of minor importance. The main plaza, called Central Park, following the usual design in the country, has become a beautiful garden with brick paths running all through it. There are also two other well-kept public parks and a multi-sports center. The cemetery is worth mentioning because of its large number of tombs and mausoleums.

The first town of Heredia, founded in the Eighteenth Century, has moved several times and has had different names. The first (1706) was located in what is known today as Barrio Lagunilla, but, as that spot turned out to be unsatisfactory, the town was relocated (1717) to what is today the center of Heredia, first called Cubujuquí, and then Villa Vieja (Old Villa) since it was the oldest town in the western sector of San José. In 1801 the governor at that time, Tomás Acosta forbade the use of the name Villa, and from then on it was called Inmaculada Concepción de Heredia, a name it retained until 1813 when it was given the title of Villa. From 1824 on it has been called Heredia.

It has factories that make soaps and matches and several other industries that demonstrate the strong work ethic of the people of Heredia. They are also distinguished for their culture and love of the arts.

In this city there are several beneficent societies and a hospital. Its public services include waterworks, sewage removal and treatment, mail, telephones, telegraph, electrical power, and public lighting.

Barva Canton

This canton is situated north of the central Heredia Canton, on the Barva mountain mass. It is bounded on the west by Santa Bárbara Canton and on the east by San Rafael Canton. The terrain is uneven but the soil is very fertile. The climate is chilly in the higher spots and moderate in the lower areas. It produces coffee, sugarcane, cattle, and other products that thrive in cooler climates. It is drained by the rivers Pirro, Seco, Río Segundo, La Hoya, and Barva.

The districts of this canton are Barva, San Pedro, San José de la Montaña, San Pablo, San Roque, and Santa Lucía. The 1984 census showed a total population of 18,933 inhabitants.

Typical houses in the center of Barva, that constitute part of this historical center of the canton.

The Catholic Church in Barva Heredia, located on what once was an Indian burial ground.

Barva, the governmental seat of the canton is located three kilometers from the capital of the province, and it is linked to Heredia City and neighboring districts by good roads. It has a Catholic Church, elementary schools, a Town Hall, and a postal-telegraph office. Its average temperature is 20.2°C. It has a population of 3,911 inhabitants. Here was born Cleto González Víquez, who served for two terms as president of Costa Rica.

Barva Canton was inhabited by Huetar Indians of the Western Kingdom. The name comes from the most famous chief of that tribe, Barva. The Huetars lived here until 1569 when the Spaniards came and divided the lands among themselves. In 1601 the area began to develop as it was made rest area for mule teams. By 1613 the village of San Bartolomé de Barva had formed.

The first church was built from the years 1568 to 1575 in honor of Saint Bartholomew (*San Bartolomé*) and then to the Virgin of the Assumption (until 1888). Today it is dedicated to Saint Bartholomew, and sits on what was an Indian burial ground.

The first school was founded in 1830; the current building was inaugurated in 1952.

In 1972 the *Liceo Rodrigo Hernández Vargas* opened for classes.

The canton is part of the greater metropolitan area. The center of the town of Barva is the historical center of the canton. A replica (in another site) of this first stage of the historical and cultural town was finished in 1986, but the work was not continued due to a lack of funds. It includes a complete sector built after the design of the original Indian dwellings, including the church.

In the center of the city, on one side of the church, there is a grotto dedicated to the Virgin of Lourdes, which preserves the original architecture. There is also the house of the twice president of Costa Rica, Cleto González Víquez; the house was declared a historical landmark in 1985. In the area also is the Braulio Carrillo National Park, Cordillera Volcánica Central Forest Reserve, and the lake of the Barva Volcano. The town also has town sports fields, the National University Recreational Center, two hotels, each with a lookout point (El Pórtico and Cipresal), and a historical museum, the *Instituto del Café* (Coffee Institute).

The canton has several cooperatives, a Lions Club, development associations, and a chapter of the Red Cross. Also, under construction, is a day-patient center for senior citizens.

Santo Domingo Canton

This canton, with 23,985 inhabitants (1984 census), is the second most populous after Heredia. It sits on an inclined plane, somewhat uneven at the foot of Mount Zurquí. The canton produces some of the finest coffee in Costa Rica. It is watered by the rivers Virilla and Bermúdez. Santo Domingo Canton is divided into the districts of Santo Domingo, San Vicente, San Miguel, Paracito, Santo Tomás, Santa Rosa, Tures, and Pará.

The town of Santo Domingo, the canton seat, is three kilometers from Heredia City, and 1.6 kilometers north of the San José-Alajuela railroad. It is surrounded by robust coffee plantations. The streets are wide and straight, and the community is pleasing to look at because of its neatness and singularity. It has two Catholic churches, one with an impressive style, a good high school, a town hall, an elegant Sanitation Unit building, postal service, telephones, telegraph, public lighting, and comfortable private homes, most of them distinctly Spanish in style. The people, proud of their outstanding

town, are noted for their patriotism and public spirit. Because of their untiring efforts to improve the status of their town, the congress in 1902, by the an agreement made on August 1 of that year declared the old villa of Santo Domingo to *ciudad* (city or town status).

Santo Domingo Canton, which came into being in 1869, gets its name from the chapel dedicated to Saint Domingo (1838), a name first given to the barrio, then to the district, and finally to the canton.

Part of the greater metropolitan area, Santo Domingo on its west side has a developing industrial zone called La Valencia. In the center of the San Miguel District there is also a quaint, little church, El Carmen, considered to be a historic, architectural, and cultural landmark.

Santo Domingo is one of the few towns in the Central Tectonic Depression whose urban layout was planned early in the last century, following the famous colonial Spanish Damero arrangement of orderly blocks with wide streets.

The building styles date back to when coffee was king (1860-1930), except for the moorish-style Rosario Church, which resembles other churches in Costa Rica (such as the one in Nicoya, to which it

El Carmen Church, considered a historical, architectural, and cultural landmark, located in the center of the San Miguel District, Santo Domingo Canton, Heredia Province.

146

is remarkably similar, especially if it were restored to its original state).

The second church, a delightful Basilica erected during the height of the coffee boom, is more neo-classical in its style (see Annie Emistre, 1984). Other important buildings in Santo Domingo are the Municipal Building, the health center, and several school buildings. The heart of the town infrastructure is located between Central to Ninth Streets and Third to Fifth Avenues. Also notable here are the many colonial houses made of adobe and wood, and others from the beginning of this century made of brick. Modern buildings include those of the cooperative, the fire fighters' station, and the high school. The central park designated 25 years ago in the historic center of the district, was recently the gathering place for centennial festivities.

It also has several landmarks, although they have not been declared as such: its 100-year-old arch bridges made of stone and brick over its main rivers, its two churches, the cemetery, and its entire downtown area, as well as some small district centers such as San Miguel and Santa Rosa, are historic works of notable colonial influence.

It has excellent communication services and roads; its local roads are good condition all year round. The streets of the downtown area are all asphalt and have clearly marked traffic signs.

Santo Domingo has all essential public services: waterworks, public lighting, public telephones, buses and taxicabs, telegraph, bank branches, post office, and others.

Santo Domingo has an abundant subterranean water supply, that even supplies other areas outside the canton. To handle the water needs of its own district, it has a pumping station in Santa Rosa. It also has good roads and streets, as well as bus and mini-bus services providing efficient transportation both within the city and to and from the capital.

This canton, as others, due to its proximity to the capital, is exposed to a rapidly expanding urbanization process extending out from San José, that is quickly turning it into a "bedroom city" (a place to sleep at night while working in San José). In spite of this, however, coffee continues to be the chief agricultural product, just as wheat, sugarcane, and tobacco were in years past. Vegetable farming continues to dwindle, but in some district it remains relatively strong.

Santa Rosa has a growing industrial zone with more and more factories and assembly plants, as it is one of the areas recommended by governmental planning for industry.

River fishing has practically disappeared due to today's deforestation and pollution. Tourists in Costa Rica prefer the purer, larger rivers in the northern and eastern parts where they can catch trout or *barbudos*.

The central district has great potential for the tourist industry, but it needs investment from the municipalities and the corresponding institutions (ICT, IFAM, etc.) in order to generate a constant flow of tourists. Nonetheless, anyone who admires colonial architecture, traditions that date back to the last century, scenic and ecological beauty, and other features of this canton, will find it an ideal place to enjoy.

Santa Bárbara Canton

This canton lies between the Alajuela Province on the west, Barva Canton on the east, Heredia Canton to the north, and Flores Canton to the south. It has a total population of 16,643 inhabitants, and is divided into the districts of Santa Bárbara, San Pedro, San Juan, Jesús, Santo Domingo, and Puralá. Its principle products are coffee, sugarcane, and vegetables. Its climate is moderate. The somewhat rugged terrain is watered by the streams La Cruz and Rosales and the rivers Ciruelas and Portrerillos and others.

The town of Santa Bárbara, the canton seat, with 3,667 inhabitants, has a Catholic church, a school, a rural guard post, and telephone, telegraph, and postal services. Its streets are straight, forming square blocks. The town is located six kilometers northwest of Heredia City.

The canton was founded in 1882, preserving the name that according to a popular account originated as follows: "A citizen named Bárbara, having obtained from a Franciscan priest a small image of Saint Barbara, made an alter to her in her house. Whenever storms (which were quite frequent) would come up, she would always seek refuge at her altar. Gradually the neighbors, hearing of her faith, unanimously followed her devotion." The first chapel erected was named after that saint. (*Atlas Cantonal*, 1987).

The Catholic Church in San Rafael, Heredia, an elegant gothic-style temple, a true marvel of its kind.

148

The name Santa Bárbara began to be used after 1821; previously the village had been called Churruca or Surrucho. The first chapel was built in 1837, and in 1852 a church was built, which was declared the parish church the following year. In 1860 the first school was opened, and in 1951 the present Juan Mora Fernández School was inaugurated. In 1973 the first high school was inaugurated: *Liceo de Santa Bárbara*.

Santa Bárbara has an office of the Ministry of Agriculture (MAG), branches of the National Bank and Bank of Costa Rica, attorneys' offices, topographers' offices, photo studios, a well-kept park, the El Banco de Mariscos Restaurant, a discotheque, good shopping centers, stores, a canton farm center, and Civil Guard and Rural Guard posts. In addition, the municipality, in conjunction with the sports committee and the development association have made plans to build a recreational center, and the land has already purchased for this purpose.

The most pressing problems of the canton are related to health, in as much as it has no sanitary land fill area, and its supply of potable water is insufficient. In addition, its local roads are in poor condition since the municipality lacks the necessary machinery to maintain them.

This canton, which is part of the greater metropolitan area, is also of great national interest since 17% of it is devoted to the Cordillera Volcánica Central Forest Reserve.

San Rafael Canton

Northwest of the central canton of Heredia is San Rafael Canton. With partly uneven terrain, it has an average temperature of from 20 to 22°C, depending on the altitude. It is drained by several small rivers, all tributaries of the Virilla. It produces coffee, vegetables, and sugarcane. It has a population of 22,871 inhabitants and is divided into the districts of San Rafael, San Josecito, Santiago, Los Angeles, and Concepción.

Situated on the south end of the canton, two kilometers from Heredia, is the town of San Rafael, the canton seat. It has an elegant gothic-style Catholic Church, a true marvel of its kind. It also has two elementary schools, a high school, a town hall, and postal, telephone, and telegraph services.

Until 1826 the town that later became the canton was called Piedra Grande. In 1818 the name was changed to San Rafael, as historical documents indicate, a name chosen by lottery as province authorities simultaneously chose the names of all the cantons from a selection of saints.

San Rafael was created in 1848 with five districts. In 1862 the first chapel was built. The present church was completed in 1962. As early as 1862 there already was an elementary school, and the present one, Pedro María Badilla School, was inaugurated in 1927. The *Liceo Ingeniero Carlos Pascual Z.* (high school) began its activities in 1967. Electric lighting was installed in 1917, and plumbing in 1910. In was in 1963 that it was classified as a *ciudad* (city or town status).

The canton, which belongs to the greater metropolitan area, has a clinic, the La Joya Hydroelectric Plant, and several places of public interest: the *Bosque del Río de la Hoja* (Leaf River Forest) and the *Paradero Monte de la Cruz*, the Castillo Tourist Center (private), Las Chorreras Farm, a stone bridge on *Calle Puente Piedra* located in the first district, and another beautiful bridge located in Barrio Santa Trinidad in San Josecito (Santa Trinidad was the original name of San Josecito).

The main problem hampering the canton is insufficient water supply, stemming from the fact that water intake was not planned in accordance with population growth. However, three wells are being dug, and the water intake mechanisms for Río Segundo and the El Gallito rivers are being improved.

The poor condition of the local roads is another problem facing the canton, but a project has been submitted to repair them. Funding for this project would come partly from the Ministry of Public

Works and Transportation (MOPT) and partly from the coffee producers.

San Isidro Canton

This sixth province of Heredia is located eight kilometers to the east. It is bounded on the north by Heredia Canton and Vázquez de Coronado, on the south by Santo Domingo, on the west by San Pablo and San Rafael de Heredia, and on the east by Moravia (canton no. 14 of San José Province).

With an elevation of 1,360 meters above sea level, temperatures here range from 16 to 25°C. San Isidro covers a total land area of 25,84 kms².

On June 13, 1905 the Central Government of Costa Rica decreed the formation of the new canton of San Isidro, the sixth in the province of Heredia, comprising the districts of San Isidro, San José, and Concepción.

The district and town of San Isidro, the governmental seat of the canton, includes the following townships: Santa Cruz, Lourdes (Las Quebradas), San Francisco, and Barrio María Auxiliadora (Calle Chaves).

The second district includes the townships of Santa Elena and Santa Marta. Concepción has only the township of Santa Cecilia.

San Isidro has a municipal building with the Delegation of the Rural Guard office, the Agricultural Extension Office of the Ministry of Agriculture (MAG), the Savings, Credit, and Multiple Services Cooperative (Coopeisidreña, R.L.).

In the canton seat there is a majestic parish church, considered to be, architecturally speaking, one of the best church buildings in Central America. There are also six Catholic chapels located in the various districts and townships.

The National Production Council has an outlet in this canton, from which it supplies many food products and other articles to the public.

There are six elementary schools, one junior high school, and another institution that offers diversified education.

There is a health center, which since 1988 has been known as the *Centro*

Integrado de Capacitación (Integrated Training Center). Finally, there are two penitentiaries of the Ministry of Justice and Grace (José Amparo Zeledón and the *Centro de Confianza San Luis*) located in Santa Elena, San Isidro de Heredia.

Regarding public services, the canton has electrical power, telephones, a post office, bus services to Heredia and San José, health and educational services, and others.

The most pressing problem hindering the canton is the insufficiency of its drinking water supply, lacking catchment sources, especially in the dry season.

San Isidro is an agricultural zone in which the single crop, coffee, predominates. Vegetables, fours, and ornamental plants are also grown, and there are several dairy farms.

The canton has within its limits a forest reserve in the northern sector of Heredia, and also the Braulio Carillo Colinas National Park. The opening of the highway from San José to Pococí (Guápiles), crossing this canton, has greatly benefitted this canton. Because of it, in 1987 traffic to and from San José increased considerably.

As for streets in the canton, currently there are a total of 18.8 kilometers of asphalt streets and 45.6 kilometers of gravel streets.

Eight kilometers from Heredia City is San Isidro, at an elevation of 1,360 meters above sea level, with gorgeous panoramic views to the west, and an average temperature of 17.4°C. The town of 5,813 inhabitants is centered on a small square with narrow, straight streets. It has a lovely Catholic Church, schools, and postal, telephone, and telegraph services. In the surrounding areas there are sugar and coffee processing plants. Some time ago there were found in this district some stone figurines of Indian origin, worthy of study for their fine detail and symbols, that resemble sacred figures of Chinese and Egyptian mythology.

The name of the canton dates back to 1861 when the first chapel was built and dedicated to *San Isidro Labrador*; subsequently the barrio was given the same name, shortly afterwards the district, and finally the canton. Today it has a population of 8,528 inhabitants and makes up part of the greater metropolitan area.

Belén Canton

West of the central canton of Heredia, Belén canton stretches over a very picturesque, generally flat plain. It has a healthy, pleasant climate with an average temperature of 21.7°C. Belén is drained by the rivers Virilla and Río Segundo. Its chief products are coffee, sugarcane, rice, beans, tomatoes, onions, corn, and cattle. Also located here is one of the most important electrical generating plants in Costa Rica generating electrical power for most of the country.

Belén Canton has 11,993 inhabitants and comprises the districts of San Antonio, La Ribera and La Asunción. San Antonio, the canton seat, is eight kilometers southwest of the Heredia City, to which it is linked by two highways. It has a magnificent church surrounded by gardens, a school, good postal, telephone and telegraph services, and spacious, elegant private homes. There are fine stores and prosperous businesses. The streets are straight and in good condition. The people of San Antonio, Belén have always been known for their religious devotion and temperance, jealous of their traditions, moral principles, and good manners. Crossing the town is a branch of the National Highway that goes from San José to La Garita, and Puntarenas, as well as the Pacific Railway that runs between San José and Puntarenas. The governmental seat has a population of 5,895 inhabitants according to the 1984 census.

Until 1791, when the Spaniards arrived, this canton was inhabited by Huetar Indians. By the beginning of the Nineteenth Century there was a chapel dedicated to the Virgin of the Assumption. The first chapel was built in 1856, and in 1967 the first parish church was built in honor of Saint Anthony (*San Antonio*).

In the year 1800 the first elementary school was opened, in 1919 the first high school (Benedicto XV) was inaugurated

Ojo de Agua swimming resort, main recreational center in Belén, Heredia.

but it only lasted for five years. By 1929 the España School was completed, named in honor of a Spaniard who had promoted its construction.

The development of what was first the canton started in 1843 when coffee began to exported to European markets, facilitated with the opening of an access route between the Puntarenas port and San José, which made Belén a necessary rest point.

At first the canton, when it was only a village, was called Potrerillo, then Barrio de la Asunción, San Antonio, and now it is called San Antonio de Belén. It gets its name from the fact that Monsignor Joaquín Llorente-y-La Fuente, who on two occasions conducted the Christmas Eve Mass here, indicated that he would continue to call the place San Antonio de Belén (Belén meaning Bethlehem). In 1907 the canton was formed with that name. This canton, forming part of the greater metropolitan area, has an developing industrial (La Ribera) and the Ojo de Agua swimming resort, its main recreational center.

Flores Canton

This canton is situated between the central canton of Heredia and Santa Bárbara Canton on flat, fertile ground that produces mostly coffee, sugarcane, oranges, beans, and corn. Its population of 9,015 inhabitants is divided into the districts of San Joaquín, Barrantes, and Llorente.

The governmental seat of this canton is San Joaquín, located four kilometers west of Heredia City, and crossed by the railroad going between San José and Alajuela. In the center of town, situated in a small park, there is a magnificent Catholic church made of granite stones. There is also a modern, spacious elementary school building, a high school, the town hall, waterworks providing excellent drinking water, and lovely private homes indicative of the comfortable lifestyle of the people. Within the district there are coffee plantations and several sugar mills, as well as various business establishments.

This place was called during the colonial period *Llano del Alto de Nuestra Señora de la Soledad de Barva* (High Plain of Our Lady of Solitude of Barva), and as the land was divided up into parcels of new settlements, the name was changed to Quebrada Seca and then to San Joaquín. When the area became a canton in 1915 it was given the name Flores,

151

in memory of Dr. Juan J. Flores-Umaña, a beloved benefactor of the province. The second district of the canton, Barrantes, was named after another patron of the canton, Lorenzo Barrantes.

Development of the canton was favored during the Nineteenths Century by the construction of the railroad from San José to the Caribbean, since it passed through it.

Elementary education was launched in 1813, with boys-only private schools. In 1890 the first building was built for the public elementary school in what is now the canton seat, and was inaugurated in 1944 with the name *Escuela de Estados Unidos de América*. In 1966 the *Liceo Regional Flores* (Flores Regional High School) began its classes.

This canton, too, belongs to the greater metropolitan area. It has developing industrial zone (Barreal), the Lic. Jorge Volio Clinic (in the canton seat), and a Catholic church that has been declared a historical and architectural landmark.

San Pablo Canton

By legislative decree on July 17, 1961 what was San Pablo District (the second in Heredia Province) was elevated to the rank of canton. It is bounded by the San José-Heredia highway on one side; and the Bermúdez River and the central canton of Heredia, Quebrada Seca, the Pirro River, and San Rafael on the other sides. It has a population of 11,802 inhabitants, with only one district of 7.55 kms[2].

The large quantity of archeological remains found in this canton are evidence that this territory was once inhabited by Huetar Indians of the Western Kingdom. By 1792, according to historical documents there was a village, first called Sabanilla de Villalobos and then just Sabanilla (1803). By 1819 it appears under the name of San Pablo.

The first chapel built in 1863 is today a historic landmark. In 1912 construction was begun on the present-day Catholic church.

In 1916 the telegraph building was opened. By 1930 the canton had electrical power. The name of the canton resulted from a lottery selection in 1818 by province authorities. (*Atlas Cantonal*, 1987).

The chief agricultural products of the canton are coffee and cattle. Within its jurisdiction are the townships of Cruces, Uriches, and La Puebla.

The canton has good public services, a post office, a Rural Guard post, a health center, which is doing an important work in the field of health. There are also fine recreational centers, such as the APSE Recreational Farm (APSE = *Asociación de Profesores de Segunda Enseñanza* = Secondary Teachers Association), a sports plaza, and a gymnasium under construction.

In addition, plans are underway to build a plaza in honor of the former Costa Rican presidents, which will be a welcomed recreational spot for the whole canton.

Sarapiquí Canton

This last canton in Heredia Province, was established in November of 1970. It is bounded on the north by the country of Nicaragua, on the south by the cantons of San Carlos, Grecia, and Alajuela, and on the east by Pococí Canton.

The first dwellers of this region were Voto Indians, who occupied the plains of Sarapiquí. Settlement of this region came about as a result of the desire, first of the Spaniards and then of the country, to open up an access route to the San Juan River through the north. By 1915 Sarapiquí appeared as a district of Heredia Canton.

It was made a canton in 1970. Its main town, now the canton seat, formerly called Sarapiquí, is Puerto Viejo.

The canton has three districts: Puerto Viejo, the canton seat, with a land area of 692.94 kms[2], and a population of 4,107; La Virgen with 881 kms[2] and 4,451 inhabitants, and Horquetas with 566.44 kms[2] and 18,909 inhabitants.

Its principle agricultural products are coffee, corn, cacao, cardamom, bananas, palm hearts, tree fruit, and cattle.

The first elementary school, *Escuela de Puerto Viejo*, was built in 1952. In 1972 the *Colegio Técnico Profesional Agropecuario* (Technical Agricultural High School) opened for classes.

The current Catholic church dedicated to Saint Augustine (*San Agustín*), was erected in 1970.

The canton has good public services, a regional office of the Ministry of agriculture, the Río Frío Clinic, located in the town of Río Frío, a branch office of the National Banking System, electrical power, and telephones.

In this canton there are vast zones of world interest in terms of conservation: the Cordillera Volcánica Central Forest Reserve, Braulio Carrillo Park, and the La Selva Protective Zone, as well a two-kilometer wide buffer wide zone parallel to the Nicaraguan border.

La Paz Waterfall, Sarapiquí region.

El Angel Waterfall, Sarapiquí region.

153

*Papagayo Gulf,
Guanacaste.*

GUANACASTE PROVINCE

The province of Guanacaste is bounded on the north by the country of Nicaragua, on the east by the provinces of Alajuela and Puntarenas and the Gulf of Nicoya on the south, and on the west by the Pacific Ocean. It has a total land area of 10,140.71 kms². The landscape of this province is completely different from that of the others, as are the customs and general personality of the people.

Practically the entire province consists of an expansive plain, drained by long rivers flowing westward and emptying into the Gulf of Nicoya: the Tempisque, Bebedero, Cañas, Las Palmas, Belén, Liberia, El Viejo, and others. These rivers during the rainy season often cause flooding in some towns precariously

Nosara, Guanacaste.

155

located near the banks of the rivers. Some of the towns most affected are La Guinea, Ortega y Bolsón, Cañas, Las Palmas, and Belén.

The curious formation of the land of Guanacaste has prompted serious studies with respect to the periods of the land's origin. The unique conformation of the geological layers and types of soil, homogeneous over wide expanses, have made it difficult to determine which components came first and, hence, to ascertain the relative age of the region. Some plains having a sandy surface appear to have once been a sea bed. In the northwest end of the province there are the picturesque beaches of Sámara, Bahía Salinas, Tamarindo, Bejuco, San Juanillo, Marbella, Brasilito, Bahía Culebra, Nancite (very important as a spawning area for green turtles), Murciélago, Punta Descartes, and others.

River beds are mostly sandy with practically no stones, although in some spots igneous stones are found. The terrain of the province is, for the most part, an immense plain with large expanses completely flat, and even the low mountains seen in the distance do not alter this vista throughout the province. East of Guanacaste is the *Sierra Volcánica*, whose slopes are steep and largely dry, with numerous folds making them very pleasing to the eye. In Nicoya peninsula there are the Hills of San Blas, La Habana; la Hoz, and Barrahonda (declared a national park).

The current in the rivers is so mild that they appear not to be moving at all, thus many of them lending themselves to easy navigation. The largest of these is the Tempisque, navigable by small steam boats for 40 kilometers. The major tributary of this river, the Río Blanco (formerly called Las Piedras), is also navigable. Emptying into Río Blanco are the rivers Salto, Liberia, Colorado, Bolsón, Los Ahogados, and other smaller ones. On the Nicoya Peninsula, the Matina River also serves as a transportation route.

The climate is generally hot, but more moderate temperatures are found on higher ground. The people here make their living principally from cattle. Also, the fertile land of the province is quite suitable for rice and cotton, to mention two of the most important crops. Various kinds of fruit are abundant and have and exquisite flavor. Sugarcane is another crop produced in abundance. The melons grown here are of very good quality, and the dry lands of Bagaces are ideal for olive trees. On the *Sierra Volcánica* there are rich gold mines, and in other areas, coal, magnesium, and marble are extracted. There are also traces of petroleum.

In the Gulf of Nicoya magnificent quality shrimp are caught. In addition, from the forests of Guanacaste the most precious woods known in the tropics are cut, and industry that provides considerable income to the province. Cattle production has been greatly developed here, for the export of beef and cattle on the hoof.

Other crops very important to this region are corn, sorghum, vegetables, coffee, citrus fruits, and beans. Beekeeping and fishery are also important industries.

With the fine Pan-American Highway, good passenger and transport services, and dependable routes to other cities of the province, the production of this rich region of Costa Rica has substantially intensified.

This province owes its name to the guanacaste tree found here in the Eighteenth Century at the intersections of the roads leading to Nicoya, Bagaces, and Rivas, where today the Liberia Park is located. Settlers back then called the place *Paisaje del Guanacaste* (Guanacaste Landscape), a name later given to Liberia Canton and then to the province.

Guanacaste Province is politically divided into 11 cantons (see Map No. 14). Hojancha and La Cruz were given canton status in 1971 and 1969 respectively.

The cantons with the biggest land area are Liberia with 1,436.47 kms² and La Cruz with 1,383 kms². Those with the largest populations are Nicoya with 36,626 inhabitants, Santa Cruz with

31,133, and Liberia with 28,067. The least populous is Hojancha with 5,879 inhabitants living on a land area of 261.42 kms². The total population of the province is 195,208 inhabitants, 32,808 more than in 1950. This population increase occurred even though the land has been in the hands of few owners, but possibly the cultivation of sugarcane has instigated immigration to it.

Liberia Canton

This canton is bounded on the north by La Cruz Canton, on the east by Bagaces and Upala cantons, on the south by Carrillo, and on the west by the Pacific Ocean and La Cruz Canton. Liberia Canton has a population of 28,067 inhabitants and comprises the districts of Liberia, the governmental seat of the canton, Cañas Dulces, Mayorga, Nacascolo, and Curubandé. The terrain here is flat toward the center and the south, and slightly uneven in the northern sector. It is watered by the rivers Tempisque, Liberia, Salto, and other smaller ones.

Liberia City

This is the governmental seat both of the Liberia Canton and Guanacaste

Typical house in Liberia City.

Province. It is situated in a very flat area, along the banks of the Liberia River, covered with white sands, which glaringly reflects the suns rays in the daytime, but at night with the light of the moon affords a spectacular view. Thus, the town is called *"Ciudad Blanca"* ("White City"). The climate is hot (average 27.2 to 28°C) but dry enough to be healthy. It gets an average annual rainfall of from 1,480 to 2,399 millimeters.

It has five schools, several churches, a town hall, a Rural Guard Unit, electrical power, plumbing, a postal-telegraph office, and the Doctor Enrique Baltodano

Catholic church in Liberia City.

157

Hospital. Moreover, since 1972 it has had a Regional Center of the University of Costa Rica, and since 1973, when the National University was founded, it has had a branch of that university (located in what was the *Escuela Normal de Liberia*). It also has Ministry of Government Building considered to be of historical interest, and all sorts of public services, making it unnecessary for people to go to San José for business.

The downtown area is quite extensive. It has a population of 22,522 inhabitants –twice that of 35 years ago. It is linked to the interior of the country by the North Inter-American Highway, which is part of the of the Pan-American Highways Project.

An important transportation link with the rest of the province is a water route, including the Blanco River (formerly Las Piedras), the Tempisque River, and the Gulf of Nicoya. The distance from Liberia to Bagaces is 60 kilometers, and from Liberia to the Nicaraguan border is 70 kilometers. There are also highways going from Liberia to Bagaces; from Liberia to Filadelfia through Santa Cruz to the southern part of the province; and to Nicaragua is the Pan-American Highway. In addition, through the Tomás Guardia Airport one can travel by air to a from the rest of the country.

Within this canton there is an ongoing irrigation project for the lower watershed of the Tempisque River, covering 32% of the canton, whose purpose is to increase production and modify land tenure, as well as permit new crops, making use of this valuable water resource. These objectives are being met with the production of cantaloupe, watermelon, cacao, and some vegetables such as sweet peppers.

Nicoya Canton

In 1988 this canton celebrated its centennial. It was created on December 7, 1988 as the second in Guanacaste Province.

During the pre-Colombian period the territory that today corresponds to Nicoya Canton was part of the indigenous provinces then called Chorotegas, which extended all the way to Lake Nicaragua. This region was inhabited by several tribes, one of whose chiefs was Nicoa (from whence comes the name Nicoya).

The region was discovered by Gil González Dávila in 1523. He was warmly welcomed by Chief Nicoa, who gave him gifts of gold and other valuables.

Around the year 1544 the Parish Church of Nicoya was built, the oldest one founded by the Spaniards in Costa Rica. The church was destroyed by fire in 1634, and with it, a file in which valuable documents were stored. The parish church erected in the second half of the Nineteenth Century was declared a national landmark by Law No. 141 of July 28, 1923.

On July 25, 1824 the Municipality of Nicoya, representing the people of the region, in an open meeting freely decided to join the Free State of Costa Rica. This meeting was attended by the Political Leader, Manuel Briceño, who presided, and the town councillors, Toribio Viales, Ubaldo Martínez, and Manuel García.

The canton occupies the southern part of the Nicoya Peninsula and has a population of 36,626 inhabitants, who make their living mostly from farming and ranching. The terrain here is varied, in some place there are large valleys, in others hills and low mountains, making for a varied climate as well. The land is fertile and drained by the rivers Morote, Nosara, and Tempisque, to mention the most important.

As in most of the rest of the country what were once abundant forests of fancy woods such as mahogany, cedar, and *cocobolo* are constantly disappearing. Today, however, the Municipality, the *Colegio Agropecuario* (Agricultural High School), and other public service institutions are making every effort to reforest this region.

The roads and other transportation means are constantly being improved in this area. The general public here, and political leaders are becoming increasingly aware of the importance of tourism. Nicoya has 45 kilometers of coastline in the process of being developed, beginning with a small section of *Playa Carrillo*, then the beaches of Sámara, Buena Vista, Barco Quebrado, Barrigona, Pavones, Garza, Guiones, Nosara, *Playa Pelada*, and others.

Sámara has become an extremely popular beach, with two hotels, consisting of several options for family lodging, and one luxury hotel on an island in the middle of the bay. Barrigona and Punta del Indio beaches are beginning to develop for the tourist industry; Garza Beach has the Hotel Villagio La Guaria Morada; Nosara shows the most rapid tourist development in the country with 1,100 hectares occupied exclusively by retirees for different countries of the world, including renown politicians, artists, scientists, and intellectuals.

The canton has 78 kilometers of gravel road, now being paved, which will facilitate travel to and from the Tempisque Ferry Boat, saving 200 kilometers of travel to tourists who will not have to go the roundabout land route through Liberia.

The *Cavernas de Barra Honda* (Barra Honda Caverns), today a national park, attract many tourists and are an converging point for scientists from many parts of the world. These caverns are comprised of La Terciopelo, Nicoa, La Capilla, Santa Ana, La Cuevita, La Trampa, Organo, and El Mirador. There are plans to install here a cable car (unique in the country) to take tourists around these caverns.

The town of Nicoya, the canton seat, has very good hotels, including the outstanding Hotel Curime, which has an air terminal located beside the local airport.

The *Hospital de La Anexión* with 250 beds provides medical service to the inhabitants of Nicoya Peninsula. The National Banking System has several branch offices: the National, Costa Rica, Anglo, and Popular. There are three central high schools, and two rural ones, and elementary schools dispersed in all the villages of the canton.

Barra Honda Caverns, Nicoya

159

Nosara region in Nicoya Canton

The Costa Rican Electrical Institute (ICE) and the Guanacaste Rural Electrification Cooperative provide electrical power and rural telephone service.

The canton has modern waterworks for drinking water, as well as modern buildings for the municipal market and bus terminals.

Following the Chorotega tradition, the arts and crafts produced here are of excellent quality, especially in the Indian villages.

Politically the canton of Nicoya is divided into the following districts: Nicoya, La Mansión, San Antonio, Quebrada Honda, and Sámara.

The town of Nicoya has a population of 21,455 inhabitants. It is situated in a pretty valley 80 kilometers from the town of Liberia, at an elevation of 123 meters above sea level. It has an old rubblework Catholic church, that was constructed during the period of the first Spanish governors.

Today's town is not is the same site as the original Nicoya, now called Nicoya Vieja. The newer town, now called Pueblo Nuevo, was the largest Indian town when the Spaniards arrived. Nicoya is one of the oldest settlements in Costa Rica. It is named after the most important Indian chief of the Spanish colonial days. Manuel María de Peralta states, "Nicoya is an indigenous word meaning 'a land with water on both sides'". Today living in this canton is an indigenous community of the Chorotega (Matambú) ethnic group.

The town has a good hospital, the Barra Honda National Park, and the Ostional National Wildlife Preserve.

Santa Cruz Canton

This canton stretches over a beautiful, fertile valley with a hot but healthy climate among the La Lechuza, Campana, and Tigre hills. It is drained by the rivers Diriá and Enmedio, which along with the Cañas River comprise the Bolsón River that divides Santa Cruz from Carrillo Canton. It is also bounded on the southeast by Nicoya Canton and the West by the Pacific Ocean. It has a port on the Bolsón River, navigable by small craft, and it is the principle access route to the gulf. It is linked to the interior of the country, passing through Liberia, by a fine asphalt highway that connects with the Pan-American Highway. The distance from Bolsón to the town of Santa Cruz is 18 kilometers.

Santa Cruz Canton has a population of 21,133 inhabitants who make their living primarily from cattle ranching. The canton is divided into the following districts: Santa Cruz City, Bolsón, Veintisiete de Abril, Tempate, Cartagena, Cuajiniquil, and Diriá, the last three having become district only a short while ago.

This region was discovered a year before Nicoya was (1522) by Gil González Dávila. By 1760 the first Spaniards had settled near what is today known as the town of Lagunilla.

When Bernalbela Ramos, daughter of one of the first settlers, married, she placed a wooden cross on her house west of the Diriá River, a place called Las Delicias. In honor of that cross every year a rosary prayer was offered up. Soon it became tradition, and eventually the name of the town was changed from Delicias to Santa Cruz (Holy Cross).

The canton has had a good elementary school since 1875, a high school since 1955, a university extension service offering humanities and other courses given by the Regional University of Costa Rica since 1975. It has two clinics, a rural electrical cooperative, and an arts and a Chorotega arts and crafts cooperative (Guaitil Cooperative). The town of Santa Cruz itself was declared the "Folklore City" by the Central American Institute of Tourism.

The canton seat of the canton, Santa Cruz is situated in a lovely valley that makes it one of the prettiest towns in Guanacaste, 50 kilometers from Liberia City. At 49 meters above sea level its climate is hot but healthy. It is drained by the Diriá River on the west. Its streets are straight and white. It has a Catholic church, good public services, business establishments, and a landing strip for smaller planes.

Santa Cruz Canton, besides its charming town folklore attracting many tourists, has more special tourist areas than any other canton in the province. Part of the Guacamaya tourist center is here, as well as splendid beaches such as Potrereo, Conchal, Brasilito, Nombre de Jesús, Grande, Tamarindo, Langosta, Avellana, Junquillal, Manzanillo, Veracruz, Ostional, Nosara, and others. Also in this canton is part of the Ostional National Wildlife Preserve.

Farming in the canton consists primarily of corn, beans, tubers, tree fruits, and, on an extensive level, sugarcane, coffee, and cattle.

Tamarindo, Santa Cruz, Guanacaste.

161

Bagaces Canton

This canton is on partly flat, stony, and not as fertile as other surrounding areas.

Bagaces became a canton during the presidential term of Dr. José María Castro-Madriz in 1848. In 1918 the Bagaces District was classified as a *ciudad* (town or city status).

The birthplace of General Tomás Guardia-Gutiérrez, glorious son of the motherland, is canton number four in Guanacaste Province. It was created on December 7, 1848 with a land area of 1,273.49 kms². It has a population of 10,009 inhabitants, and the central district is at an elevation of 80 meters above sea level.

Its districts are Bagaces, La Fortuna, and Mogote. It is bounded on the north by Upala, on the northwest by Liberia, on the west by Carrillo, on the southwest by Santa Cruz, on the south by Nicoya and the Tempisque River, and on the east by Cañas.

The principle buildings in the center of Bagaces include the parish church, the National Bank of Costa Rica, the General Tomás Guardia Elementary School, the high school, the Municipal Building, and a building complex in which there is the

Municipal Market, a bus station, stores and other businesses, and offices. There is also a magnificent and costly arena, ICE buildings, and other smaller buildings such as the Sanitary Unit, the Social Security Building, and school buildings, including the kindergarten and pre-kinder school. An attractive park is situated in the center of the city, and there other plans to make others in the other districts.

Among the most notable monuments, is a bust of General Tomás Guardia G., on a pedestal in the city park. Historical buildings include the old adobe brick house a block away from the elementary school, and another one in front of the park, both of which are over 200 years old.

Public services include electric power, plumbing, telephones, health centers, a slaughter house, a municipal market, telegraph, and buses in all directions. The streets and roads are mostly all paved.

The districts of La Fortuna and Mogote have been experiencing rapid growth, and already in operation in those areas are Social Security health services, good roads, a high school, elementary schools, and large business establishments. The most important

Miravalles Volcano, 15 kilometers from Bagaces; a dormant volcano but in its cone there are continuous rumblings and solfataras. Located on it is the Miravalles Thermal Project.

means of livelihood here are cattle ranching, vegetable and grain farming, and dairy farming. Agricultural production in this region is very important to the national economy. In La Fortuna and in the center of Bagaces there are regional dance bands and musical ensembles.

Some potentially attractive tourist resorts for the future would be the Miravalles Volcano, where there are boiling hot *hornillas* and a geothermic project already in progress. In this region several agricultural and conservation projects are also operating: San Ramón, Bagatzi, and the Biological Reserves of Palo Verde and Lomas de Barbudal, wildlife areas protected by the National Parks Service of Costa Rica, totally in a tropical forest setting, where there are preserved many varieties of fancy wood trees, rare species of animals, and over 150 species of birds worthy of admiration and study.

Agricultural productions include rice, beans, cotton, sorghum, beef, and lumber cut for export. Bagaces is a poor town, but full of hard-working people. The people have the general feeling, though, that government help has been insufficient and that if the government would help a little more, the town could develop more rapidly. They also feel that government assistance should be aimed at agriculture.

The canton has a population of 10,103 inhabitants who make their living mostly from farming and ranching. North of the canton are the Miravalles and Güipilapa volcanoes, the former still active and the latter dormant (although those who live near it say they often hear strong rumblings coming from it). At the foot of Miravalles there are *hornillas*, holes with deposits of sulfur, mud, pure water, and mineral waters in a constant state of boiling.

The principle river flowing through the canton is the Las Piedras, which is the best communication route from Puerto Bebedero on the gulf. Other rivers include the Salto, Bebedero, Tenorio, Potrero, and Río Blanco.

In the town of Bagaces, the governmental seat of the canton, many of the houses are old, and the climate is very hot. It is located 25 kilometers from Liberia to which it is linked by the National Highway. It has a Catholic church, a Municipal Building and an elementary school. In this little town (now 5,509 inhabitants), was born the former Costa Rican president, Tomás Guardia. This canton has a number of tourist attractions, including the Cordillera Volcánica de Guanacaste Forest Reserve, the Laguna Mogote (Mogote Lake), located in the district with the same name, the Enmedio River Dam, the Lower Tempisque Watershed Irrigation Project, the dams on the Blanco and Tenorio rivers, the Doctor Rafael Lucas Rodríguez Wildlife Preserve, the Lomas de Barbudal Biological Reserve, the Palo Verde National Park, and the Rincón de la Vieja National Park.

The name of the canton evolved from the name of the Indian Chief Bagatzí, who lived in the region at the time the Spaniards arrived.

Carrillo Canton

This canton comprises the districts of Filadelfia, Palmira, Sardinal, Belén, and has a total population of 18,475 inhabitants. It is bounded on the north by Liberia Canton, on the south by Santa Cruz and Bagaces cantons, on the east by Liberia Canton, and on the west by the Pacific Ocean. The region is drained by the Tempisque River, which provides easy access to the Gulf of Nicoya. There is a road that links it with Liberia, Santa Cruz, and the Pacific Ocean. Its climate is generally hot but healthy. The predominate industry here, as in the rest of the province, is cattle raising. The soil is fertile and in some spots a special clay is found, that is just right for making fine china.

The town of Filadelfia, the canton seat, is positioned on a plain between the rivers Palmas and Tempisque, 30 kilometers from Liberia. It covers a land area of 125.01 kms². The climate is hot but healthy. The streets are narrow and

Playa Hermosa; in the background, Punta Cacique and Montosa Islet.

straight. The main buildings include a Catholic church, an elementary school, a town hall, and a postal-telegraph office. It is linked to the river port of Bolsón by a highway that goes from Liberia and runs south along almost the entire peninsula. It has a population of 5,353 inhabitants. It was given the status of *ciudad* (city or town) in 1947.

Carrillo Canton also has a clinic in Filadelfia, good public services that include a unit of the Rural Guard, a chapter of the Red Cross, several bank branch offices, and a variety of stores and other business. The Tempisque Lower Watershed Project is also operating here.

It has five areas classified as tourist resorts found in an area that covers most of the coastal area of the canton. They include Golfo de Papagayo y Guacamaya, Playas del Coco, Bahía Culebra, Playa Hermosa, and the Brasil River Dam.

The canton was named after the former Costa Rican president Braulio Carrillo Colinas.

Cañas Canton

The region corresponding to the canton of Cañas was discovered in 1522. In 1739 the first chapel was built and dedicated to San José.

Before becoming a canton in 1878, Cañas was a district of the Occidental Department, and along with Bagaces, made up the fourth canton of Guanacaste Province.

The town used to be called Escarbadero, but after José María Cañas visited it, it was named after him. It was granted the status of *ciudad* (city or town) in 1921.

Cañas Canton has only one district with a total land area of 682.20 kms² and a population of 17,284 inhabitants. Of that population 45.5% is economically active and 7.6% is unemployed. The labor force is concentrated in the primary sector with 41.6% and 30.3% in the tertiary sector (according to the 1984 census).

The canton is geographically centered equidistant from the cantons of Tilarán, Bagaces, Abangares, and Upala. It is linked to the capital and other provinces by the Inter-American Highway; the highway that goes between the cantons of Bagaces, Liberia, and La Cruz; and by the national highways that link it to the cantons of Abangares, Tilarán, and Upala. Thus, due to its geographic location it is referred to as a "cosmopolitan capital".

Among the state institutions represented in the canton are the following: the *Universidad Estatal a Distancia* (State Extension University) (Academic Center), the National Education Institute (School of Developing Irrigation Systems), National Production Council, the Agricultural Extension Office, the Enrique Jiménez Núñez Experimental Station, the Costa Rican Electrical Institute (an branch office, a sub-station, the Corobicí Hydroelectric Plant).

The most important buildings here include beautiful Catholic church, a Town Hall (the first module), the Monseñor Luis Leipold Herbert Elementary School, Antonio Obando Elementary School, CEN-CINAI, the Municipal Gymnasium, *Liceo Miguel Araya Venegas* (high school), the Postal-Communications (CORTEL) buildings, a branch office of the National Bank of Costa Rica, the Fire Fighters' Station, the Integrated Health Center, the National Refrigeration Network, and the SENARA Building.

The town of Cañas has a main park with gardens, pleasant arbors, and benches surrounded by nice shady trees. Running alongside this park is a spacious cultural and sports plaza.

Within the town there are three monuments: one dedicated to Monseñor Luis Leipold Herbert, located in the parvis of the church, another to Pedro Ferrandino-Calvo, in the southeast corner of the park, and another to Gerardo Gómez-Ramírez, located in the Town Hall yard.

The streets and avenues of the center of town are wide, paved, and in good condition. The paving of the streets was inaugurated during the presidential term of Trejos-Fernández on July 27, 1968.

The canton has good public services. Since 1968, it has had electric power generated by the Costa Rican Electrical Institute (ICE), and today there are 3,481 customers. Public lighting was transferred from the hands of the Municipality to ICE in 1973.

In 1966 the Costa Rican Waterworks and Sewage Treatment began serving 600 families; today it serves 2,350. Water is drawn from deep wells by electric pumping stations.

Telephone several was installed in 1970. Today there are 750 private customers, and 30 public telephones are distributed in the center of town and the barrios.

The town of Cañas, the only district, has 23 townships: Porozal, Santa Lucía, Tuquirusas, Níspero, Buenos Aires, San Miguel, Higuerón, Lajas, San Juan, Javilla, Taboga, Begedero, Sandial, Palmira, San Isidro, Agua Caliente, Nueva Guatemala, Vergel, Hotel, Colonia San Luis, Paso Hondo, and Tenorio.

Bebedero was, for many years, the main river port, since it was the communication route between the cantons of Liberia, Bagaces, Tilarán, and Cañas. It was used not only to transport people, but also farm produce, lumber, salt, livestock, and other things.

For many years there has been talk about transforming the township of Bebedero into a tourist center, by so far nothing concrete has been done. In the town today there is a health center, an elementary school, a nutrition center, a chapel, a postal-telegraph office, a police station, and services of electrical power, drinking water, and public telephones. Employment is found mostly in the sugar mills in Taboga and Las Piedras.

In Hacienda Taboga people make their living from sugarcane. In addition to growing it, there is also a sugar mill and a gasohol factory.

The township was founded by the same company that owns the sugar mill. It has also provided housing, an elementary school, a recreational park, a community house, a public telephone, and other facilities.

San Miguel Township is 10 kilometers from Cañas, along the Inter-American Highway. Its economy is based on agriculture and cattle ranching. It has an elementary school, a chapel, an athletic field, athletic field, a public telephone, a development association, and other public services.

The local roads in Cañas are in good condition and well maintained, especially around the sugar plantations. The law here requires that the roads be adequately maintained at all times.

The main agricultural products here are sugarcane, rice, sorghum, cotton, and beef. On a lesser scale, corn, beans, and fruit such as cantaloupe and watermelon are also grown.

In this region are located the forest reserves of Taboga and Manglado, comprising respectively 1% and 6% of the canton's total land area.

Cañas Canton has very little industry since most of the people here make their living from ranching and farming. The industries found here include sugar processing, an ice factory, concrete products, ironworks (gratings for windows and gates), jewelry, furniture, a tortilla factory, and a factory that makes leisure and athletic shorts.

The most visited places are the La Pacífica (a swimming pool with restaurant and cabins), the Magdalena River Dam, the forest reserves of Taboga and Manglado, and the Corobicí Hydroelectric Plant. Fishing is only done at the mouth of the Tempisque River, in El Níspero Township.

Most of the people who live here are descendants of the Corobicí Indians, but they have not conserved their indigenous roots. Being a commercial center, they have mixed with many people from the rest of the country. Moreover, groups of specialists of other nationalities have settled here: Japanese, Spaniards, Italians, Israelis, and others, who have in one way or another helped to shape the culture of this region. As the people of Cañas are known for their friendliness and hospitality, their town has been called *"Ciudad de la Amistad"* ("Friendship City").

Operating in this canton is the Arenal-Tempisque Irrigation Project, managed by SENARA (*Servicio Nacional de Aguas Subterráneas, Riego y Avenamiento* = National Service of Subterranean Water, Irrigation, and Drainage), created by Law 6977 on July 27, 1983. This project has brought great benefits to the canton: jobs, distribution of lands, improved living conditions for the people, diversification of farm production, expanded commerce, political participation of broad sectors of the population, including women involvement in the process of introducing irrigation, modernized farming techniques, increased crop yields, and efficiently utilized lands that had heretofore been poorly used.

Abangares Canton

Abangares is situated among the cantons of Tilarán, Cañas, Puntarenas, San Ramón, and Golfo de Nicoya. The region has a substantial quantity of gold and several gold mines, some of which are still in operation. The land is partly flat and fertile. The climate is mostly dry tropical but in some places it is moderate and even chilly on the mountains of La Sierra de Tilarán.

The most important economic activities here are in agriculture, the chief products being sorghum, rice, beans, beef (in the low-lying areas), and dairy cattle (on the higher areas).

Industry in the canton includes the Pacific Cement Factory in Colorado, the Conaprosal Salt Processing Plant. These industries are a source of jobs for residents here. Mining is now expanding rapidly with the investments of foreign countries. Also in the area of the Nicoya Gulf the fishing industry is very important.

This canton is divided into the districts of Las Juntas, with 229.35 kms² and 6.568 inhabitants; La Sierra with 141.47 kms² and 1,562 inhabitants, San Juan with 109.17 kms² and 1,475 inhabitants; and Colorado with 195.77 kms² and 2,970 inhabitants. This comes to a total population for the canton of 12,575 inhabitants (only 975 more than the population of 35 years ago).

The national highway from Barranca to Liberia (the most travelled route for commerce with the central part of the country) crosses the canton. This highway is asphalt from Las Juntas to Puerto Yglesias on the Gulf of Nicoya, and from Omonal to Puerto Moreno where one can take the El Tempisque Ferry to the Nicoya Peninsula.

Las Juntas, is the canton seat with 6,568 inhabitants. It is located six kilometers northeast of La Irma off of the Inter-American Highway. Some of its streets are paved with stones. In this town there are buildings with modern structures, such as the Municipal Building, the fire fighters station, the Red Cross building, and the Municipal Market. Las Juntas has an agricultural high school. It also has the basic services of electrical power, drinking water, telephones, bank branches, a Social Security office, and others. Abangares has many interesting spots for tourists, and one of the fastest growing in popularity is the Minero en La Sierra Museum-Park located where gold had been extracted at the beginning of the century. The idea is to offer tourists a historically interesting site at the same the plants and animals of the region are protected.

The main roads are in fair condition, and there are regular bus services facilitating travel to San José, Cañas and nearby districts such as Colorado.

Mining is affecting the environment, and should this situation continue it will eventually lead to serious detriment to the population.

Regarding health in this canton, the most significant hindrance to the people's well-being is the quality of the drinking water in Las Juntas, although the Municipality is now promoting a project to set up a treatment plant in the near future.

Since 1885 the principal activity of the canton has been mining, which has brought with it very harsh working conditions, and a high mortality rate among workers due to inadequate security. These conditions in 1912 led to the first labor strike in the history of the country.

The labor force of the canton is concentrated mostly in the primary sector with 53.4%, followed by 17.3% in the secondary, and 17.3% in the tertiary; 43.9% of the population is economically active and 7.5% is unemployed (according to the 1984 census).

The irrigation project is partially located in district of Colorado, and in the La Sierra District, the Arenal Forest Reserve.

The town of las Juntas is drained by the Abangares River, flowing from east to west. This river often causes flooding when it overflows its banks.

Tilarán Canton

Situated on the *Sierra Volcánica de Guanacaste*, north of Abangares Canton, the canton of Tilarán includes the districts of Tilarán, the governmental seat, Quebrada Grande, Tronadora, Santa Rosa, Líbano, Tierras Morenas, and Arenal.

The districts of Tronadora and Arenal were founded in 1980 after the waters of the Arenal Lake was raised to 545 meters above sea level, resulting in a lake 72 kms^2, for the purpose of building the Costa Rican Electrical Institute (ICE) hydroelectric plant. As a result, the following towns were flooded: Arenal, Tronadora, Mata de Caña, Piedras, and part of San Luis. At that time some 2,500 residents were affected and had to abandon their lands and work.

The total population of this canton is 14,586 inhabitants. The terrain is mountainous and the climate is moderate and healthy. It produces coffee and subsistence foods, but most people make their living from cattle raising, which has steadily developed.

The town of Tilarán is linked to Cañas Canton by a good road with adequate bus services. Communication with the interior of the country is also facilitated by this road. The town has a population of 5,926 inhabitant and it is the episcopal headquarters of Guanacaste.

During the early colonization days, this zone was favored by immigration due to the mines of Abangares and the cedar forests. The town used to be as called La Cabra, but in 1910 the name was changed to an Indian word, Tilarán.

The people have earnestly sought development, and by 1924 it had electric lighting, plumbing, a chapel, and an elementary school; by 1945 it had grown into a good sized town; in 1952 it inaugurated a high school; and in 1961 the church that had been built in 1931 was elevated to the rank of cathedral.

Within the jursidiction of Tilarán Canton is Laguna de Arenal (Arenal Lake), with great tourist potential. From it one can observe the impressive Arenal Volcano.

Today there is a clinic and a hydroelectric plant (Arenal). The people make their living by raising vegetables and fruit, coffee, corn, beans, macadamia, cardamom, and cattle.

Within the jurisdiction of this canton are two conservation reserves (Cordillera Volcánica de Guanacaste and Arenal) and **Arenal Lake, which have great tourist** potential, and even now are being used to that end to some extent. There is a tourist complex with hotels, several restaurants, fishing areas, cabins, and coasting vessels. To the south of the town of Tilarán there is a cross that was placed in honor of the Tilarán Diocese.

Today the canton is suffering from housing problems and roads in poor condition as the irregular topography is conducive to landslides.

The labor force is concentrated in the primary sector with 56%; in the secondary sector there are 14.4%, and in the tertiary with 24.8%. Employment can be found on the coffee plantations at picking time; two coffee cooperatives help to place workers. There is also a savings and loan cooperative for business.

The town of Tilarán has all sorts of public services, including three bank branch offices (Anglo, Nacional, and Bank of Costa Rica).

Nandayure Canton

In 1961 Costa Rican legislators created through law this canton of Nandayure in the territory that was called Colonia Carmona, founded at the onset of the current century by Father José Daniel Carmona.

The canton is bounded on the north by the Gulf of Nicoya and part of the Golfo de Nicoya Canton, on the south by the Pacific Ocean, on the east by Puntarenas Canton and part of the Gulf, and on the west by the Pacific Ocean and part of Hojancha Canton.

It has a total population of 9,604 inhabitants, most of whom have immigrated from the provinces of Alajuela and San José, a factor that has caused them to develop much differently from the other cantons of the province.

Nandayure's districts are: Carmona, the central district, with 1,654 inhabitants; Santa Rita with 1,423; Zapotal with 1,508; San Pablo with 1,299; Porvenir (also called Cerro Azul) with 1,338; and Bejuco with 2,383.

This canton has shrunk by 3,896 people in less than 30 years, primarily in the districts of Santa Rita, which had 1,938 inhabitants in 1963 (151 less in 1984), and the Zapotal District had 1,969 (461 less in 1984). The same thing has occurred in the districts of San Pablo and Bejuco, which in 1984 respectively had populations of 439 and 2,018. This decrease may be due to a lack of jobs, and partly because Hojancha, previously a district of Nandayure, seceded to become a separate canton in 1971.

This canton was first settled in 1910 by a colony of farmers led by Father Daniel Carmona-Briceño, and it was in his honor that the canton seat is today called Carmona. Those first settlers had come from Atenas, San Ramón, and Palmares. They built a chapel in 1910, an elementary school in 1912, and a high school in 1910.

In 1962 the Carmona Colony was made a canton through a plebiscite vote, and it was called Nandayure, after a popular legend about the area.

Nandayure Canton has all kinds of public services: post office, a Canton Delegation, a Regional Delegation of the Ministry of Education, a clinic, and since 1972, electric power.

The chief agricultural products of the region are rice, sorghum, corn, beans, coffee, and cattle.

One of the main problems the canton faces, as in almost all cantons in the country, is the poor condition of its local roads. There is also a shortage of public telephones.

There is a very good tourist potential here that has not yet been tapped. The canton has the best beaches on the coast, among which six have declared apt for tourism: San Miguel, Coyote, Caletas, Comosalito, and La Islita (now in the process of development). It also has marshlands that form part of the Gulf of Nicoya to the northeast.

La Cruz Canton

This region was discovered by Spaniards in 1522, who had come from Leon Nicaragua. It was subsequently settled by people who came from Rivas, Nicaragua.

The Santa Elena Peninsula is part of district number four, and is it is in this district that the Santa Rosa National Park is located, the place where the battle against William Walker was fought. Remaining evidence of this battle is the Casona de Santa Rosa, today a national landmark.

La Cruz Canton came into being in 1969 as canton number 10 of the province. This one, along with Hojancha Canton, are the newest cantons in Guanacaste.

Although it became a canton in only in 1969, it has had an elementary school since 1906, a chapel since 1923, and public plumbing since 1946. Its high school was inaugurated the same year it became a canton.

The origin of the name of the canton goes back to when a cross was placed because of the death of a rancher named Cruz (meaning Cross). Later this cross served as a reference point for travellers, and finally the name was given to the town.

The canton is made up four districts: La Cruz, the governmental seat with 5,517 inhabitants; Santa Cecilia with 3,042; La Garita with 1,341; and Santa Elena with 976, for a total of 10,876 inhabitants, of whom 68.2% make their living from farming and 7.7% are unemployed (according to the 1984 census).

The canton has all types of public services: a clinic, bank branch offices, post office, etc. But its most pressing problems have to do with too few recreational areas and facilities, poor local roads, excessive unemployment, and the inconvenient location of the elementary school. As far as the school is concerned, the town is now discussing moving it from the park to another location.

Tourists attractions in the canton include the *Mirador La Cruz* (La Cruz

Bahía Salinas (Salinas Bay) seen from La Cruz Lookout Point, La Cruz Canton, Guanacaste Province.

Lookout Point), and the Santa Rosa National Park. There are also plans to build a multi-sports center and an athletic field.

Its beaches are gorgeous: Jobo, Cuajiniquil, Puerto Soley, Las Nubes, Bahía Salinas, and Manzanillo. But they still have not been exploited for their tourist potential, even though they are within the 10 zones declared suitable for coastal tourism. Further, it also has a two-kilometer wide forest buffer zone along the Nicaragua border, part of the Cordillera Volcánica de Guanacaste Forest Reserve, and the Isla Bolaños Reserve. Most of the people of this canton make

Fishery development, Cuajiniquil, Santa Elena Bay, La Cruz, Guanacaste.

their living from cattle ranching, but they also grow rice, beans, and corn.

Hojancha Canton

This last canton of Guanacaste Province is bounded on the north, northwest, and west by Nicoya Canton, on the south by the Pacific Ocean and on the southeast by Nandayure Canton. It is comprised of only one district, Hojancha, and it has a small costal zone that has been declared suitable for tourism, on which is Carrillo Beach. Also in this canton is the Chorotega Indian Reserve of Matambú.

The canton was first settled by inhabitants of San Ramón, Atenas, and Palmares. Today it has an elementary school, a Catholic church since 1925, public plumbing since 1957, and electrical power since 1972.

It has a population of 5,879 inhabitants and occupies a total land area of 261,42 kms². Most of the people make their living from farming, producing primarily vegetables and fruit, rice, sorghum, corn, beans, honey, and beef.

The canton gets its name from a tree the natives called "wide leaf" ("*hoja ancha*").

Virgin of the Sea festivities in Puntarenas City.

PUNTARENAS PROVINCE

This province encompasses: 1) the southeast coast of the Nicoya Peninsula toward the entrance to the Gulf of Nicoya and the islands of that gulf; 2) the territory between the *Sierra Volcánica de Guanacaste* and the Gulf of Nicoya, from the Lagartos River to the Jesús María River; 3) the whole western coast of the country from Jesús María to Punta Uvita; 4) the territory between the *Cordillera de Talamanca* and the Pacific Ocean, from Punta Uvita to the Panamanian border. The total land area of Punta Arenas Province is 11,276.97 kms².

The region of this province was at first inhabited by Brunca, Cocto, and Burica Indians, and starting around 1522 the Spaniards began to colonize it.

In 1847, when its population was beginning to grow, Puntarenas was declared a free port. It became then, as Limón on the east coast, the most important city west of the Central Region.

Today Puntarenas Province has 265,883 inhabitants, making it the fourth largest in population of the seven Costa Rican provinces. It is the largest in terms of land area. Its terrain is naturally flat in most places, and the climate is hot, although there are some mountainous regions with moderate to chilly climates. The province is divided into the cantons of Puntarenas, Esparza, Buenos Aires, Montes de Oro, Osa Aguirre, Golfito, Coto Brus, Parrita, Corredores, and Garabito.

Catholic church In Puntarenas City.

172

Buenos Aires Canton is the largest in area with 2,382.61 kms². The largest in population is Puntarenas City with 74,135 inhabitants, and the one the least populated is Garabito with 3,144 inhabitants.

The chief agricultural crops of the region are rice, pineapple, various fruits, palm oil, sorghum, sugarcane, bananas, beans, vegetables, tubers, corn, coffee, cacao, tobacco, and beef. Two other important sources of income are beekeeping and fisheries.

The province has been diversifying its economy. The business sector, although only recently, is beginning to surge ahead. The industries thriving here include the fishing industry, shipbuilding, a fertilizer factory, tourism, and arts and crafts. Even the small saltworks after having formed cooperatives, are now producing enough salt so that it no longer must be imported.

Among the most serious problems troubling the province now, and which could worsen in the future, are the pollution of the Gulf of Nicoya, the lack of good roads, particularly to the beaches, slum housing, especially in Puntarenas City, insufficient infrastructure to accommodate tourists, and unkempt beaches.

Puntarenas has many interesting spots: two higher learning institutions, a metalwork factory (ALUNASA), and shipyards. There are five hospitals in the province, located in the cantons of Palmar, Puntarenas, Ciudad Neily, Osa, and Golfito. Communication to and from the city includes roads, water routes, and a railroad. Moreover, construction is almost completed on the Southern Coastal Highway.

Very important to this province has been the opening of a new port, Caldera, in 1972, which has incorporated new domains into the general flow of national life, with resulting new communication routes, new industries, and other development for the Nation.

Puntarenas Canton

This canton includes the eastern coastal region of the Gulf of Nicoya, from

Opposite page: Estuaries formed by the Sierpe River in Sierpe District, Osa Canton, Puntarenas Province.

Carnaval in Puntarenas.

the Lagartos River to Punta Judas, the islands in the Gulf of Nicoya, and the southeast coast of the Nicoya Peninsula. It has a population of 74,135 inhabitants distributed among 11 districts: Puntarenas with 29,224 inhabitants, Pitahaya with 3,402, Chomes with 2,686 (where the Spaniards built the second church in the country in 1556), Lepanto with 9,064, Paquera with 4,727, Manzanillo with 2,868, Guacimal with 1,119, Barranca with 15,882 (the largest population after Puntarenas), and Monte Verde with 1,467, Cóbano (which became a district in 1986). There is also the district of *Isla de Coco* (Coco Island) which has no population, but is now a national park.

It is believed that the population increase came about as a result of declaring Puntarenas a free port in 1847; the construction of a burro trail between Barranca and Puntarenas; and the construction of a railroad between San José and Puntarenas (completed in 1910). By 1942 it had elementary schools and a high school, and in 1972 facilities were installed for extension university services of the University of Costa Rica. In 1980 the *Colegio Universitario de Puntarenas* (Puntarenas College) was created.

The canton is still important since its beach is the most visited by tourists, but port activities have been transferred to Puerto Caldera, and Punta Morales has docks and loading facilities for sugar transport.

In Puntarenas Canton is the Monseñor Sanabria Hospital (one of the best in the country), three Social Security clinics (located in Puntarenas, Chomes, and Jicaral –all districts of Puntarenas), and 23 zones declared suitable for tourism.

Puntarenas City

This city is the capital of the province and the governmental seat of the canton with the same name. It has a population of 29,224 inhabitants. Once it was Central American port. Situated on a narrow strip of land consisting of dirt and black volcanic sand, in the eastern part of the Gulf of Nicoya, it is located 116 kilometers from the country's capital. It is linked to the interior of the country by and electric railway and by very good highways.

Hat sale in Puntarenas City.

Puntarenas is a picturesque town. Its streets are all asphalt, narrow, and straight. It has many attractive public and private buildings, most of them made of wood; and shipping dock that used to accommodate large ocean vessels. North of the city there is a beautiful calm estuary constantly rippled by small boats, sail boats, and canoes that move back and forth along the gulf. On the side of the Pacific Ocean is the beautiful *Paseo Cortés*, which is today a tourist ride.

The town has electric lighting, excellent plumbing (all the way from Alajuela Canton), and telephone services with San José City, as well as many comforts befitting of modern cities. There is a beautiful park, a Catholic church, a large Customs Building, which was the best in the city, and bath houses much frequented by vacationers from the center of the country; a good municipal market, a public slaughtering house, several grocery stores, clothing stores, and every business necessary in a tourist center: plenty of good hotels, inns, and restaurants. There are also branch offices of the Bank of Costa Rica and the National Bank, a well staffed hospital, and a fire fighting station. Private industries here include factories that make soft drinks, ice, soap and candles.

In addition salt is processed and sold by an important company organizing the labor force in a place called Pueblo Nuevo.

Previously Puntarenas was the only port in the country for exporting and importing, but since the Caribbean Railway was built, shipping was distributed between Puntarenas and Limón. Puntarenas is still active as a port, but now mostly as a transit station for travellers and merchandise from Guanacaste Province and the coastal Pacific region. Further, commercial movement through Puntarenas has been increasing with the recent conditioning of lands in the southeast of the province and the establishment of new towns along the coast, all of which has helped to intensify traffic, and greatly enhance the value of this old port.

Puntarenas City presents several characteristics worth noting. First, is that it is located on an arrow of sand formed only two centuries ago, from whence come its name meaning "an arrow of sand". Second, is a result of the first fact: due to limited space every bit of land has been maximized. And, third, its condition as a port has favored its economy and fishing industry, even through foreign maritime commerce has been transferred to Puerto Caldera.

Out in front of Puntarenas, near the western coast of the Gulf of Nicoya is San Lucas Island, used as a State prison since 1873. It has a total area of 20 kms^2. Being very fertile, it is well farmed by the inmates. There are several well-maintained roads on it, it has good drinking water, and it is frequented by visitors arriving from the port.

Esparza Canton

This canton is bounded on the west by the cantons of Montes de Oro, Puntarenas, and Golfo de Nicoya; on the east by the cantons of San Ramón, San Mateo, Orotina, and Garabito; on the north by Montes de Oro; and on the south by Golfo de Nicoya and Garabito.

Esparza in 1848 was the second canton of Alajuela Province, but in 1851 it seceded to become the second canton of Puntarenas Province.

Puerto Caldera, within the jurisdiction of this canton, began functioning as a port in 1577, and in 1834 the operations of Puntarenas were transferred to Caldera. But in 1840 Braulio Carrillo rehabilitated Puntarenas as a port for State commerce, and it was not until 1981 that Caldera's port facilities were inaugurated. This has contributed to the development of the canton, especially regarding the improvement of thoroughfares.

The town of Esparza was founded in 1574 when the town of Aranjuez was moved to what was then called Espíritu Santo. It was built over the wedge formed by the confluence of the rivers Barranca and Esparza, where today resides the Hacienda Pan de Azúcar. But when the governor of the Province of Costa Rica was changed in 1577, the town was moved to its present site and named Esparza in honor of the Villa de Esparza, the hometown of Diego de Artieda. And this move doubtlessly had to do with Puerto de Caldera, since it was at that time used as a port, and this new town was the headquarters for staff and authorities in charge of overseeing port activity as to the "registry and dispatch" of ships, accounting, and collecting of taxes.

The first Catholic church of this region was erected in 1574, the year the building that today is the Town Hall was built. There has been a high school here since 1976. There is also a fire fighting station, a branch office of the National Bank of Costa Rica, several kindergartens, a Social Security office, a Ministry of Agriculture office, a Canton Delegation, and a movie theater. Public services include electrical power, drinking water service and plumbing, rural telephones, both private and public.

One historical-cultural landmark here is the *Puente de las Damas* (Bridge of the Ladies), located at the canton limit with

Puerto Caldera, Esparza Cantón, Puntarenas Province.

San Mateo on the Jesús María River. There is only one park, *Parque Pérez*, and no historical buildings. On the south side of the park there is a bust of Diego de Artieda y Chirino, the governor and founder of the town of Esparza. In front of the bank there is a monument to Luis Vasco Coto, the first deputy of Esparza.

Esparza Canton has five districts: Espíritu Santo with 9,649 inhabitants; San Juan Grande with 1,579; Nacacona with 1,947; San Rafael with 1,041; and San Jerónimo with 982. Thus, the canton has a total population of 14,998 inhabitants of varied origins: China, Poland, Germany, Mexico, USA, Belgium, Peru, Argentina, and Portugal, and others.

Within Esparza Canton there are four beaches that attract many tourists: Doña Ana, Caldera, Tivives, Mata de Limón, and Puerto de Caldera.

The canton has had a stone road between it and Alajuela, and since 1945 it has been linked to San José by the Inter-American Highway.

Since pre-Colombian times throughout the region now occupied by Esparza Canton the following crops have been cultivated: corn, beans, cassava, and various fruits, especially medlars, sapodilla plums, *nancites*, avocados, *caimitos*, *jocotes*, cashews, and papaya, which has made fruit growing in this canton a very important enterprise. It also grows plantain bananas, sugarcane, and rice. Other industries include poultry raising, beekeeping, and salt processing, but farming and ranching are the primary means of livelihood.

There are seven enterprises in the canton (only one is financed with foreign capital): Macacona, mining gold and silver; Industria el Prado, producing fruit drinks, syrups, and canned fruit; Roinsa, manufacturing gunpowder; and Alimenticios Goya S.A., a flour mill. All of these are located in the Macacona District. In the district of Espíritu Santo is Productos Caribe S.A., which processes clay; and in San Juan Grande, Procesadora de Pescado (a fish processing plant) and Procesadora de Aluminio (ALUNASA, a manufacturer of aluminum ware). Other substantial sources of income include the tourist industry, gold mining, and coal mining.

Buenos Aires Canton

This canton comprises part of the Diquis Valley with very fertile soil, and a chilly climate in the heights of the Cordillera de Talamanca, and moderate to quite warm in other places. It is drained by tributaries of the Diquis River (also called Térraba), and by the Diquis itself near the canton limit with Osa, forming a very effective natural irrigation system.

The canton was originally inhabited by Boruca Indians, but white men began to settle here in 1870 when a road was opened between El Guarco to Boruca. Then the name was changed from Hato Viejo to Buenos Aires. But real development of the region began with the construction of the stretch of the Inter-American Highway to the south between the towns of San Isidro del General and Buenos Aires in 1961. The canton is divided into the districts of Buenos Aires, Volcán, Potrero Grande, Boruca, Pilas, and Colinas. The canton covers a total land area of 2,382.61 km² and a total population of 8,295 inhabitants.

Within Buenos Aires Canton there are several indigenous communities: Cabagra and Guaymí in the Potrero Grande District, Salitre and Cabécar de Ujarrás in the Buenos Aires District, and in the districts of Boruca, Pilas, and Colinas the Boruca, Térraba, and Curré Indian Reservations, situated near the Ceibo River, a tributary of the Diquis (also called Térraba).

In these vicinities are found vestiges of very old constructions, bearing witness to the existence of a people that once lived there and whose importance is evidenced by uncovered grave sites (*huacas*), in which gold Indian figurines and jewelry have been found. Other very interesting findings from here are some perfectly spherical granite rocks.

To get from Buenos Aires to the Pacific Coast one can travel by the valleys of the Térraba River, or by boat or canoe in the river itself. By land one can get to the country's capital taking the Pan-American Highway that passes through San Isidro de El General and then to Cartago.

The main activity of the canton, pineapple growing, is coordinated by the PINDECO Cooperative (having to do with pineapple development). Other important farm products are coffee, corn, beans, rice, sugarcane, papaya, and beef cattle. Cattle ranching has been a part of the economy since early settlement days, and today dual-purpose cattle has been gaining in economic importance in the highlands such as Volcán.

Deposits of bauxite (aluminum ore) have been found but have thus far not been exploited. There are plans to build a hydroelectric dam on the Térraba River at a place called Cajón (the project is called the Boruca Hydroelectric Project). This would form a lake covering approximately 200 kms^2 (three times that of Arenal Lake), but it would involve changes of such proportions that water would cover a large section of the Inter-American Highway, as well as part of the Boruca Indian Reservation, and then travel would have to be redirected over the new highway now in construction (Southern Coastal Route). At any rate, the project still has not materialized due to a lack of resources.

Montes de Oro Canton

This canton is bounded on the north by Alajuela Province, on the east by the province and canton of Esparza, on the south by the central canton of Puntarenas, and on the west by Puntarenas as well. The terrain here is dry and stony. But there are gold mines, highly exploited, especially by foreign investors.

The canton seat, Miramar (meaning "sea view") used to be called Los Quemados (meaning burnt, supposedly because of its color).

The name Miramar was proposed in 1897 by a visitor who observed that the ocean could be clearly seen from here.

The name of the canton (meaning "mountains of gold" has to do with the rich gold deposits in the mountains of

the region. The canton is divided into the districts of Miramar, La Unión, and San Isidro, and it has a total population of 7,500 inhabitants.

The town of Miramar is linked to Puntarenas and the rest of the country by the highway that leads to Barranca, and the Pacific Railway Station. It has a Catholic church, a postal-telegraph building, an elementary school, good commercial establishments, as well as public plumbing and electric power. Miramar is a very progressive town with 3,950 inhabitants and an average temperature of 26°C.

Osa Canton

This canton is bounded on the north and the east by the cantons of Aguirre, Buenos Aires, Pérez Zeledón, and Golfito, on the south by the Pacific Ocean and Golfito Canton, and on the west by the Pacific Ocean.

The fifth canton of the province, it has a population of 26,294 inhabitants. It is crossed by the Inter-American Highway on which there is a bridge over the Térraba River, 343 meters long.

It is divided into three districts: Puerto Cortés (population 7,368); Palmar (population 14,845); and Sierpe (population 4,081). The total land area is 1,930.24 kms^2.

This canton really began to progress when the banana plantations were moved in from the Caribbean region (1938), and a landing strip was set up and a dispensary a housing were built for the workers. This motivated settlement in the area and the construction of an urban zone now called Palmar Norte.

Since 1957, Puerto Cortés has been the governmental seat of the canton. At the time it was settled, it was called El Pozo. This port used to be the principle point of communication between that region and Puntarenas city through vessels that would arrive by sea near the mouth of the Térraba River.

It has good services: an agricultural high school since 1962; the Doctor Tomás Casas Hospital and the Palmar Sur Clinic; good stores and other businesses.

The main agricultural products from here are rice, cacao, corn, sorghum, beans, oil palm (a crop that replaced bananas when it became more profitable for the company since it required less manpower, and thus was less conducive to social and economic strife; moreover there is a great internal demand for palm oil).

The cultivation of bananas has been increasing again, and coffee growing is more important to the economy than palm oil.

In the Palmar District of this canton is the Curré Indian Reservation; in the Sierpe District is the Dulce Gulf Forest Reserve and the Corcovado National Park (where a series of conflicts have arisen regarding the indiscriminate use of the gold reserves, causing the loss of other protected resources). There are also seven zones declared as suitable for tourism, that hold out great potential for the future. These potential tourist zones include beautiful beaches such as Tortuga, Play Hermosa, and Playa Dominical.

Manuel Antonio National Park, Aguirre Canton, Puntarenas Province. Its beaches are immensely beautiful.

Aguirre Canton

This region was first settled by Huetar Indians and then was discovered by the Spaniards in 1522, and since that time until the end of the colonial days it was known as San Bernardo de Quepo in honor of the indigenous tribe the lived there.

The main village disappeared around 1746 and was not resettled until the end of the Nineteenth Century, by some Costa Ricans who travelled only by sea from Puntarenas. Real development began, however, in 1930 when the banana company moved in and built offices, a hospital, workshops, and the shipping dock that was inaugurated in 1939.

In 1948 this area became a canton, with Quepos as the governmental seat, and it was called Aguirre in honor of Rolando Aguirre-Lobo, a man who contributed greatly to the social and economic progress of the canton.

The canton seat is located near the shipping dock, that since 1972 has belonged to the State. Today the dock is in poor shape and offering only coasting vessel services. The town is small (only 9,093 inhabitants at the 1984 census) with basic services. It has an elementary school and a high school. Ample tourist services are available, especially in the private, commercial sector.

Aguirre Canton has three districts. Quepos, is the first and the governmental seat, with a land area of 229.16 kms². It has a shipping dock, and is a very popular town for vacationers who come to enjoy the beaches of the canton.

The district of Savegre has a land area of 216.2 kms² and a population of 2,466 inhabitants. Its main activities are the cultivation of African palm and tourism on its beaches, including Matapalo. The terrain here is flat and drained by the rivers Savegre, Hatillo, Portalón, Guaba, and Barú, which have made this zone a broad alluvial plain.

The last district is Naranjito, the smallest in land area with 104.64 kms², and a population of 1,760 inhabitants. The terrain in this district is somewhat uneven since it is situated right where the mountainous zones of Dota and Tarrazú begin.

The canton is geologically formed of sedimentary and tertiary rock, giving it two morphological units: one of tectonic and erosive origin corresponding to the mountainous zones, and the alluvial plain formed of sedimentation deposited by the rivers. This makes it necessary to set management policies for 39% of the canton's soil, and to dedicate 15% of the land to protected areas. The rest may be used for agriculture, with some limitations.

The canton has a hospital and a beautiful tourist center (Nahomi) in the center of Quepos. The chief farm products are African palm, beans, sorghum, tobacco, and plantain bananas.

Aguirre canton presents good conditions for the tourist industry: the Manuel Antonio National Park in the Quepos District and four zones that have been declared suitable for coastal tourism, and are already are quite well developed with adequate infrastructure, special areas prepared for tourists, and a diversity of attractions.

Golfito Canton

This canton covers a total land area of 1,7531.96 kms² and is divided into three districts: Golfito, the governmental seat with 708.76 kms² and a population of 14,937 inhabitants (according to the 1984 census); Guaycará with 324.66 kms² and a population of 9,380 inhabitants; and the Jiménez District with 720.54 kms² and 4,766 inhabitants. This last district is separated from the rest of the canton by the Dulce Gulf, and has some of the oldest lands in the country (on the Osa Peninsula). Here, too, is the Corcovado National Park.

The first dwellers in this region were Brunca Indians, some of whose descendants still live in the area today. In 1519 the first Spaniards arrived, and the region was resettled by Costa Ricans beginning around the year 1874. Development here has been propelled by the opening of the Southern

A beach in Jiménez, Golfito Canton, Puntarenas Province.

179

Corcovado Lake in Corcovado National Park in Golfito.

Inter-American Highway, and the banana plantations. The main population center of the region today occupied by the canton was once called Golfo Dulce, and also Santo Domingo, but in 1949 when the canton was founded, it received the name of Golfito (little gulf), due to fact that the coastline at the entrance to Gulf Dulce has the shape of a little gulf.

With the arrival of the banana company, many people migrated to this zone, but when it pulled out in 1984, many residents left to find jobs elsewhere. Now this problem has been eased by the opening of a free port here in 1989, which has greatly increased the daily flow of tourists.

In this canton rocks are found from the Cretaceous era, especially in the hills that surround the Dulce Gulf, corresponding to forms of tectonic and erosive origin. There are also limestone formations from the Quaternary era comprising the alluvial plains, the land unit of marine origin represented by the arrow-shaped sandy coastal strip occupied by the whole of the Golfito District.

The canton is drained by numerous rivers that empty into the Dulce Gulf: the Esquinas, Coto Colorado, Conte, Golfito, Sábalo, and Mazanillo, and others

such as La Vaca and La Vaquita, which have been causing serious problems for the past few years due to flooding.

In this canton there are 11 costal zones that have been declared apt for tourism, including Zancudo Beach, Puerto Jiménez, Punta Agujas, and others. There is also the Golfo Dulce Forest Reserve, the Corcovado National Park, the Guaymí Indian Reservation in Conte Brunca, and the Golfito National Wildlife Preserve.

The canton has a hospital, and a palm oil processing plant. Palm oil, rice, cacao, corn, beans, and beef are the chief products.

Coto Brus Canton

Coto Brus, canton number eight of Puntarenas Province, has a population of 31,650 inhabitants and covers a total land area of 935.52 kms², according to the 1984 census. It has four districts: San Vito, the canton seat, with 393.13 kms² and 12,864 inhabitants; Sabalito with 356.16 kms² and 9,063 inhabitants; Agua Buena con 59,82 kms², the smallest district in land area, with 6,446 inhabitants; and Limoncito with 126.41 kms², with the least population, 3,277 inhabitants.

The primary source of services for this canton is Costa Rica's neighbor country to the south, Panama, which has greatly influenced the development of the trade and customs of the people, especially in the Sabalito District.

The canton has several tourist attractions, such as the Las Tablas Protected Zone located in the Sabalito District, the La Amistad International Park in the San Vito District, and the Guaymí Indian Reservation of Coto Brus located in the Limoncito District.

As most of the other cantons in this zone, Coto Brus was once inhabited by Brunca Indians, and then settled by Spaniards, in this case beginning in 1571.

In 1601 development began to spring forward with the opening of the mule trail from Cartago to Panama, used for trade with the neighboring country. This development was influenced by coffee growing starting in 1949, and the arrival of an Italian community of farmers, which with the help of Costa Ricans gave a healthy boost to the economy.

The main activities of the zone involve coffee, sugarcane, plantain bananas, corn, beans, and dual-purpose cattle. These are favored by the terrain and soil of the zone, corresponding to the unit of land formed by alluvial sedimentation, represented by the deltas of the rivers General and Potrero, where the best soils of the canton are found.

Two watersheds drain this canton and make possible its economic and tourist development: that of the Río Grande de Térraba with tributaries including the rivers Coto Brus, Sabalito, Limón, Las Gemelas; and that of the Esquinas with tributaries such as the Caño Seco and the Corredores. These watersheds constitute rich resources that are used for fishing, swimming, irrigation, and fertilization of the lands near their rivers' banks.

In this canton are the foothills of the *Fila Brunqueña* and the high plateaus of San Vito; the first has become the main water catchment zone, and the high plateaus serve as sites for several towns,

such as La Unión, Cañas Gordas, Campo Tres, and Torre Deto.

The name of the canton, and the river of the same name, is of Amerindian origin, in honor of an Indian Chief and his tribe, who lived in the region long ago.

Parrita Canton

This ninth canton of Puntarenas Province, as almost all of Costa Rican territory was inhabited before the Spanish colonization by indigenous peoples, in this case the Huetars. The Spaniards began to colonize the region in 1522.

In 1924 a young German installed the first banana plantation near the Pirris River (also called Parrita River), which prompted the migration of people from the provinces of San José and Guanacaste, and the country of Nicaragua. By 1941 the zone was made into a canton with one single district.

The name of the canton, according to a popular account, has to do with a woman called Rita, who lived on one of the original settlements, and who had a business in which she received packages. The phrase "*Es pa'Rita*" ("It's for Rita") was so often heard when speaking about packages addressed to her, that they finally called the canton, Parrita.

This canton, as of the 1984 census, had 9,774 inhabitants distributed over a total land area of 478.79 kms². The people make their living primarily from African palm (an activity that has replaced bananas and rice), corn, plantain bananas, beans, cacao, sorghum, various fruits, and beef cattle.

In this canton one can observe two distinct geomorphological units: one of tectonic and erosive origin corresponding to the mountainous zones of the *Fila Brunqueña*, the Susubres, and the Chonta; and the Llanura and Los Marisinas zone, and the Parrita River delta, a land unit formed mostly from river sedimentation.

The canton is drained by the rivers Damas, Pocaritos, Palo Seco, Chires, Jicote, and Parrita (also called Pirris), which present serious flooding problems as they cut across main population centers in the canton, such as Plazón, Surubres,

Sardinal, and Pueblo Nuevo, located very near the mouth of the river.

There is one palm oil processing plant in the canton. Here are also deposits of peat (carbonaceous deposits occurring principally in marshy places, composed of partly decayed vegetable matter which can be used as fuel when dried).

The first Catholic church was built in 1942, and that same year the first elementary school was established. The *Colegio Técnico Profesional Industrial* (Technical Industrial High School) has been functioning since 1973. Plumbing and electric power were installed by the Banana Company (*Atlas Cantonal*, 1987).

Parrita holds out many advantages for the tourist industry, since it has good infrastructure services and businesses, a Social Security clinic, a high school, good public lighting, and an extensive coastal region of which three zones have been declared suitable for tourism, that cover practically the entire coast of the canton. Further, there is a good highway that links this canton with the central part of the country, and soon it will be connected to the Southern Costanera Highway, which will extend over much of the Pacific coast.

Corredores Canton

As the other cantons in this region, this area was first colonized by Brunca Indians, and then by Spaniards, but true progress began with the arrival of the banana company to the Pacific Southwest, particularly in Golfito, since it was that activity that brought on the immigration that made development possible. The Corredores District, the canton seat, is also known as Ciudad Neily, since that town has been the most developed since 1940, when a citizen of Lebanese origin, Ricardo Neily, installed a commissariat used by the workers of the banana company of Golfito Canton and then by those of Valle de Coto. The main population center of the region from the beginning has been the land owned by Ricardo Neily, on which he had made a elementary school, and installed electrical power, drinking water facilities, and

several other services. These services were expanded when Mr. Neily sold his property and more immigrants arrived.

Corredores is named after the Corredor River that crosses the district in which Ciudad Neily is located. It has three districts and covers a total land area of 620.60 kms² distributed among the following districts: Corredor with 272.19 kms² and 13,846 inhabitants; La Cuesta with 226.08 kms² and 9,449 inhabitants; and Canoas with 122 kms² and 5,071 inhabitants (according to the 1984 census).

In the canton one can observe several geomorphological forms that serve to beautify the land and make it attractive for tourists: the alluvial plain of the Coto Colorado, the delta area of Paso Canoas; the marshes of the Corredores River; the Esquinas River Valley, a result of the surrounding ridge; and the high plateau of San Vito (a flat area of the *Borunqueña Fila*), which is of volcanic origin. Other tourist attractions include the indigenous communities of Abrojos de Montezuma, and part of Conte Burica, as well as a region where gold can be found, and which is now experiencing a great influx of tourists.

Available in this canton are most of the essential community services: hospital, elementary and high schools, a warehouse in the La Cuesta District, and good tourist resorts since the Corredor District is a strategic point for vacationers from San José who visit Paso Canoas and the other cantons of the region.

The principal activities of the canton are agricultural including the production of palm oil, bananas, cacao, rice, corn, vegetables, beans, sorghum, and beef. The activities are favored by the geography of the canton, including the numerous rivers that drain it: the Colorado, which waters the region, Corredor, Abrojo Conte, and La Vaca, which sometimes overflows its banks causing flooding, but also fertilizes and irrigates the soil.

Garabito Canton

This eleventh canton of Puntarenas Province was created in 1980 with only one district, Jacó, when it was separated from Puntarenas Canton. It gets its name from one of the most well-remember Indian chiefs of these lands, who lived here before Spanish colonization.

The governmental seat, Jacó, designated as such in 1980 when the canton was created is primarily involved in the tourist industry.

In the town of Jacó are concentrated social and economic services such as tourist resorts (including hotels, restaurants, sodas, tourists complexes), and infrastructure services, such as drinking water, electrical power, and good roads. But the most important attractions here are the lovely beaches throughout the canton, including Jacó, Play Hermosa, Bahía Herradura, and Punta Leona, situated within the eight zones declared apt for tourism. (Sadly Tárcoles Beach, belonging to this canton is the only zone that is unsuitable for tourism because of the fecal wastes emptied onto it by the Río Grande Tárcoles, carrying sewage down from San José, and transformed it into a dead beach.) Other tourist attractions in the canton are the Carara Biological Reserve and the Caldera Reserved Port Zone, since it borders with Esparza.

There are also three beautiful geomorphological units that embellish the landscape of the canton: the mountains and deep valleys corresponding to the denudation unit; the terraces of Esparza and Orotina, the alluvial plain of Herradura and Jacó, and the alluvial plain of the Tusubres, Agujas, and Jesús María rivers; and tectonic-erosive unit corresponding to the *Chiclera Ridge*.

The canton is drained by the following rivers: Tusubres, Seco, La Gloria, Copey, Cama Blanca, Agujas, Tárcoles, Río Grande de Tárcoles, and others. Except for the Río Grande de Tárcoles, all of these have good quality water. These rivers are important to the canton, in addition to its thriving tourist industry, since some of people here make their living from farming, producing corn, fruits, beans, and livestock.

The most pressing problem of this canton is in Jacó, as it is not actually conditioned to receive the 30,000 tourists that arrive during the high season (the dry season). This has led to greater pollution of the beaches, resulting from the wastes of commercial and social services, and consequently the ocean as well, given the shallow water table.

Jacó Beach in Garabito Canton, Puntarenas.

183

LIMON PROVINCE

This province occupies the whole eastern side of Costa Rica, from Punta Castilla to the Sixaola River. It is bounded on the west by parts of the provinces of Heredia, Cartago, and Puntarenas; on the north by the Caribbean Sea, and Costa Rica's northern neighbor, Nicaragua; on the east by the Caribbean Sea; and on the south by the country of Panama.

The terrain is flat and marshy, especially in the coastal regions and in the north, but it gets progressively more mountainous going toward the south. It covers a total land area of 9,188.52 kms². Its forests present a great variety of species, including many containing substances useful in industry and medicine. For many years the chief crops of the province have been bananas, cacao, coconuts, and, on a lesser scale, various kinds of fruit. Some of its land has been dedicated to pasture lands for cattle. The principal and navigable part of all the rivers that empty into the Caribbean is in Limón Province. Of these, the most important are: the Colorado, the Jiménez, the Parismina, the Reventazón, the Pacuare, the Matina, Río Banano, La Estrella, and the Sixaola.

It was a spot on this Caribbean coast (now Uvita and formerly Cariari) that Christopher Columbus disembarked in his fourth voyage to the New World.

Practically speaking, this province has no dry season. It rains during the whole year, although it eases up somewhat in the months of September and February. Hence the intertropical climate predominates, which, along with the topographical characteristics of the region, cause the rivers to frequently change their courses. Moreover, the vegetation is similar to that which is found in the rest of the intertropical world: very wet forests with trees up to 40 meters tall, where the ground is covered with ferns, mosses, and likens. These forests are found principally in Tortuguero, and in the southern part of the mountains (where little remains of the original forests).

Canalization, the lagoons of the Tortuguero, and the use of the canals as transportation routes have led to the emergence of important centers of production and trade in the region. Here today are huge banana and cacao plantations, and much of the territory is accessible by railway.

Limón Province is divided into the cantons of Limón, Pococí, Talamanca,

Opposite page: Beach in the Refugio Nacional de Fauna Silvestre Gandoca-Manzanillo (Gandoca-Manzanillo National Wildlife Preserve), Talamanca, Limón.

Breakwater in Limón, City.

Matina, Guácimo and Siquirres, with a total population of 168,076 inhabitants, many of whom are descendants of blacks from the Antilles originally brought to the country to work on the cacao and banana plantations and on the railroads during early colonial days. Today the population of the province is a mixture of races: blacks, whites, orientals, as well as Cabécar and Bribí Indians, and others, forming a heterogenous society with little socio-cultural cohesion.

Economic development of this province began with the cultivation of

Vargas Park, Limón City.

cacao, the first export product of Costa Rica. Toward the end of the Nineteenth Century and the beginning of the Twentieth the cultivation of bananas was encouraged, and the plantations prospered well until they were hit by disease: Panama blight, mold, and sigatoka. This led to the introduction of a new crop, cacao. Then during the decade of the sixties bananas began to be grown again, this time using more advanced technologies, which with rapid transformations brought about through new infrastructure and services, and the contributions of some private enterprises, made this province once again an attractive region. Evidence of this is that in less than 30 years its population grew by 92,956 inhabitants, making it one of the fastest growing areas in the country. This growth has been concentrated particularly in the cantons of Limon, Siquirres, and Pococí.

Communication routes are generally in poor condition, except for the Turrialba-Siquirres-Limón, San José-Guápiles-Siquirres highways, and the canals of Tortuguero (mentioned above) to the north, and a coastal highway that goes south as far as Sixaola. The rest of the transportation routes consist of penetration roads that are often impassible due to the many rivers and streams crossing them. The other important route to the socio-economic development of Limón has been the railroad linking Río Frio-Guápiles-Limón, and Valle La Estrella with Limón, currently out of service.

Today the port development complex in Limón managed by JAPDEVA is the chief driving force of the urban economy in Limón, because of the other industries that depend on it: stevedore companies, customs and insurance agencies, and others. Also very important in this area is the new port at Moín, and more recently the *Escuela Superior del Trópico Húmedo* (EARTH = Higher School of the Wet Tropics).

Limón Canton

Located among the cantons of Talamanca, Turrialba, and Matina, it is

José Joaquín Trejos Fernández Highway between Puerto Limón and San José, the country's capital, making travel by automobile between the two cities possible in around three hours.

bound on the east and the north by the Caribbean Sea.

In is located the Indian reservations of the Cabécars, the Cabécars of Tayní, the Cabécars of Telire, and the Cabécars of Talamanca; and the Chirripó National Park. The area occupied by this canton was discovered by Christopher Columbus around the year 1502; it was then called Cariari. But the zone went uninhabited until the road between Cartago and Moín was built, and a port on the Caribbean was opened for coffee export after the country's independence. Not until the end of the Nineteenth Century, however, with the new railroad and the banana growing industry, did development really began to take hold. The name of the canton, according to popular versions goes back to when there was a big lemon tree used

Boats on Bonita Beach.

La Estrella River,
Limón Canton.

as a point of reference, right where the Government Building is today.

Limón City

The capital city of the province and the most commercially active port in the country, it is situated on rocky terrain on the small Limón Harbor in front of La Uvita Islet.

Limón City has available all the conveniences and services expected in a modern city. Protecting it from the sea is a costly breakwater, over two kilometers long. The rocky surface of the land has been filled in with two to four meters of dirt all over. Its asphalt streets are wide, straight, and in good condition. The buildings, most of two or three stories, are spacious, comfortable, and some elegant.

Near the sea there is a lovely park, a docking complex to which large ocean vessels arrive each day. Public buildings include one very well conditioned one containing the customs offices and spacious merchandise warehouses, a

Catholic cathedral and several Protestant churches, a municipal market, a modern municipal and government office building, a police station, a plaza command post, and a city jail, department and other stores, and hotels. For vacationers there is a nice modern public swimming pool with all the necessary facilities. There are good elementary schools a public high school, and a vocational high school. In addition, there is a postal-telegraph office, and Limón has telephone communication with the capital, and air transport for passengers and mail.

The city has public lighting, and electric power for the homes, suitable drinking water, and a complete sewage removal and treatment system.

Health services have greatly progressed in this port city, which was a death trap until the end of the last century, due to rampant yellow fever. Today it is healthy, albeit hot and humid, with a population of 52,602 inhabitants.

Puerto Limón is linked to the capital by a fairly new highway that makes travel between the two cities by car possible in around three hours.

In this town is the Regional Headquarters of the University of Costa Rica, a clinic, a regional center of the National Learning Institute, and the Isla Uvita National Landmark Park (which the Indians call Quiribrí, and the place where Christopher Columbus landed in 1502, calling it La Huerta). It has an ethnic-historical museum, also a historical landmark, as well as the Costa Rican Oil Refinery (RECOPE), and Canales de Tortuguero wharf.

This canton has many tourist resorts in constant development, such as the Portete Recreational Park and the Moín Tourist Stop. Also covering part of this canton are the national parks, Talamanca and Chirripó, and the Hitoy Cerere Biological Reserve. It also has a costal zone declared apt for tourism, encompassing the areas of Vizcaya, Cieneguita, Boca del Río La Estrella, Estero Negro, and Isla Uvita.

The main problems facing this canton are the shortage of adequate housing, and not enough jobs to go around. The first problem is being addressed by several urban projects: Navarro Construction, INVU, IMAS, and BANHVI (the latter three government housing agencies). As for jobs, several new factories (clothing, biscuit, potatoes, and plantain bananas), and farms are helping to diminish unemployment.

In the kiosk in Vargas Park in Limón City is one of the most important monuments in the canton, that depicts a legend about three fishermen.

Pococí Canton

Pococí canton, number two of Limón Province, covers a total land area of 2,403.49 kms² and has a population of 44,187 inhabitants according to the 1984 census. It has six districts: Guápiles, Jiménez, Rita, Roxana, Cariari, and Colorado. Guápiles, which has been classified as a city since 1966, is the canton seat.

The canton of Pococí owes its settlement to Mainor Keith's contract to

Tortuguero National Park in Pococí Canton.

exploit the railroad, and to the Carrillo Road in 1882 when the government decided to sell lands in the region in order to encourage migration to this area from San José Province.

Development of this canton has been tied to the banana industry right from the start. The relationship was only affected when the banana company moved to the Pacific Southeast due to the problem of disease here.

This canton has had a Catholic church since 1907, an elementary school since 1908, and the *Colegio Técnico Profesional Agropecuario* (an agricultural vocational high school) since 1969. It has a hospital and a clinic in the Cariari District.

The canton was named after the Pococí Indians who inhabited this land before the colonial period.

The principal means of livelihood in the canton is banana growing, an activity that was revived starting in 1960. Other farm products from here include corn, beans, tubers, pejibaye, several kinds of fruit, and livestock. The canton also has

promising tourist potential, which only recently has begun to be tapped. In this canton is the Barra de Colorado National Wildlife Refuge covering almost the whole Colorado District; Tortuguero National Park in the same district, and part of the Cordillera Volcánica Central Forest Reserve, as well as two zones declared suitable for coastal tourism that encompass the beaches of Tortuguero National Park and Barra del Colorado National Wildlife Refuge; and the navigable canal that links Limón with Villa Barra de Colorado.

In addition to these tourist attractions, there are several scenic zones, such as the river plains, the swamp, the river deltas, and the volcanic hills of Coronel, Caño Moreno, and Las Lomas de Sierpe, the coastal ridges, and the lagoons on the north side of Limón.

The zone is one of the best drained in the country, by the three most important watersheds in the country: those of the rivers Tortuguero (where the navigable canal is located),

Another view of Tortuguero National Park with its lush vegetation.

The Parismina River, which serves as a boundary in part of its course between the cantons of Siquirres and Pococí.

Reventazón-Parismina (the roughest river in the country), and the Chirripó.

Siquirres Canton

On September 19, 1911 the *Villa de Siquirres* was declared canton number three of Limón Province. It occupies a land area of 869.19 kms².

The canton has several spots of interest to tourists: the Pacuare Tourist Center, Barra del Parismina, Barra del Pacuare, and Laguna Madre de Dios, frequented mostly by foreign foreigners.

The population centers are found mainly along the railroad, and some important highways such as the Limón-Guápiles Freeway. The canton is divided into five districts: Siquirres, Pacuarito, Florida, Germania, and Cairo.

Tortuguero Hill, the only important elevation near the Tortuguero Lagoons.

Its transportation means include buses and small craft on the navigable rivers (Pacuare, Parismina, Reventazón).

Many of these communities already have the most essential public services, but some seem to have been forgotten, having few resources and scant means of mobilization.

Most of the people here make their living from farming. Their crops are quite diversified: bananas, cacao, corn, coconuts, plantain bananas, rice, cassava, *guanábana* (soursop), macadamia nuts, passion fruit, and ginger.

Only small industries exist here: sawmills, cabinetmaking, ceramics, block makers, and small bread bakeries located in the canton seat of Siquirres. The principal buildings include the Town Hall, the Costa Rican Electrical Institute, the Tribunal of Justice, the Catholic church, the Municipal Market, two shopping centers, an agricultural high school, the Ministry of Agriculture, a branch office of the National Bank, a chapter of the Red Cross, a Social Security office, and the Fire Fighters Station. It only has one park. Siquirres has many historical

buildings, for example the Casa de Cultura (Cultural Building) and the railroad station.

There are three monuments, two of which are dedicated to important contributors to the canton's progress, and the other, *Mártires del Codo del Diablo*, in honor of those who lost their lives defending the workers of the Caribbean zone in December of 1948.

The current state of the streets in the urban center is fair, but not that of the local roads, which are for the most part quite deteriorated, and thus hindering such activities as agriculture, fishing, and tourism.

The canton has suitable drinking water, electrical power, telephone, telegraph, and mail services. It also has a Social Security office, a Ministry of Health office, two high schools (one regular and the other a night school), elementary school, and numerous business establishments.

The fishing industry is quite prosperous, especially in the rivers Parismina, Pacuare, and Reventazón, where many kinds of fish are caught.

The name of the canton and its governmental seat is derived from and Indian word that means reddish colored.

Talamanca Canton

In terms of land area, this is the largest canton in Limón Province, with 2,809 kms² distributed among three districts: Bratsi, the canton seat and largest district in land area (2,399.51 kms²); Sixaola with 237.01 kms²; and Cahuita with 173.41 kms². Practically all of the Cahuita District corresponds to protected areas since located there is the Cahuita National Park, with the only corral reef in the country, and the Gandoca Manzanillo National Wildlife Refuge.

The canton also has other tourist zones in the Bratsi District such as: part of the Chirripó National Park; the Indian reservations, Cabécar de Tayní, Cabécar de Telire, Cabécar de Talamanca, Bribrí de Talamanca, and the Cocles; and La Amistad International Park.

Gandoca-Manzanillo National Wildlife Refuge in Talamanca Canton.

Coral "brain" in Puerto Vargas, Talamanca.

The canton was first settled by black immigrants from the Caribbean who had come to make their living from fishing. Thus the first village was established at Cahuita. Later, other blacks arrived from Bocas del Toro, Colón, and Jamaica and settled to work on the construction of the railroad.

Talamanca was made a canton in 1969, with the governmental seat in Bambú, now called Bratsi. According to the 1984 census it has a population of 11,013 inhabitants of whom almost all are indigenous. It has had a Catholic church since 1961, an elementary school since 1886, and a technical high school since 1974 (in Bribrí, a town in the Cahuita District), and it has a Social Security clinic in the Sixaola District. It has electrical power, and drinking water services. The chief agricultural products of the canton are bananas (all the way to Panama), cacao, corn, plantain bananas, tubers, and livestock.

Since 1921 explorations for oil have been underway, an activity that has been stepped up in the last few years, and has broadened to include exploration for coal and iron.

Talamanca Canton presents great diversity in its geomorphological forms, giving it beautiful contrasts. On one side it has formations of the tectonic and erosive origin, represented by the *Cordillera de Talamanca*, a mountain range that reaches almost to the coast giving the coast line a variety of curious forms; and on the other side, there are the river valleys of the Sixaola and the Telire, the alluvial plain of San Carlos and the Caribbean, and a permanent swamp.

Also present is the costal land unit or marine origin represented by the protruding coral platform located in the town of Puerto Viejo, Manzanillo and Punta Mona, and the area north of Cahuita; and the submerged coral reef made up of live corral, which is a complex of exoskeletons of calcareous material. There are also zones of glacial origin such as Mount Chirripó, and of structural origin corresponding to the faults along several rivers such as the Tuba, Puerto Viejo, and Watsí.

Another significant fact is the great diversity of the rivers that drain the canton, including the Sixaola River watershed, which is the international boundary, and as it flows over very flat terrain, it often changes its course, causing the country to gain or lose territory depending on the weather. Other watersheds are those of the Estrella and the Sini, which have also been troublesome due to flooding, but also beneficial as they fertilize the soil. The origin of the name of the canton is Spanish and its name has not changed since the first Spaniards arrived at these lands.

Matina Canton

The development of this canton has had much to do with the cultivation of cacao beginning in the second half of the Seventeenth Century. This product was the first export from Costa Rica, an activity financed by well-to-do citizens of Cartago. This made Matina such an important town that Fort San Fernando was built there in 1742, the first and last bulwark erected by the Spaniards in the Caribbean zone. The activity also caused this town to be declared a foreign trade port in 1811, but it was not until 1826 that there was any significant immigration to that area.

Matina Canton came into being in 1969, and today it has three districts: Matina, the governmental seat, and the largest in land area; Batán; and Carrandi. The total land area of the canton is 772.64 kms^2 and, according to the 1984 census, it has a total population of 14,723 inhabitants. The name is of indigenous origin. The people here make their living mostly from farming, their chief products being bananas, cacao, plantain bananas, pejibaye, and beef cattle. These activities are favored by the rich topsoil of this zone. The terrain can be categorized as follows: the alluvial plains of San Carlos, and the Caribbean; the swampy zone; the deltas of the Chirripó and Zent rivers, the foothills of the *Cordillera de Talamanca*, which is a good catchment source; the coastal ridges, the lagoons situated around the mouths of the Pacuare and Matina rivers.

In addition to its scenic beauty, this canton has a great diversity of rivers that drain it and permit tourist and other economic activities. Among these rivers are the Matina, Moín, and Madre de Dios with its tributaries the Chirripó, Barbilla, and Toro. The canton also has a zone declared suitable for tourism that encompasses the navigable canal of Tortuguero, Villa Barra del Colorado, and the indigenous communities of Chirripó located in the Matina District, and the protected zones of the Pacuare River, and Barbilla, as well as the Matina-Pacuera Forest Reserve located in the Batán District, which constitute the principal tourist potential of the canton.

The Chirripó Atlántico River, Matina, Limón Province.

Tortuguero, Limón Province.

Guácimo Canton

In 1971 Guácimo became canton number six of Limón Province, with five districts: Guácimo, the governmental seat, Mercedes, Pocora, Río Jiménez, and Duacarí, for a total land area of 576.48 kms^2, and a population of 16,472 (according to the 1984 census), The people are dedicated mostly to farming, their chief products being bananas, cacao, tubers, and livestock.

This canton, as most, was once inhabited by indigenous groups and then conquered and colonized by the Spaniards. Its development stems from the banana industry and the construction of the railroad between Siquirres and San José.

Guácimo has had an elementary school since 1914, a agricultural vocational high school since 1974, and a parish church since 1966. It also has a Social Security office in the canton seat, and numerous commercial and social services available.

Tourist activity here is favored by the railroad crossing the canton from east to west; and the many rivers that drain it, including the Reventazón-Parismina (already quite developed for tourism), and the Chirripó; and the Cordillera Volcánica Central Forest Reserve, where there is great diversity of flora and fauna. This canton is located among the cantons of

Pococí, Turrialba, and Siquirres. It is named after a luxuriant tree called the *guácimo*, that used to grow in the place where the first village sprang up, and which today is the governmental seat of the canton.

Another view of the Tortuguero; in the background a surá or guayabón tree (Terminalia oblonga-combretaceae).

195

10 Economic and Social Aspects

AGRO-EXPORT ECONOMY

Toward the end of the colonial era, and the early years of independence, tobacco growing, and to some extent mining, gave a substantial impetus to the Costa Rican economy. Nevertheless, it was coffee that enabled the large-scale evolution of the economy in this country for it was with the export of this commodity that Costa Rica was inserted into the world economy. And it allowed Costa Ricans to gain access to many imported products that they had never known before.

Costa Rica was the first Central American country that discovered the importance of coffee as an export crop. The risks the first coffee growers took, as well as the incentives they received from the government through land grants and the construction of roads, propelled the expansion of this commodity. Initially Chile, and later on England, were the principal external markets for coffee. Since coffee growing for export began in 1820, this has been Costa Rica's most vital export crop.

Coffee used to be exported through Port Puntarenas from where it was shipped to England by sailing around Cape Horn. But since transportation over this route was quite costly, Costa Ricans sought a communication route to the Atlantic Coast so that coffee could be shipped from there more directly to England.

After several attempts to build a road to the Atlantic, during the presidential term of Tomás Guardia, the construction of the Atlantic Railway was begun with English financing. Minor Keith, the brother of the railroad builder, introduced banana growing in order to make more intensive use of the railway.

The cultivation of bananas was concentrated primarily in Limón Province, which was for many years a banana coast *par excellence*. It encompassed Línea Vieja, Siquirres Canton, and the zone between Limón and La Estrella River. But banana growing was halted there due to disease, and in the thirties of this century, the crop was introduced in the Pacific coastal region. Subsequently, production on the Atlantic Coast was reactivated, and in the eighties banana production was abandoned on the Pacific side. Since the introduction of coffee until the decade of the sixties of this century, the driving force for economic growth was coffee and banana exports. Price variations of these products has had a heavy impact on the national economy, inducing both bonanzas and crises.

Opposite page: Vegetable patch in Escazú.

The driving force of the Costa Rican economy until the sixties of this century was coffee and banana exports.

THE COSTA RICAN ECONOMY AFTER 1950

Industrialization of the country

In the fifties a concern mounted in the country over the problems involved in the country's economical dependence on only a few export products. Then a policy was drafted in which industrial production would be given incentives with an eye to diversifying the Costa Rican economy. This process culminated with Costa Rica's incorporation into the Central American Common Market. The new arrangement was characterized by the following:

a. Free trade was established for industrial products among the countries of Central America. Thus, for example, products produced in Costa Rica would be sold without import duty in Guatemala, and vice versa.

b. High tariffs were established for goods imported from outside Central America but very low ones for imported raw materials. Thus, for example, a high tariff was set for soaps produced outside of Central America, which allowed national manufacturers to transfer resources to the production of soaps, since they were protected from competing imported products. This has been termed the "import substitution policy".

c. Tax exemptions were established for industrial enterprises involved in production for Central America.

This set of policies had important consequences, noteworthy of which was:

a. Growth. At the onset this process of substituting local products for imported ones was very dynamic, and during the sixties and at the beginning of the seventies production rose sharply. But when the possibilities of substituting imports were gradually depleted, the process lost its initial momentum, due to the small size of the Central American market. The process, moreover, suffered from political upheavals occurring in other Central American countries. In 1969 there was a war between El Salvador and Honduras, and following that there was intense fighting in Nicaragua and El Salvador.

b. Dependency. The new industrial sector was depending heavily on imported raw materials. This made the foreign revenue generated by traditional export items (coffee, bananas, beef, especially) extremely crucial in enabling the industrial sector to import its raw materials. So what was happening, in reality, was not the substitution of imported goods by local production, but rather consumer goods (soap, for example) were being substituted by imported raw materials (ingredients to make the soap, for instance).

c. Slower growth in exports. The import substitution policy redounded in the greatest benefits for those entrepreneurs that invested their resources in producing for the Central American market rather than for markets outside the isthmus. This, in

In recent years the country has been making a significant effort to modernize its industries to enable it to export to broader foreign markets.

turn, caused traditional exports to lose their momentum. All of these factors, coupled with the needs for raw materials on the part of the industrial sector resulted in a constant deficit in the country's trade balance (exports minus imports).

d. Fiscal problems. The policy of tax exemptions as incentive to the industrial sector led to reduced tax revenue for the national government, and a series of consequent problems in dealing with the fiscal deficit (income minus expenditures).

Agricultural Modernization

In the sixties beef cattle and sugarcane began to take on importance, adding to the well-established export products, coffee and bananas.

In the fifties and sixties the highest growth in agricultural production stemmed from cultivating new lands, since it was still possible to use heretofore unfarmed lands. In the seventies, however, the farm frontier was coming to an end, and agricultural production increases since then have come about mainly through technological changes. This has enabled substantial productivity improvements with respect to the available resources. Especially noteworthy in this vein is the increased productivity achieved in coffee, bananas, and rice.

Population and Employment

The growth of the economy depends much on the number and quality of the workers. In turn, the number of workers depends on the population growth and age distribution. Around 1960 the population growth rate reached its highest level, 3.9 percent per year. This rate had diminished by the eighties to around 2.7 percent. Around 1960 the average woman by the time she reached the end of her fertile years would have seven children, but by the end of the seventies that figure had dropped to four children. This gradual reduction in the population growth rate has caused a general "aging" of the population, evidenced by the following facts: In 1963 60 percent of

the population was 12 years old or over, and by 1985 that figure had risen to 70 percent. In other words, over the last two decades there have been more and more people of working age.

As for the incorporation of people of working age into the labor market, several important phenomena are observed. First, there is less participation by young people, who now postpone their involvement in the labor market preferring to stay longer in the educational system. Second, women participate more in the labor market today than ever before.

Regarding working population, several significant changes are worth mentioning:

a. Declining importance of agriculture. In 1950 55% of the population was employed in agriculture, while in 1989 only 26% was engaged in that sector. The sectors that have gained most in importance are those involved in services and industry. This has occurred as a consequence of the decreasing contribution of agriculture to the total national production and

In the seventies the farm frontier was coming to and end, and increased production from that time on had to come about mainly relying on technological advances.

199

In 1950 55% of the population made its living from farming; in 1989 only 26% did.

the greater technification that has made it possible to produce more with less manpower.

b. Prominence of the public sector. More people today are employed in the public sector. In 1950 6% of the labor force was employed by the government, in 1980 20%, and in 1989 17%.

c. More salaried workers. From 1950 until the present the trend has been an increasing relative importance on salaried workers with the total labor scheme. In other words, fewer and fewer workers are self-employed.

The Role of The State

The Costa Rican Government has played a very important role in the development of the country's economy. During the last century and the first half of this one, the action of the State has focused on providing the country with essential physical infrastructure (highways, bridges, port facilities, waterworks, etc.) and in improving the conditions of education and health of the general population.

Since 1940 until the present the State has intensified its involvement in the Costa Rica economy. In the decade of the forties, during the presidential term of Rafael Angel Calderón Guardia, the Code of Labor was established to regulate relations between workers and employers, and the current Social Security system was also established. In 1948 the existing private banks were taken over by the national government, thus giving it a monopoly as to time deposit accounts. Another State institution was created for the generation of electricity: the *Instituto Costarricense de Electricidad* (ICE = Costa Rican Electrical Institute). In the sixties the government's intervention through taxation and exemptions sought to provide incentives for market production through an import substitution policy. In the seventies the government vowed to fight poverty, and to this end it created the *Instituto Mixto de Ayuda Social* (IMAS = Institute of Combined Social Assistance), and the Family Allocations System. Also in the decade of the seventies the *Corporación Costarricense de Desarrollo* (CODESA = Costa Rican Development Corporation) was founded. This agency grouped together a number of enterprises engaged in producing a variety of products, such as cement and sugar. Most of these enterprises, however, due to their inefficiency, left the country with heavy financial losses, and, consequently, they eventually had to be shut down or transferred to private hands.

All of this expansion of State involvement in the economy has been, of course, financed through taxation. Nevertheless, a substantial part of the national deficit public expenditures was largely financed by foreign indebtedness, at least until 1980. Moreover, these high deficits had a very notable effect on inflation.

Growth, social conditions, crises, and structural adjustment

The following points highlight the Costa Rican economy for the years 1950-1980.

a. Growth, stability, and declining poverty

The evolution of the Costa Rican economy from just after the Second World War until the crisis of the eighties showed satisfactory performance, achieving economic growth, economic and political stability, and a substantial reduction in the poverty level, principally through the increased availability of jobs, as mentioned above. The rapid economic growth was accompanied by an even more rapid improvement in the living conditions of Costa Rican families. Notable, for instance, were lower infant mortality rates, higher life expectancy, higher educational levels of the population. These exceptional results in comparison with other Latin American countries, were possible thanks to economic growth, broad access to foreign savings, and effective management of the institutional mechanisms that seek equity.

It is also important to mention that by around 1950 the country had achieved unequivocal progress in the fields of education and health. That is, the initial conditions of modern Costa Rica were extraordinary in comparison with the other Latin American countries. For example, the life expectancy of Costa Ricans at the end of the last century were superior to the average in Latin America, occupying at least fourth or fifth place among those countries in that category. Along with these economic achievements, the country enjoyed exemplary political stability, whose roots go far back in the history of the nation. In Costa Rica there has been a decided preference for peaceful solutions to conflicts through dialogue and public debate. This last characteristic has also had a profound effect on the formulation of economic policy, in that the nations leaders must always have broad political approval before going ahead with new policies. This consensus constitutes an important basis for the political and economic stability, although it has been extremely costly, as the negotiations this system involves have resulted in many concessions that have ended up becoming "rights" to public remunerations for privileged beneficiaries. Hence, those rights, placing a heavy burden on public finances, largely explain the crisis of the eighties, as well as the subsequent problems in bringing about stability and reactivating the economy.

b. Increasing availability of resources and productivity.

From 1950 to 1980 the work force tripled, increasing the size of the local market and the availability of human resources needed for economic growth. Initially, the increased labor force was mainly associated with the expansion of the farm frontier, since at the beginning the fifties the Costa Rican population occupied only 19 percent of the national territory. The increased cultivated area (corresponding to the increased availability of resources) constituted, therefore, another determining factor in the growing national production. This made it possible to employ a high percentage of the work force. By 1973, farmlands represented 73 percent of the national territory. The gradual disappearance of opportunities for agricultural expansion was subsequently compensated by substantially increased physical productivity as a result of technological advancement.

c. An important investment process was associated with increased production.

Between 1966 and 1979, investments rose to an average rate of 10.4 percent per year in real terms; investments came to represent 17 percent of the GNP in the seventies; and in the coffee bonanza year (1976-1977) they had risen to 28 percent.

During this process several changes took place. First, investments in the industrial sector took on greater importance as the country joined the Central American Common Market. Second, investment in the public sector gained in importance as it enabled the country to carry out a series of infrastructure works: highways, electrification, health, drinking water systems, education, making it possible for large segments of the population, now prepared for greater productivity, to benefit from the new markets. Third, toward the end of the period while investment in the State was being promoted, public enterprises (such as CODESA) were favored. But these investments turned out to be highly unprofitable, and were one of the elements that led to the economic crisis of the eighties.

d. The internal effort to finance the process of generating material assets was very limited.

The net national savings as a proportion of the available national revenue was actually reduced from nine percent in the fifties and the early sixties to six percent toward the end of the seventies and the beginning of the sixties. During the first phase, foreign debt was tied primarily to private foreign investments in the agricultural and industrial sectors. Then, the public sector began to accumulate debts with public international agencies. Subsequently, at the end of the seventies debts were financed mainly through private banks.

Likewise, there were several phases in the use of external resources. First, private foreign investment was oriented toward highly profitable projects. Second, debts were incurred to soften consumption fluctuations in the face of transient external disturbances (drops in foreign exchange terms and natural disasters). In the third phase, beginning in the seventies, foreign debt was acquired in order to sustain Costa Ricans' purchasing power really beyond the long-term growth capacity of the economy. This last practice began to sow the seeds from which sprang the serious economic crisis of the eighties –a typical case of a policy which when assessed on the short-term presents apparent broad benefits, but in the long run turns out to be extremely costly.

Parallel to the extraordinary achievements of the 1950-1980 period,

the elements contributing to the broad-sweeping economic crisis of eighties were already breeding. On the one hand there were what appeared to be clear triumphs: economic growth, stability, and reduced poverty. But on the other hand, the germs that would undermine this bonanza were being cultivated. In fact, even though the economy was swiftly expanding in the seventies, the growth rate was even then steadily slowing down.

Gradually, the Costa Rican economy went on to accumulate a set of elements that would slow economic growth to almost a standstill. Those elements had to do with changes in the availability of production resources, with growing distortions in prices that reflected the national protectionist policy, and the growing relative importance of the public sector with as opposed to the private, and with new forms of State intervention that tended to foster the squandering of resources, as they were often destined to unproductive activities, but which did generate "profit" for select groups as a result of their involvement in the political arena.

At first, as mentioned earlier, import substitution in the context of the Central American Common Market did accelerate economic growth, as new opportunities were created, both for intra-regional trade and national market production. Hence, industrial production initially rose rapidly as imports were replaced by local production of consumption goods. Over time, however, these "easy" possibilities for substitution of imports were gradually reduced since the corresponding market was small.

The policy instruments used to encourage the substitution of imports (high tariffs coupled with a great dispersion) caused economic resources to be destined more for the Central American Common Market and less for exports to the rest of the world. For that reason, the sector involved in world export gradually lost its momentum. At the same time, some agricultural sectors sought and got governmental protection from foreign competition. This process ended up in a labyrinthine system of protection, subsidies, and extremely complex transfers in which no one knew with certainty who the real beneficiaries are. Invaluable economic resources were allocated to manage this system and, therefore, detoured from more profitable alternative uses.

In the early seventies Costa Rica experienced significant external deviations from the norm. Some of the most notable were the two international oil crises, the coffee bonanza, the political and economic unrest in Central America, the worldwide recession, and the rising interest rates at the onset of the eighties. These aberrations brought on far-reaching macro-economic adjustments that unfortunately tended to accelerate the economic crisis.

The coffee bonanza, occurring from 1976 to 1977 was perceived by most Costa Ricans, and especially by government authorities, as a permanent blessing, rather than the passing phenomenon that it was. People and government acted as though spending could continue increasing forever. Then, when exchange terms, beginning in 1978, fell to below what they were before the bonanza, government authorities attempted to postpone urgent adjustments, preferring instead a policy of massive foreign indebtedness and ever-expanding fiscal spending. But imbalance in the economy was so deep-rooted that finally in 1980, the symptoms of the crisis began to be felt in the money exchange market, and in the impossibility of complying with the obligations of awesome foreign debt. No longer having access to external resources and with little political support to carry out the necessary adjustments, the presidential administration of Rodrigo Carazo was overwhelmed by the crisis. The way the foreign exchange market was handled led to chaos. Devaluation and inflation rose to unprecedented levels in the history of the nation. Production fell, as did real salaries, as unemployment climbed. The Costa Rican economy was plunged into an wild whirlpool of impoverishment.

As an example of the uncontrollable exchange rate, which had remained throughout the seventies at 6.65 colons (₡) per US dollar, had climbed to ₡47.78 per dollar by January of 1985, to ₡54.85 by April of 1986, and to ₡86.76 April of 1990.

The momentum and magnitude of the crisis were influenced by external phenomena, as well as the macro-economic measures applied, but the causes of the crisis had been sown long before. Thus, the task of rescuing the economy in the post-crisis period has not been an easy one. If the crisis had simply been the result of "chance" events, just going back to doing things as they were done in the past, the problem would have been solved. But it wasn't that simple: the challenge the Costa Ricans face lies precisely in making those fundamental changes necessary restore a healthy economy to the nation.

During the 1983-1989 period, undoubtedly the Costa Rican economy, in relative terms, recovered some of its lost stability. The fiscal and foreign deficit were substantially brought down from the levels of 1980 and 1981.

Further, inflation and devaluation began to decline. Stability, however, did not reach anything like that of the fifties and sixties. Moreover, the average internal inflation for the 1983-1989 period was above the international level.

In addition to seeking stability, the national economic policy has attempted to reactivate the economy through what has been termed a "structural adjustment policy". The most important characteristics of this policy are outlined below.

a. The structural adjustment policy has sought greater participation of the national economy in the international market.

The government has sought to stimulate increased exports as a key element it achieving economic growth.

b. The structural adjustment policy has been a mixture of government and market intervention.

In some ways this policy has tried to eliminate distortions so that the economy can function in a freer market, for example, through the tariff and financial act. In other ways, the State continues to intervene, for instance, by subsidizing non-traditional exports.

c. The structural adjustment policy has been developed independently from the stabilization policy.

The immediate policy, before the crisis, was aimed at economic stability; structural adjustment measures came later. In a way, government authorities of the 1982-1990 period viewed both policies as independent from one another, or even contradictory, and hence, harmonizing them was a difficult task.

d. The structural adjustment policy has been implemented gradually.

Shock treatment has definitely not been applied. As a rule, measures have been announced beforehand and their execution has been gradual. Such has been the case with the tariff and financing reforms.

e. The international financial agencies have influenced the structural adjustment policy.

Two structural adjustment programs were implemented with the World Bank, and structural adjustment measures were established in conjunction with agreements between the Costa Rican Government and the Agency for International Development (AID).

The principal change observed in the Costa Rican economy after the 1981-1982 crisis was the appearance of a new non-traditional export sector that targets markets other than those of Central America.

PLANT PRODUCTIONS

Before the introduction of coffee to Costa Rica, the land was used mostly for livestock grazing, and food crops grown by small farmers, known as *chacra* crops.

By the middle of the Eighteen Century farmers cultivated such basic crops as corn, wheat, plantain bananas, sugarcane,

National Stock Echange, San José.

tobacco, and tree fruits; but only tobacco and sugarcane were grown commercially, under government controlled systems in which colonial authorities and then the National Government regulated production and sales.

In 1820, with the gold mining in the Aguacate Mountains, the first source of capital accumulation began. This capital was invested shortly after the development of the coffee growing industry, introduced in the Americas by the French, and then carried on by the British. Although no one knows exactly when this activity was initiated in Costa Rica, it is important to point out that it started to pay economy dividends in 1820 when the first exports were sold in Panama.

Coffee, the first export crop

Coffee continues to be an major contributor to Costa Rica's economy, perhaps the most important.

The first coffee beans were brought to the country from Havana, Cuba and planted in Cartago. Coffee plantations were developed for the most part around the main population centers of the Central Tectonic Depression.

Up until several decades ago in that region grew the coffee trees that supplied seed to the rest of the country and even to all of Central America. The coffee plantations in Nicaragua and Guatemala were established by Costa Ricans. The propagation of this precious bush came about gradually thanks to the efforts of a few people who foresaw the vital role this crop would play and the great advantages it would bring to the country.

Regarding the cultivation of coffee, it is pre-planted nurseries, and when the plants grown for a year, they are taken to the plantation and placed in long rows two meters apart. After four years, when the bushes grow to a height of two meters, they begin to produce to their full capacity.

In April, with the first rains, the small white coffee blossoms cover the bushes,

and their jasmine-like fragrance permeates the air. In November shiny red berries start showing up against the dark green leaves.

Coffee growing requires continuous care throughout the year. The amazingly fertile soil cause weeds to grow so rapidly and abundantly that as soon as weeding is finished, it must be begun again. As soon as the berries are picked, each bush is examined and weak branches are pruned or cut off in preparation for the next harvest.

Coffee opened up a new possibilities in business and prosperity for most beginning small-scale farmers, who were the primary beneficiaries of the new economy. This situation continued throughout much of the Nineteenth Century, but gradually, in addition to the small-scale growers, medium-sized plantations began to develop. In this business there are few year-round salaried workers, but there is a great need for seasonal hands (to pick coffee for example).

Several factors, however, worked against the initial development of this

In addition to the essential crops, Costa Rica grows many others both for export and domestic consumption.

crop. The low technological level of the farmers hindered them from obtaining high yields per area unit, but in 1950 the government, in an effort to remedy this situation, began to sponsor programs that involved, for example, replanting with new varieties and fertilizers. Another thing that contributed to the improvement of crop yields was the organization of coffee growers into cooperatives.

Until 1935 the land devoted to coffee was concentrated in the Central Tectonic Depression from Turrialba to San Ramón. After 1935 the industry began to spread out to less favorable regions: Coto Brus, El General Valley, San Carlos, Sarapiquí, and Nicoya, and others, rendering a lesser quality product.

In 1861 Costa Rica was exporting 45,000 kilograms of coffee; in 1975 85 million; in 1980 100 million; in 1985 nearly 120 million; and around 150 million for 1990.

The development of this industry wrought extensive changes to the country, which are summarized below:

– New technologies have been created; new manual industries such as basket and cart making; the number of people able to study abroad and trade with other countries increased; other countries, such as France and England became more affluent. Part of landscape the central region of the country was altered; the prices of certain foods rose as they were grown less to make room for coffee; there was greater economic activity as jobs were created; commercial activity was stimulated and this favored greater imports, the formation of private capital, improvement of communication routes; and many commercial enterprises emerged.

Today Costa Rica has the highest coffee yields per area unit in the world.

Bananas

As mentioned earlier, with the construction of the Caribbean Railway to improve coffee exports, emerged bananas as a new export product. With this new crop the Tropical Trading and Transport Company was founded, which in 1899 merged with the Boston Fruit Company, to form the United Fruit Company with which banana growing was stimulated, and which monopolized everything (shipping, plantations, docking, railroads, etc.) and so became one of the most prosperous enterprises in all of the Americas.

Banana plantations were first set up on the Caribbean side of Costa Rica in the zones of Línea Vieja, Siquirres, and south of Limón City to the La Estrella River region. Then, as already stated, in the decade of the thirties of this century, other plantations were established on the Pacific side, and for some years the Atlantic side was all but abandoned. The plantations on the Pacific encompassed mainly the regions near the rivers Pirrís, Paquita, Diquís and the Dulce Gulf. In the eighties the United Fruit Company succeeded in having rescinded its contracts with the Costa Rican Government, and abandoned the intense

Today Costa Rica has the greatest coffee productivity per area unit in the world.

cultivation it had been involved in. This resulted in difficult social and economic problems for the South Pacific Region, and consequently, for the whole country. Today that company maintains a strictly commercial attitude with respect to banana growing, and has, in fact, now engaged in growing African palm used to make cooking oil. Some Costa Ricans purchased land from the company, which they are now using to grow bananas.

The move by the banana companies from the Caribbean to the Pacific side was precipitated by problems experience on the Caribbean due to diseases that were assailing the plantations, such as Panama blight and Sigatoka. Hence, in 1938 a planting program was undertaken in Golfito, Coto Colorado, and Palmar. This led to the arrival and settling in these areas of some 30,000 workers, between the years of 1938 and 1960. By 1965 the banana industry had already left Quepos and Parrita, and then the same occurred in southwest part of the country, where today African palm is grown and cacao is once again being promoted.

Today bananas are grown mostly on the new plantations on the Caribbean where the national government has supported this activity by improving the infrastructure of that zone.

In 1880 the first 360 bunches of bananas were exported, and since that time production has continually climbed: in 1884 425,000 bunches were cut; 900,000 in 1888; in 1967 banana plantations covered some 10,000 hectares and aground nine million bunches per year were being exported to the United States and Great Britain. Today the yearly production of bananas grown for export is approximately 57 million boxes of bananas. Therefore, if current trends are maintained, Costa Rica in a few short years will be the largest banana exporter in the world.

Bananas are cut and gathered during all months of the year, and the plants do not require a great amount of care. Each plant grows to a height of from six to eight meters and produces one

large bunch. From its roots sprout new shoots that go on to form other thick bunches, hence multiplying the production. Once the bunch is cut from the plant, the plant itself is cut down and left to decompose and return to the ground the nutrients it absorbed from it.

The banana industry did not have the same happy consequences as coffee growing did, since the latter was sown on heretofore virgin lands, with the investment of foreign capital (the United States) by large corporations that intervened even as to the organization of farmlands and the cultivation techniques employed; that was not the case with coffee.

Sugarcane

Sugarcane farming is dates back earlier than coffee in Costa Rica. The first plantations were located in the western part of the Central Plateau region and over time kept extending, as coffee did later, toward the areas of Turrialba and Grecia, and finally, during the last few decades to Guanacaste and other

Banana plants grow to a height of six to eight meters and produce one large bunch of fruit. As soon as the bunch is cut the plant is cut down.

zones of the country. Over 70% of Costa Rican sugarcane is grown by small farmers, of whom there are over 14,000 in the country.

Sugarcane farming requires a great deal of manpower especially at the time of year when that manpower is not needed to harvest coffee. Thus, many peasant families work part of the year on the sugarcane plantations and the other part picking coffee, and in this way have a fairly steady income throughout the year. Often sugarcane and coffee are even combined on the same farm, be it big or little, in an effort to make better use of the farmhands. Also, sugarcane farming is closely tied to the industrial sugarcane processing. Sugar mills, in fact, are the most common industrial plants in the country. This industry provides employment and considerable added value to the commodity. Moveover, in agro-industry sugarcane has found firm footing in the national cooperative movement as evidenced by the numerous sugar mills that are affiliated with cooperatives in different parts of the country.

The great magnitude of the national sugar industry, and the major role this activity has come to fulfill in the economy, has necessitated the organization of farmers and industrialists, under the direction of the government into a system that encompasses all production zones, and all export and marketing activities.

In 1940, Law No. 359 created the *Junta de Protección a la Agriculture de la Caña* (Sugarcane Growing Protection Board). Since then, a organizational process was begun in conjunction with farmers, industrialist and government that has culminated in the consolidation of the most comprehensive, productive, distributive agro-industrial system in Costa Rica: the *Liga Agrícola Industrial de la Caña de Azúcar* (Agricultural-Industrial Sugarcane League), founded by an act signed into law in November 1965. This league is a public cooperative agency that groups together sugarcane farmers and processors from all over the country.

Currently, and in the immediate future, sugar exports may have a substantial impact on the national economy, if sugarcane production can be maintained, since presently the country only meets 40% of its allowable export quota with the United States, even though its soils and industrial capacity

A sugarcane plantation. Over 70% of Costa Rican sugarcane is produced by small farmers.

Port terminal at Punta Morales, used for sugar export.

would easily allow for doubling production in a short time. Despite this promising outlook, however, sugarcane production, which had been increasing since 1960, began to level off at the 1972-1973 harvest, and lately production has been sharply declining. Meanwhile, internal consumption has steadily increased. Consequently, the export potential of this commodity has also fallen.

In 1970, Costa Rica exported 50.3% of its sugar production, while it exported only 20% of its 1981-1982 harvest. To make matters worse, in 1981 the country actually had to import sugar to meet internal demand. Should the present trend continue, future imports could rise even higher. The harvest for 1990 was estimated at 230,184.75 metric tons.

But the future of Costa Rica's sugar production is not limited to supplying the national market with white sugar, and exporting bulk sugar. There are many options: for example, the production of syrups is becoming increasingly important in the production of alcohol, animal feed concentrates, yeasts, and other products. The demand for syrups from the *Central Azucarera Tempisque, S.A.*

(CATSA = Tempisque Central Sugar Company), the National Liquor Factory and other animal feed companies could not be met for 1982 due to the insufficient production of processed sugar.

In the case of the National Liquor Factory, and CATSA, the country already has installed a great industrial capacity that could be highly profitable if it were provided with the necessary raw material.

Under-utilization of this installed industrial capacity for processing and exporting sugar and sugar derivatives is perhaps one of the greatest ironies in Costa Rica's economic panorama. Currently sugar mills are operating at 60% of their capacity. Alcohol distilleries are even more under-utilized. Finally, the port terminal at Punta Morales only operates a few days a year since their isn't enough sugar to export. This situation, however, is in the process changing.

Cacao

The cultivation of cacao was originated in Mesoamerica by indigenous peoples. It was also grown on some of the first colonial plantations, especially on the Caribbean between the Pacuare

Cacao plant with its fruit. Today the total land area in the country planted with cacao is over 20,000 hectares, mostly concentrate around Limón and Upala.

plantations. Cultivation of this crop was carried on from the early Eighteen Century to the end of colonial days and continued to expand until the end of that century. Then it began to decline for the following reasons:

- the development and prosperity of the plantations in Isthmus of Rivas;
- the development of the crop in another country (Venezuela);
- the tobacco monopoly began to dominate commercial agriculture in Costa Rica;
- thievery by the Zambo Mosquito Indians.

It is important to bear in mind that cacao was the first commercial product of Costa Rica. The profitable yields of this crop stemmed from the fact that the climate was just right, and the plantations were so close to the coast, that it was relatively easy to market.

This product eventually became an illegal trade commodity between the English and the Indians of Costa Rica. This illicit trade, though, enabled these indigenous peoples to purchase their freedom using the proceeds that received from selling cacao.

and Matina rivers. These plantations were worked by black and Indian slaves with the purpose of selling the cacao outside the Captaincy General of Guatemala. The owners, practically all residents of Cartago, scarcely ever visited their

Cacao beeing dryed.

The cacao grown in Costa Rica is of excellent quality, especially that which is grown in Matina. Earlier in history it was extremely important, but its importance was eventually surpassed by bananas, as they appeared to have more profitable yields. In recent years, however, cacao is on the rise again, and there are already large cacao plantations in Limón Province. In 1963 there were 48,000 hectares planted, and 10,000 kilograms a year were exported, in addition to a large amount sold locally.

Today there are 20,000 hectares of cacao plantations in the whole country, and most of them are in Limón Province, and Upala, Alajuela with an annual harvest of nearly 5,000 tons. Especially, on the Caribbean side, however, diseases (such as Monilia) have wiped out entire plantations. Thus, cultivation of this crop has intensified in other regions (Golfito, Sarapiquí, Llanuras del Tortuguero, Alajuela, and Llanuras de San Carlos), and technology has produced more resistant varieties of the plant.

Corn

Corn thrives all over Costa Rica; robust cornfields are seen even at altitudes of 2,000 meters above sea level. The total area covered by this grain has been estimated at 60,000 hectares rendering an annual yield of nearly 55.000 tons.

One of the staples in the Costa Rican diet, it is eaten in a variety of forms, from corn on the cob, to tortillas, to tamales, and a host of other dishes. The most popular way to eat corn is in tortillas, thin little disks made of *masa* (corn dough), lightly cooked. They take the place of bread for most farmers' families, and many city folks, as well, can not live without this national food item.

Corn was one of the chief harvests the Spanish settlers depended on to subsist in the economy of the New World.

Beans

Beans, along with corn and rice are the main staples of the Costa Rican people; they are served at the tables of the poorest to the most well-to-do. These commodities are produced in all parts of the country.

The total land area dedicated to this crop is estimated at nearly 30,000 hectares. The most popular variety is the black bean but many other kinds are grown on a lesser scale: white, red, brown kidney, and others. None, however, is so nutritious as the black bean.

The bean plant is one of the most demanding with respect to soil conditions, temperature, and moisture, being very susceptible to temperature extremes and heavy rains. Soils must be a mixture of sand and clay, with plenty of nutrients and adequate drainage. In Costa Rica the best zones for growing beans are found at 400 meters elevation, principally in the southern part of the country.

It has always been necessary to import large quantities of this commodity since local production has not been able to keep pace with demand, and to make matters worse there is really no place in the country that is ideally suitable for growing beans. (DGEC, 1981).

Other crops

In addition to special crops in Costa Rica such as coffee, bananas, sugarcane, cacao, corn, rice, and beans, which constitute the principal wealth and food base of people, many other important crops are grown, both for local consumption and export.

In Cartago Province and other cool climate zones excellent potatoes are grown, providing a good living for farmers. In fact, of all annual crops grown in the country, potatoes show the highest yields per unit of area. Cartago Province and Alfaro Ruiz Canton (in Alajuela Province) supply 90% of the country's demand for this tuber.

Rice is grown mainly in the provinces of Puntarenas and Guanacaste, but it also does well in other temperate or hot regions, such as Parrita, Quepos, Palmar Sur, Coto, San Carlos, Sarapiquí, Guápiles, Los Chiles, and Upala. Since the total annual production of around 140,000 tons per year is not enough to meet the national demand, more and more rice must be imported. This occurs because of the rising population, and the low production and technological capacity in the country at this time. The situation was turned around for a while during the sixties, but for the past few years the country again has had to import because of new problems (DGEC, 1981).

Good quality tobacco is produced, especially in Palmares Canton, which specializes in this crop. It was known and used by the indigenous peoples of these lands before the arrival of the Spaniards, who learned from them how to use and cultivate it. Tobacco became an important factor in the economy, since it was exported to Nicaragua and Panama, and induced people to move toward the northwest of the Central Tectonic Depression of San José, where this crop gained in prominence. In 1912 the Republic Tobacco Company was formed. This company initiated controlled, mechanized industrialization of tobacco. Later, the *Tabacalera Costarricense, S.A.* (Costa Rican Tobacco Company) was founded, and it managed to get the

Papaya plantation.

activity regulated and standardized through Law 2072 of November 20, 1956, referred to as the "Regulatory Law on Relations between Tobacco Producers and Industrialists". From that time on tobacco growing, with very few exceptions, has been engaged in through contracts between growers and the cigarette factory.

Tobacco, depending on specific agricultural conditions, is grown in four definite regions of the country: (1) the region between San Ramón and Alajuela (cantons of Atenas, Naranjo, Palmares, and San Ramón cantons), all located in the northwest part of the Central Tectonic Depression; (2) Puriscal, including Puriscal and Mora cantons (the main sun-dried tobacco area); (3) Quepos (Aguirre and Parrita cantons); (4) the Brunca region comprising the cantons of Pérez Zeledón and Buenos Aires, the main region producing Burley and Virginia tobaccoes. Tobacco farmers have an arrangement whereby they receive technical assistance and guaranteed earnings, even if they experience crop losses due to disease or natural phenomena. (DGEC, 1981).

Textile plants such as pita, henequen, and hemp are valuable in making rope and string. Vegetables are grown on the largest scale in the provinces of Cartago and San José, some of which are exported to Panama.

Cassava (*Manihot aipi*) provides high quality starch for local consumption, and some is has even been exported obtaining very good prices in foreign markets. Processing the starch is quite easy and can be done with very little capital investment. Cassava grows well on all kinds of soil, and it can be cooked much as the potatoes are for a tasty side dish.

The most used varieties of this crop are the Mangi and the Valencia. The plant has a growing period of from seven to 18 months from planting to harvest. Yields satisfy national demand, and the land area devoted to this crop has been increasing substantially, due to recently acquired customers in the United States and Europe. The pealed product is shipped frozen in plastic bags. (DGEC, 1981).

Other similar delectable starchy root plants include the *camote* (like a sweet potato), the *ñame*, and the *tiquisque*, preferentially grown in hot tropical climates. The *chayote* (vegetable pear) is a popular vegetable which can be prepared in a number of ways. It is served at practically every Costa Rican table. Other vegetables such as several kinds of squash, tomatoes, eggplant, pimento, and green peppers are also common in the Costa Rica diet. All of these products, too, are fast becoming non-traditional export items.

The spices, black pepper, cinnamon, nutmeg grow very well in this country, but they are produced very little. *Achiote*, from which red food dye is extracted, is used particularly in coloring yellow cheeses and butter. This would be an prime candidate for export if cultivated more actively since in Europe it is sold at good prices due to the excellent properties the Costa Rican variety.

On some farms in Costa Rica edible fruit is grown as a special crop. Fruit can be found growing almost anywhere: in the midst of plantations, gardens, residential yards, and even on fences.

The most common varieties of fruit are oranges, lemons, peaches, pomegranates, cantaloupes, and quince, which were originally brought from Europe but actually grow better here; and native varieties such as anonas, avocados, *zapote* (sapodilla plums), papayas, *manzana rosa* (rose apples), mangos, *granadillas* (similar to pomegranate), *jocotes*, coconuts and other fruit from several kinds of palm tree, others from cactus plants, different types of berries, and a host of other small fruits. Pineapples, mentioned in conjunction with the section on Alajuela Province, are of very good quality there, especially in Grecia and Naranjo cantons, having ideal soil and climate for that crop. That fruit is quite popular in foreign markets because of its exquisite flavor and pleasing appearance. Currently, the PINDECO company is producing them in Buenos Aires Canton, and exporting great quantities.

Guinean and plantain bananas have been grown since colonial days. Costa Ricans use several kinds of Guinean bananas (squared, purple, green) in various ways, both for human consumption and for livestock and poultry feed.

There are also several varieties of plantain bananas. The *curraré* and the *dominico* are the most popular, the *curraré* being the most widely accepted. Plantain bananas are grown mostly by small farmers. Recently they were being shipped to other countries in Central America and the Caribbean, as well as to the United States and Europe.

Sweet basil is also grown on the grown on the east coast. This herb could bring in millions of dollars were it promoted as an export item.

Cinchona, from which quinine is extracted, began to be grown as an emergency crop, during the Second World War.

Coconut nursery.

Recently, the cultivation of certain fruits (cantaloupe and mangos, for instance), ornamental plants, and flowers has been substantially increased to take advantage of favorable export conditions.

Lumber

"Costa Rica has extensive forests, and they are one of the major sources of natural resources in the country. At one time much more extensive areas were covered by lush natural forests, but they have been rapidly disappearing in ways that really provide very little benefit to most of the population. The natural forests of Costa Rica have a rich composition; that is, there are a great number of species per hectare, varying in kind and quantity depending on the life zone in which they are located. Costa Rica has over 1,200 different tree species of which 100 are commercial. Micael Junkov estimated in his analysis made in 1984 that 64% (32,728 kms^2) of the national territory that once was fit for forestry, only 26% (13.397 kms^2) was left, of which only approximately 5,000 kms^2 would be exploited, while the rest (8,397 kms^2) must be preserved for protection of the land and environment. In 1987 only 3,000 kms^2 of productive forest was left, and of those 500 kms^2 were buffer zones, i.e., areas that must be protected for ecological reasons. Also according to Junkov's report, in 1984 only 19.7% of the country was covered by thick forest, and 13.9% with sparsely wooded or open areas. In the Atlantic zone 44.8% of the forest land is virgin or at least practically untouched, in the Southern Pacific zone, 20.8%, 18.6% in the Central Pacific zone, and only 2.5% in the Northern Pacific zone (encompassing one fourth of the country). Originally, 99.8% of Costa Rica was covered with natural forest, but the present rate of deforestation is alarming –from 40,000 to 70,000 hectares per year, according to different sources. Illegal logging continues to be a difficult problem to curb. The first initiative to reverse the process of deforestation was taken in 1969 with the first version of the Forestry Law. The General Forestry Department created through this law has the responsibility of executing the main policies having to do with the management and use of forest resources. The reforestation required in Costa Rica amounts to 1.3 million hectares (26% of the country). Of these reforested lands, 70% could be lumber production plantations and the rest would have to be totally protected (Junkov, 1984). Given the favorable conditions of the country, lumber can be extracted from a plantation in five to eight years. The total reforested area in Costa Rica for 1987 was 12,560 hectares. Most reforestation has been initiated since 1979 when a system of fiscal reforestation incentives went into effect. The Forestry Department deems it necessary to prolong the useful life of the existing timber resources, maintain and augment the resource, and generate new foreign exchange sources as follows: increase the efficiency of utilization of the areas cut; increase the yields of the raw material destined for industry; initiate a rigorous management program for existing forest lands in the country, combined with reforestation in suitable lands presently cleared; and promote the necessary training of human resources to meet the technical demands of this program. The combination of these measures would reduce the volume of logging, increase production and yields, ensure the supply of this much-needed raw material, and would achieve an effective forest industry integration." (B.Gustafsoon and A. Westermark, 1989).

Medicina Plants

In every part of the Costa Rica an abundance of medicinal plants are found: for example, the castor-oil plant, croton, cassia, sarsaparilla, ipecac, ginger, rhubarb, and tamarind. Some, such as wormseed (Mexican tea, *Chenopodium ambrosiosies*), mallow, and rue, are preferred herbs for home remedies in Costa Rica.

Many other medicinal plants, due to there manifest healing properties, have warranted study by pharmaceutical researchers. Among them are: copalchi (from which copal is extracted) for colds, *targúa* (*Croton xalapensis* and *C. gossypiifolius*, from which an oil is extracted used in making dentifrice); *zontol* or "lemon grass" for colds, and many others for which there is great market demand.

Other plant riches

Fine essences can be extracted from numerous plants very common in the country: jasmine, storax, sandalwood, and Tomka beans, for example. Generally speaking, flowers from Costa Rica, such as verbena, heliotrope, Joseph's staff, violets, render much more perfume than similar varieties in Europe, even through they are not given any special care. Over the past few years flower growing, as an export item systematically produced by commercial gardens, has been greatly increased.

Rubber trees abound in Costa Rica's forests. Initial rubber exports totalled around 26,000 kilos a year. There are also found a great number of trees and bushes that produce all sorts of resins, most of them unknown; several species of *quiebra-hacha* ("break-axe"), which yield a gum similar to gum arabic; copal resin is abundant in the northern plains, but it is not exploited.

On the Pacific Coast many Myroxlylum varieties are found, that produce *tolú* and the coveted gum of Peru The *higuerón* (wild fig), the *mastate*, and the sapodilla all render abundant latex.

Vanilla actually grows wild in the hot zones, but it has been exploited very little, despite its many uses in pharmaceutical applications, industry, and foods.

Established in Turrialba with modern buildings and facilities for the purpose of studying all these natural riches is the Inter-American Institute for Experimentation and Research (a department of CATIE, the Tropical Agricultural Research and Training Center).

INDUSTRY

As for industrial development, indigenous arts and crafts can be considered the first products manufactured in this land when grain was used as money. By 1577 the first wheat flour mill was operating; in 1565 with the introduction of the wheel the first sugar mills were set up; and by 1665 sugar, flour, syrups, cured tobacco, twined pita, and other products were being exported.

With the cultivation of coffee, then bananas, all sorts of imports were introduced, and by 1852 there were installed a brewery, several sawmills, a tile factory, and an iron and copper foundry.

Industrial development was of a local nature and, therefore, most of the industrial installations were modest and usually family-owned and operated.

The participation of the industrial sector in the Costa Rican economy, for all practical purposes, goes back to the fifties of this century, when the Economic Commission for Latin America (CEPAL) proposed to the Central American countries a development model involving the substitution of imported goods.

Costa Rica joined the Central American Common Market in 1963, and a policy of credit and tariff exemptions was implemented to offer incentives for industrial development. Also, important infrastructure, such as highways and roads and electrification, were installed for the same purpose.

Foreign capital began to flow due to these conditions, and soon was helping to bring about the development sought. In this way a number of corporative subsidiaries were formed: Firestone, Colgate, Coca-Cola, and others.

As time went on, both small and large industries continued to grow and develop, and today there are industrial zones in La Uruca, Heredia, Curridabat, Calle Blancos, Autopista General Cañas, and others.

Production from industrial manufacturers, mines, and quarries for 1990 rose to 2,647.2 million colons (approximately US$398 million), equivalent to 21.64% of the gross national product. The volume of industrial production for that year can be broken down into the following markets: 81.1% to the internal market, 6.9% to Central America and Panama, and 12.0% to the rest of the world.

The 1990 figures reveal meager industrial growth as compared to previous years, and it is alarming that 41% of all Costa Rican industrial companies showed negative variations. (José A. Bontempo, 1991).

In recent years the country has been making a significant effort to modernize its industries in order to prepared them for export production destined for much broader markets.

Cattle

Toward the middle of the Sixteenth Century the first cattle were introduced to this land; these cattle would be the base of today's cattle industry. The development of cattle ranching here has had many setbacks due to disease, as well as the attempt to raise them in inadequate places and the use of inappropriate techniques.

Until the end of the last century cattle raised here have been of deficient breeds with respect to production, their only virtue being the resistance they developed over the years to enable them to subsist in an adverse environment.

By mid-Eighteenth Century the first specialized breeds of cattle were imported. This elevated cattle raising to a new level of improvement, which with some setbacks, has led to the today's quality

Beef cattle continues to be one of the prime agricultural contributors to the economy of the country.

breeds. Cattle ranching in Costa Rica is carried out in the following ecological zones:

a. Central Plateau (including the slopes of the Cordillera Volcánica Central).

The soils of this region, due to the climate, tend toward lateralization, but their characteristics depend on the material matrix, age, and topographical conditions.

The climate is regular, varying only according to the altitude. Altitudes below 1,300 meters have a even climate with an mean average temperature of above 18°C; at greater altitudes the mean temperature is below 18°C. The average rainfall is quite varied from place to place. The lower lands and mountainsides, which are exposed to trade winds from the northeast receive fairly even rainfall throughout the year with annual average of over 2,000 mm, while the southwestern slopes of the Irazú-Turrialba mountain mass to Cartago have well-defined rainy and dry seasons.

Regarding the growth and adaptation of forage, this region is divided into two subregions: high (+1,700 m) and medium high (-1,700 m). The high subregion has the following types of forage (listed in order of priority): kikuyo (*Pannisetum clandestinum*), clover (*Trefollum sp*), rue grass (*Lolium perenne*). In the medium high region there is kikuyo, star grass, natural grasses (*Calinguero, Pitilla, Setilla, Jenjibrillo*), court grasses (giant and imperial), and pangola (*Digataria documbens*).

In the Central Plateau, for the most part, dairy cattle are raised, with some European breeds of beef cattle.

b. Dry Pacific (Guanacaste and northern Puntarenas).

The eastern zone of this region (Cañas, Bagaces, and Liberia) has volcanic soils, with slightly below medium fertility. The soils of the western region (Nicoya), with irregular topography, have low fertility.

The soils of the Tempisque Valley are of alluvial origin and have varied

216

characteristics of texture and drainage. Annual rainfall varies between 1,000 and 2,000 mm, most of which is spread throughout the seven months of the rainy season, with sporadic rains during the dry season. The areas comprised between the town of Cañas going southeast and northern Puntarenas Province, receives average annual rainfalls of between 2,000 and 4,000 mm.

The pasture grasses in this region are jaragua (*Hyparrhenia rufa*), Pará, (*Brachiaria mutica*), Guna (*Panicum maximum*), Pangola (*Digitaria decumbens*), and several natural grasses, such as jenjebrillo, deer tail, flat grass, and aceitillo.

In this region approximately 70% of the nation's cattle is raised. Most of these cattle are zebu varieties (Brahma, Indobrail, and Guir), but there are some herds of Charolais, Saint Gertrude, and Hereford.

c. Southern Pacific (cantons of Buenos Aires, Osa Aguirre, Golfito, and Pérez Zeledón).

This region has three basic types of soil: alluvial with high fertility, located on the coastal strip and the alluvions of the Térraba River and in the Coto Valley; highly fertile volcanic soils situated in the Coto Brus Valley in San Vito de Java; and multi-soils (coarse sand with reddish clay) of low fertility of the El General Valley.

The main grazing grasses include Guinea (*Panicum maximum*), onion grass (*Panicum sp*), Pará (*Branciaria mutica*), star grass (*Cynodon nlimfuensis*), *Brachiaria ruziziensis*, gramolota (*Axonopus Cynodon nlemfuensis*), jaragua, German (*Echonichloa sp*), natural (*Axonopus compresus*), gramalote (*Paspalum sp*).

In this relatively new zone beef cattle production is constantly increasing, the most popular breeds beeiny zebu varieties and Charolais.

d. Atlantic region (Limón, San Carlos, and Sarapiquí).

This region presents two types of soil: volcanic, found on the foothills of the Cordillera Volcánica Central and the alluvial plains. The first has highly fertile soils comprised of volcanic ash, and soils with a high clay content and medium to low fertility. Alluvial soils are found on part of the plains of San Carlos and Tortuguero; they are fertile and suitable for cultivation when drained. On the foothills of Talamanca (southeast of Limón) are found multi-soils of sedimentary origin, of low fertility and rough topography and are suitable for extensive grazing.

The climatic conditions in this region correspond to wet and very wet tropical zones, with average annual rainfalls between 2,000 and 4,000 mm for the regions of Siquirres and San Carlos, and from 4,000 and 6,000 mm east and southeast of the Sarapiquí region. Rainfall occurs almost daily throughout the year. The mean temperature exceeds 24°C.

The most important grasses are: star grass (*Cynodon nlemfuensis sp*), natural (*Axonopus compresus*), Pará (*Branciaria mutica*), San Juan (*Setaria sphancelata*), Guinea (*Panicum maximum*), Guinea (*Panicum maximum*), German (*Echonichloa sp*), *Brachiaria ruziziensis*, gogante (*Pennisetum purpureum*), and imperial (*Axonopus scoparius*).

This is another relatively new cattle region, producing beef cattle of zebu and charolais breeds in Limón; and in San Carlos and Sarapiquí, dairy cattle of the Holstein, Guernsey, Jersey, and Brown Swiss breeds, and crossbreeds of these with native cattle (Ministry of Agriculture).

The beef cattle industry is one of the prime agricultural contributors to the nation's economy. In the four-year period ended in 1989 the foreign exchange generated by beef exports exceeded US$55 million, although in proportion to total agricultural exports, it has decreased. The cattle population was estimated at 2.2 million according to the cattle census of 1988. That census also reported that 64% of those were beef cattle, 22% dual-purpose, and 14% specialized dairy cattle. The population of dual-purpose cattle over the past few years has been growing at an accelerated rate: from 15% in 1982 to 22% in 1989. ·

Coffee Processing Plants

Coffee processing requires a series of facilities and machinery for the phases the coffee bean must go through before it is ready for local consumption or export. There are 200 of these processing plants in Costa Rica, from very small, simple operations to complex ones involving hydraulic or steam operated machinery that output many tons of coffee each day.

The preparation of coffee as done in most of the coffee processing plants in Costa Rica involves the following steps: (1) The picked berries are machine-scrubbed and -washed with plenty of water in masonry tanks. The purpose of this first operation is to remove all of the fruity outer layer and dissolve the remaining gummy substance that clings to the coffee beans. (2) Having removed all the pulp (which is used as fertilizer on the same coffee plantations), the washed beans are sun-dried on spacious concrete patios. Some processing plants use heated machine driers for this purpose. (3) Now the beans are still covered with a leathery skin which

Costa Rican coffee is recognized as one of the fines available on world markets.

must be removed by other special machines. (4) Still, there remains a thin film that must be removed in two cylinders with rough linings that spin in opposite directions. (5) Next, the beans are sorted according to size, separating out the broken or odd-shaped ones. In this way, first, second, and third class coffee beans result. Sorting is done by hand, usually by women and children, or, in some cases it is done by machine.

The first-class beans are often separated out right after drying to be exported with skin and all where client-companies finish the processing, thus providing better yields. Coffee shipped in this way is called "coffee in parchment".

Costa Rica is famous for producing one of the finest coffees on the world market. Moreover, the yield per hectare in this country is one of the highest in the world.

Sugar mills

In Costa Rica there are over 100 sugar mills using some of the most modern machinery and methods available in the industry. But, throughout the country there are many simpler, completely national sugar processing operations commonly called *trapiches* (sugarhouses). Some of these are run by electricity or moving water, but most are powered by oxen. After squeezing out the sap, most of the water is boiled out in huge vats, and then the boiling liquid is poured into wooden molds where it cools and hardens into the form in which it is sold.

Lumber Industry

"The commercial exploitation of lumber in Costa Rica was begun at the onset of this century, but it was after the fifties that it developed into a major industry. In 1986 it involved 161 sawmills, providing a total of 2,214 direct jobs. Dominating the industry are small- and medium-sized operations. The total lumber production in the country during that same year was 356,211 cubic meters. It has been estimated that over past few

years 65% of the lumber cut has been employed in supplying forestry industries and energy production while the remaining 35% is abandoned on site. The quality of the equipment used by the sawmills is adequate, but it is poorly maintained and operated inefficiently. Paneling and veneer is produced by two plywood plants, one specializing in plywood and the other in paneling. These two plants annually consume 79,856 cubic meters. There are also two match and one toothpick factories. Regarding paper pulp industries, there is only one paper mill in the country." (B. Gustafsson and A. Westermark, 1989)

Mining

Of the many mines that have existed in Costa Rica, today only a few gold veins are being worked. In the past gold exports brought in a half a million to six million colons, when its sale was free of controls and taxation.

In 1944 Costa Rica was exporting 917 kilograms of gold bars, mined primarily from the Sierra Minera in Tilarán and the Hills of Aguacate, where today a foreign-owned company is installed and mining this precious metal. Gold is also mined by foreign enterprises on the Osa Peninsula, and the beaches of Carate and Madrigal and surrounding areas, where years ago small-time miners used to dig for it.

Other important minerals, which, if exploited, could bring great benefits to the country include limestone, sandstone, diatomite, travertine, and kaolin. Other minerals known to exist are copper, silver, manganese, chromite, zinc sulphide, and lead. Some are rudimentarily exploited: for example, diatomites, coal, and clay. The problem with some of these is that no one knows just how much of these minerals exist and how beneficial it would be to extract them, except for bauxite, magnetite sand, sulfur, limestone, and diatomites. Salt is extracted through the evaporation of sea water in Guanacaste, and there is now an industrial plant in Colorado de Abangares that produces iodized salt. (DBEC, 1981).

Other industries

In Costa Rica different companies specialize in the manufacture of woven goods, soaps, candles, ceramics, cigarettes, footwear, beer, soft drinks, cookies and crackers, and canned goods.

There are also thriving factories that make ice, glass, mosaics, and bricks; and others that produce cooking oil, and in Puntarenas, a tuna enterprise. The pharmaceutical industry is worthy of acclaim. Laboratories here produce fine medicines, cosmetics, veterinarian products, injections, and prescription drugs, as good as any imported.

Other industries work in machined metals, graphic arts, and the manufacture of appliances, such as stoves and refrigerators. Near the international airport one business specializes in the repair and maintenance of airplanes, including the large, modern jet planes. Other industries produce plastic articles, paints, aluminum ware, furniture, construction materials, and many other items.

The graphics arts industry has developed to such an extent that it not

Papaya processing plant preparing the fruit for export.

Ceramics craftsman.

prices to consumers are prohibitive. Currently the National Liquor Factory is administered by an autonomous institution of the State. Due to the magnitude of its expansion, part of its operations had to be moved to Grecia, between Alajuela and San José, where it now carries on most of its activities.

ROADS AND HIGHWAYS

All of the population centers in the country, without exception, are inter-connected by roads that the municipalities endeavor to maintain in good condition for the smooth flow of traffic. Some roads, however, become impassible in the rainy season, to the point that many farmers cannot get their goods to market.

The main highway system in Costa Rica was at first comprised of the national highway, Cartago-San José-Alajuela-Atenas-San Mateo-Puntarenas. There are also other roads, mostly dirt or gravel, such as the Barranca-Nicaraguan border, San José-Tarrazú-Santa María, Alajuela-Grecia-Naranjo-Zarcero, San Ramón-Esparza-San Ramón-Palmares-Atenas-Río Grande, San José-Puriscal, San José-Santo Domingo of Heredia-Sarapiquí, San José-Coronado-Carrillo, as well as many other local roads and dirt trails.

With the law of 1921, for the first time municipalities were given financial assistance to improve their roads, and in 1924 they were allocated a regular annual budget ("territorial tax").

In 1965 construction was completed on the General Cañas Freeway, which was the first four-lane toll road. Following that one, other freeways were built: Bernardo Soto, Madrigal Alajuela, Grecia, Naranjo, and San Ramón, finished in 1972 with the formulation of the "Highway Plan". Subsequently the "Corporative Plan" has sustained progress on the highways system, and from 1974 to 1984 improvements were made to the following highways: Pacayas-Santa Cruz-Turrialba-Alegría, San Ramón-San Isidro de Peñas Blancas,

only meets national needs but also exports books, and commercial and industrial manuals to other countries.

The National Liquor Factory

The production of alcohol and alcoholic beverages is in the hands of a State monopoly, for which purpose there is a huge building in San José. The distillery facilities there are excellent.

Rum is made from sugarcane, and even fine liquors such as whisky and cognac, wines and brandies of various kinds of fruit (specialties of the factory) are widely accepted at home and abroad. Alcohol 80% and other forms for diverse uses is prepared, and it is one of the factory's best products.

Recently State monopoly restrictions were relaxed to make way for private initiatives in the production and possible export of alcoholic products, in an effort to revitalize the production of sugarcane in areas like Grecia Canton.

Liquors can be imported, but because of the heavy import duties,

Cañas-Upala, and Vara Blanca-San Miguel-Poasito. Improvements have also been made on the highways, Cartago-Irazú Volcano, Golfito Inter-American, Nicoya-Carmona, Pavones-Siquirres, and many others.

With the financial assistance of the Central American Bank of Economic Integration (1970), vital roads were completed: between the four-lane toll road linking Curridabat and Tres Ríos-Taras, known as the Florencia del Castillo Freeway; the Próspero Fernández Highway (part of the Caldera Highway); to the north, the Los Chiles Highway; in the southern Pacific coastal region, the Southern Pacific Highway (today called the "Conquistadors Highway"), the inter-American highway, El Roble-Caldera, and the Coyolar-Caldera stretch; toward the Caribbean side the José Joaquín Trejos Fernández (Siquirres-Limón), and the San José-Guápiles-Siquirres stretch, including the Chirripó-Puerto Viejo Highway, finished in 1980.

Since 1960 proposals have been extended for a bypass road around San José. But this work has never been undertaken, and instead construction was begun on a four-lane, east-west highway south of San José, a work now almost entirely completed through a roads improvement program. From 1979 to 1984 that program also was responsible for building a four-lane radial highway connecting San José (Turnón) with the Tibás-Guápiles-Siquirres Highway, finished in 1983.

Today there is a 10% surtax on the territorial tax for the maintenance of all roads and highways in the country: 25,000 kilometers of local roads, nearly 2,000 national highways, nearly 1,200 kilometers of regional highways, for a total of 30,000 kilometers of roads in Costa Rica.

The National Railroad System

Currently two railroad services are operating in the Costa Rica: the National Railway to the Atlantic and the Electric Railway to the Pacific, which are owned and operated by a State enterprise called Railways of Costa Rica.

The National Railway to the Atlantic a short time ago cut back on its services due to serious economic problems stemming from operating at a loss, and the Railway to the Pacific, it would seem, if it does not undergo certain changes, is about to suffer the same fate.

Limón-Cahuita and Puerto Viejo Highway.

It has been determined that the costs of transportation by this means, in general, are more expensive than highway transportation, especially in the case of passengers. Some types of cargo, however, could be transported efficiently by railway. Railway transportation could become reasonably profitable if their energetic advantages were put to the best uses, and if they were employed where they can be the most efficient, such as in the transportation of bananas and concentrated cargo to and from the ports. But, this would require changes in the services so as to ensure efficient operation.

The Electric Railway to the Pacific offers two services a day from San José, leaving at 6 a.m. and 3 p.m., and passing through the towns of San Antonio de Belén, Ciruelas, Orotina, Caldera, and others and travelling as far as Puntarenas. The total length of the railway is 144 kilometers.

The Caribbean railway encompasses stretches from San José to Siquirres (not presently operating) and from Siquirres to Limón, and another going from Río Frío to Siquirres, and passing through Guápiles, covering a total distance of 471.6 kilometers. Both routes offer both passenger and cargo service.

Also, until 1982, there was a privately-owned Southern Railway, but it is presently out of service. Another railway out of service is the Valle de La Estrella branch line on the Caribbean side.

Worthy of mention also is the 600 kilometers of railway on the Pacific coast, connecting Parrita, Quepos, Puerto Cortés, and Golfito, that went out of service when the banana company shut down its operations. The possibility has often been mentioned of installing a new railway referred to as "the dry canal". It would be a modern high-speed railroad going from Moín to Puerto de Caldera, avoiding passage through the mountains surrounding the Central Plateau.

River and Maritime Routes

Coastal traffic has not grown as rapidly as ocean traffic; coastal transportation, as well as ocean transportation, is concentrated around the ports of Limón, Puntarenas (Caldera), and Quepos. In the northern part of the country there is light river traffic, for zones that lack other means of transportation: Upala, Los Chiles, Puerto Viejo de Sarapiquí, and the San Carlos Dock.

One special case is constituted by the towns along the northern coast of Limón, since the Tortuguero Canals were opened. Traffic along the Pacific Coast only involves some cattle transport from Golfito to Puntarenas. The river and sea routes are currently being used for recreation and tourism. Such is the case with Moín, Golfito, Tortuguero, Lagunas del Arenal, and Cachí.

On the Gulf of Nicoya there is a good coastal service touching all the towns of the province of Puntarenas and Guanacaste, and extends into the rivers Tempisque, Matina, and Diquis. This area of the Gulf of Nicoya uses the two largest ferries in the country to transport passengers, vehicles, and goods during the whole year. One of them goes from Paquera to Nicoya and the other provides service along the Tempisque River. The second, consisting of a string of flatboats pulled by a tow boat, transports passengers and cargo between Puerto Moreno and Puerto Níspero, situated on opposite banks at the mouth of the river. Another boat service on the Gulf of Nicoya transports cargo from Puntarenas to Paquera.

Farther down south on the Pacific side (around the Dulce Gulf, and from Puerto Jiménez to Playa Blanca, Cañaza, and Golfito) there are passenger boat services available. Along the Río Grande de Térraba at Paso Real there is barge that transports cargo, passengers, and vehicles, and another one at Ciudad Cortés along the same river. Two other boats offer similar service on the Sierpe River. On the Caribbean side this service is provided from the towns of Sixaola, Bribrí, Sarapiquí, Bambú, Shiroles, and Amubri.

Postal and Telecommunications Services

The postal service is organized in an effective manner. The Central Post Office in San José is linked to offices of all Costa Rican towns through a system of many kilometers making use of buses, railways, trucks, and airplanes to get mail swiftly to its destination. Air mail service is provided daily through the same planes that carry passengers.

Before 1963 the telephone service was quite deficient. But in that year the Costa Rican Electrical Institute (ICE) took on the responsibility of improving the service. In 1966, when it merged with the Regional Technical Telecommunications Commission (COMTELCA), Costa Rica began to acquire inter-linked telephone exchange stations and high-frequency, semi-automatic communications. In 1964 the ICE bought 50% of the foreign-owned Radiográfica's shares, and in 1975 it purchased the remainder of the company to form the Radiográfica Costarricense. With this acquisition Costa Rica then had a capacity for 90,000 telephone lines.

As of 1963 there were 10,000 telephone customers; today there are over 200,000. Moreover the needs of the most rural zones, where there is no mail service, are being met.

Today the ICE has a microwave system of over 600 circuits, 960 channels of over 1,300 kilometers, with a reserve for television transmission –the "Central American Microwave Network"– extending northward to Mexico, and southward to Panama, with over 33 stations. Hence, in 1963 the telephone system was greatly improved, when the Direct Dialing International System (MIDA) was instituted, connecting Costa Rica to the United States, Mexico, Spain and other European countries, as well as

Post Office Building, San José City

the rest of Central America. Its capacity today has been expanded to over 1,000 circuits and extends to some South American countries.

Telex services have also been much improved. Now there is installed highly advanced equipment using nineplex division with electronic tele-printers, far superior to those used in 1964, that had a capacity for only 720 terminals used to handle all international telex communications.

To handle all the international traffic, today the main Costa Rican telephone exchange station is connected with the ITT, RCA, WUR, and the TRT in the United States, as well as through direct circuits with the rest of Central America, Panama, Mexico, some European administrations, and China.

Over the past few years the use of facsimile services have become popular among ICE's clientele.

MAPS

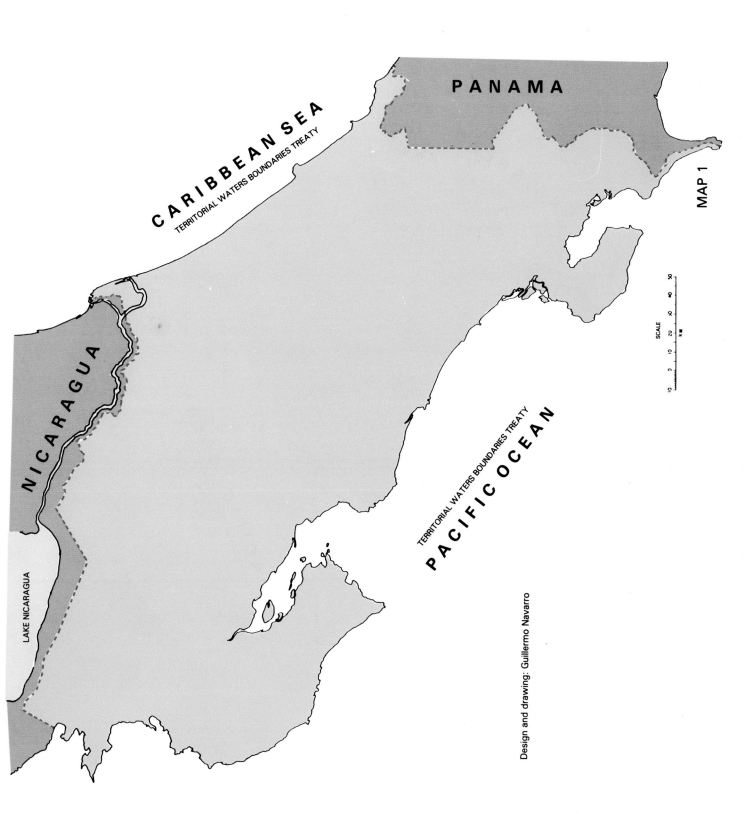

PANAMA

CARIBBEAN SEA

TERRITORIAL WATERS BOUNDARIES TREATY

NICARAGUA

LAKE NICARAGUA

TERRITORIAL WATERS BOUNDARIES TREATY

PACIFIC OCEAN

SCALE

KM

MAP 1

Design and drawing: Guillermo Navarro

227

COAST AND SEA BOUNDARIES OF COSTA RICA

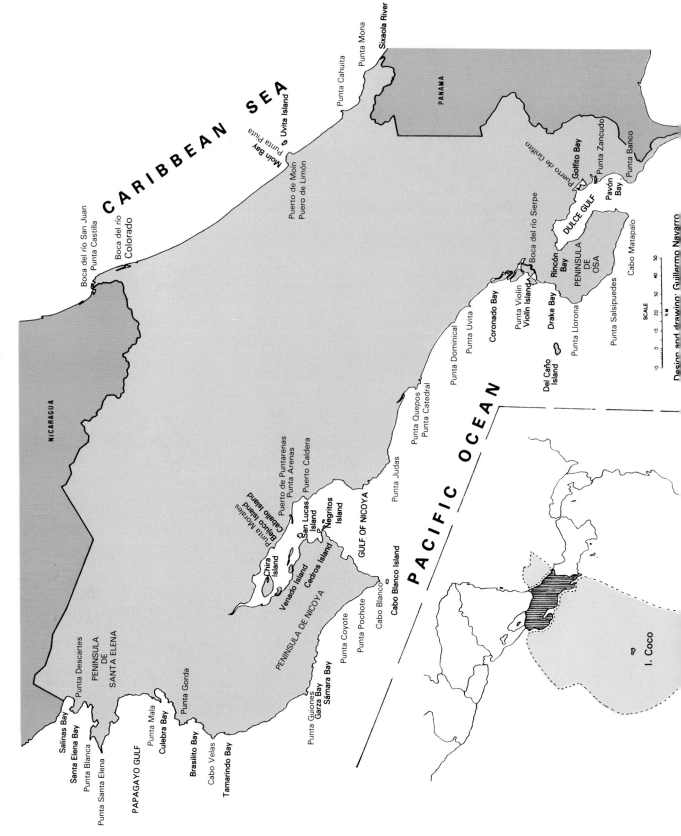

CARIBBEAN SEA

PACIFIC OCEAN

NICARAGUA

PANAMA

Boca del río San Juan
Punta Castilla
Boca del río Colorado

Puerto de Moín
Moín Bay
Punta Piuta
Uvita Island
Puerto de Limón
Punta Cahuita
Punta Mona
Sixaola River

Punta Descartes
PENINSULA DE SANTA ELENA
Punta Blanca
Salinas Bay
Santa Elena Bay
Punta Santa Elena
PAPAGAYO GULF
Punta Mala
Culebra Bay
Punta Gorda
Cabo Velas
Brasilito Bay
Tamarindo Bay

Punta Guiones
Garza Bay
Sámara Bay
Punta Coyote
PENINSULA DE NICOYA
Punta Pochote
Cabo Blanco
Cabo Blanco Island

Punta Morales
Caballo Island
Beluco Island
Puerto de Puntarenas
Punta Arenas
Puerto Caldera
Chira Island
Venado Island
San Lucas Island
Cedros Island
Negritos Island
GULF OF NICOYA
Punta Judas

Punta Quepos
Punta Catedral
Punta Dominical
Punta Uvita
Coronado Bay
Del Caño Island
Punta Violín
Violín Island
Drake Bay
Punta Llorona
Punta Salsipuedes
Boca del río Sierpe
Rincón Bay
PENINSULA DE OSA
Cabo Matapalo

Puerto de Golfito
Golfito Bay
Punta Zancudo
Pavón Bay
Punta Banco
DULCE GULF

I. Coco

SCALE
KM
0 10 20 30 40 50

Design and drawing: Guillermo Navarro

228

CARIBBEAN SEA

PACIFIC OCEAN

MAP 3

Sierra Volcánica Central

El Desagüaño Depression

paso la palma

Fila Matama

Cordillera de Talamanca

Coastal Ridge (Brunqueña)

Península de Osa

Cordillera de Talamanca

Bustamante Ridge

Laguna de Arenal

Sierra Volcánica de Tilarán

Sierra Volcánica de Guanacaste

Viejs del Oeste Mountains

SCALE
km

ISLA DEL COCO

PACIFIC OCEAN

SCALE
km

SOURCE: 1978 Aeronautical Map of Costa Rica
Design and drawing: Guillermo Navarro

VOLCANOES AND PEAKS OF COSTA RICA

Orosi V.
Cerro Cacho Negro V.
Rincón de la Vieja V.
Sta. Maria V.
Cerro Góngora V.
Cañas Dulces P.
Miravalles V.
Montezuma P.
Tenorio V.
Hills of Colorado

CARIBBEAN SEA

Arenal V.
Cerro Chato V.
Tilarán Mountains
Los Perdidos P.
Cerro Platanar V.
Porvenir P.
Volcan Viejo P.
Abangares Mountains
Cedral P.
Congo P.
Poás V.
Miramar P.
Cacho Negro P.
Barva V.
Aguacate Mountains
Turrialba V.
Irazú V.
Tigre P.
Escazú P.
Turrubares P.
Matama P.
Caraigres P.
Vueltas P.
Herradura P.
Dichibeta P.
San Gerónimo P.
La Muerte or Buena Vista P.
Chirripó P.
Nara P.
Durika P.
Utyum P.
Kamuk P.
Pittier P.
Echandi P.
Pando P.

SCALE
87°06' 87°03'
5°33'
KM
Iglesias Peak
PACIFIC OCEAN
5°30'
87°06' 87°03'

Design and drawing: Guillermo Navarro

PACIFIC OCEAN

SCALE
10 0 10 20 30 40 50
KM

MAP 4

OF COSTA RICA

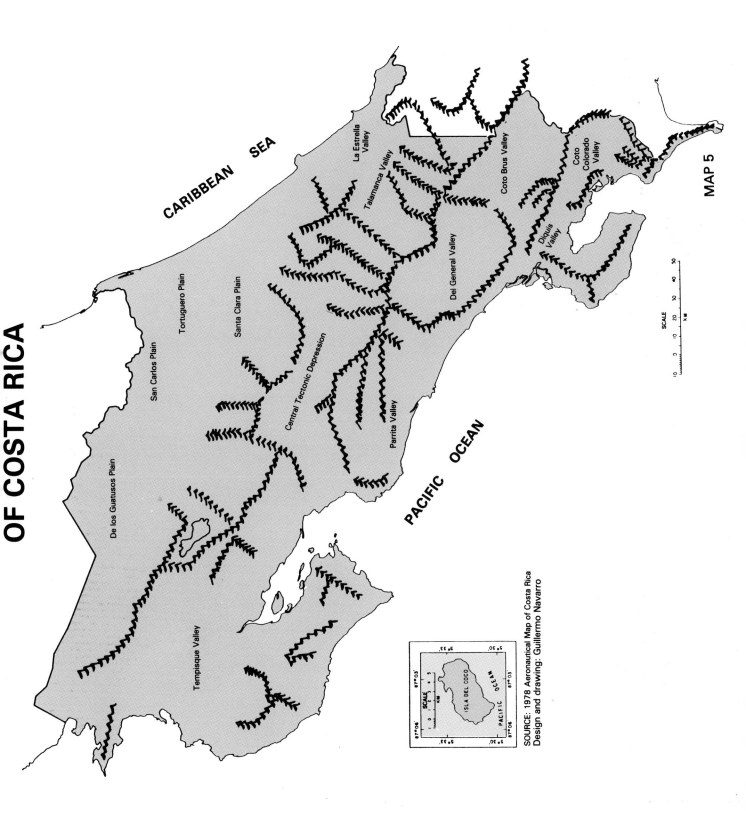

CARIBBEAN SEA

PACIFIC OCEAN

La Estrella Valley

Talamanca Valley

Coto Brus Valley

Coto Colorado Valley

Del General Valley

Diquis Valley

Tortuguero Plain

Santa Clara Plain

San Carlos Plain

Central Tectonic Depression

Parrita Valley

De los Guatusos Plain

Tempisque Valley

MAP 5

SCALE

KM

SCALE

KM

ISLA DEL COCO

PACIFIC OCEAN

SOURCE: 1978 Aeronautical Map of Costa Rica
Design and drawing: Guillermo Navarro

231

RIVERS OF COSTA RICA

Source: Costa Rican Electrical Institute (ICE)

Design and drawing: Guillermo Navarro

MAP 6

FUNCTIONAL REGIONS OF COSTA RICA

CHOROTEGA

HUETAR NORTE

CARIBBEAN SEA

HUETAR ATLANTICA

CENTRAL

BRUNCA

ISLA DEL COCO

PACIFIC OCEAN

Functional regions do not coincide with natural regions, since the former are based on demographic, economic, or territorial criteria.

SOURCE: MIDEPLAN

Design and drawing: Guillermo Navarro

SCALE
KM

MAP 7

SPECIAL ZONES OF COSTA RICA

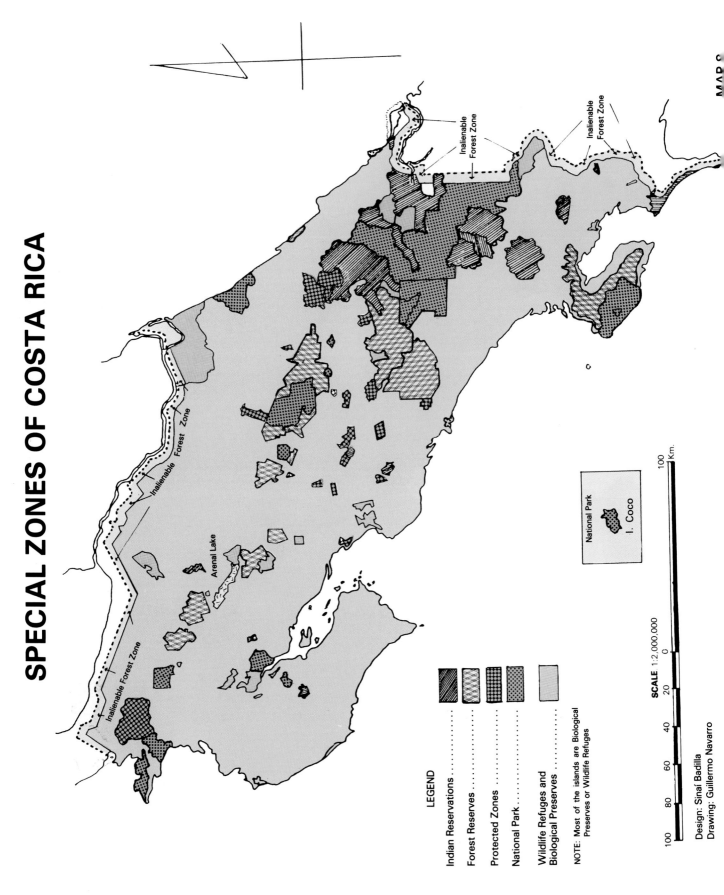

Inalienable Forest Zone

Inalienable Forest Zone

Inalienable Forest Zone

Inalienable Forest Zone

Arenal Lake

MAP 8

LEGEND

Indian Reservations . . . .

Forest Reserves . . . .

Protected Zones . . . .

National Park . . . .

Wildlife Refuges and
Biological Preserves . . . .

NOTE: Most of the islands are Biological
Preserves or Wildlife Refuges

National Park

I. Coco

SCALE 1:2,000,000

0   20   40   60   80   100

100   Km.

Design: Sinaí Badilla
Drawing: Guillermo Navarro

PROVINCES OF COSTA RICA

ALAJUELA

HEREDIA

GUANACASTE

LIMON

CARTAGO

SAN JOSE

PUNTARENAS

Drawing: Guillermo Navarro

MAP 9

235

CANTONS OF SAN JOSE PROVINCE

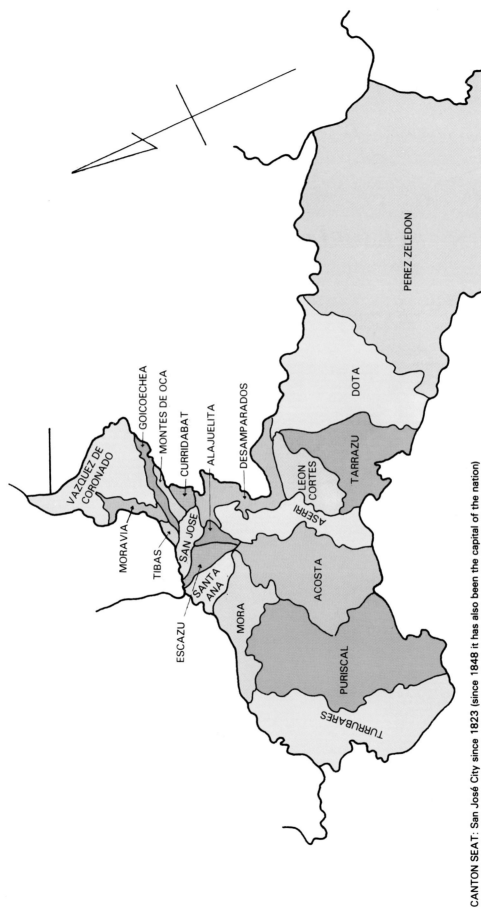

MAP 10

SCALE 1:750,000

DESIGN: Sinaí Badilla

DRAWING: Guillermo Navarro

CANTON SEAT: San José City since 1823 (since 1848 it has also been the capital of the nation)

POPULATION: 890,434 inhabitants, largest province in population.

AREA: 4,959.63 kms²

LARGEST CANTONS: Pérez Zeledón (1,905.51 kms²), Puriscal (553.21 kms²)

ECONOMY: Industry: food production to machine operated factories
Agriculture: coffee, sugarcane, tobacco, beans, fruits, vegetables, ornamental plants, beef, poultry.

236

CANTONS OF ALAJUELA PROVINCE

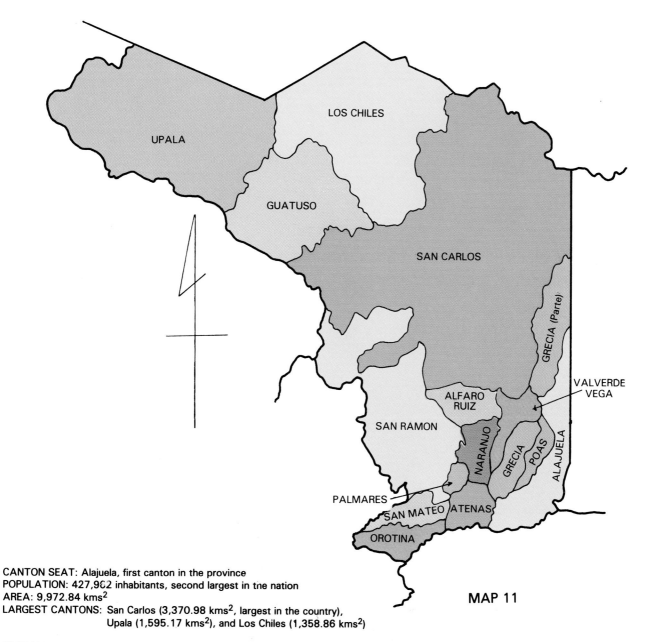

UPALA

LOS CHILES

GUATUSO

SAN CARLOS

GRECIA (Parte)

VALVERDE VEGA

ALFARO RUIZ

SAN RAMON

NARANJO

GRECIA

POAS

ALAJUELA

PALMARES

SAN MATEO ATENAS

OROTINA

MAP 11

CANTON SEAT: Alajuela, first canton in the province
POPULATION: 427,962 inhabitants, second largest in the nation
AREA: 9,972.84 kms^2
LARGEST CANTONS: San Carlos (3,370.98 kms^2, largest in the country),
        Upala (1,595.17 kms^2), and Los Chiles (1,358.86 kms^2)

ECONOMY: Industry: canned foods to machine operated factories.
        Agriculture: coffee, sugarcane, tubers, caña india, cacao, pineapple, corn,
        beans, vegetables, tobacco, beef, and others.

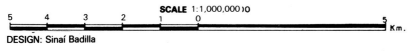

SCALE 1:1,000,000

5   4   3   2   1   0   5
                                         Km.

DESIGN: Sinaí Badilla

DRAWING: Guillermo Navarro

CANTONS OF CARTAGO PROVINCE

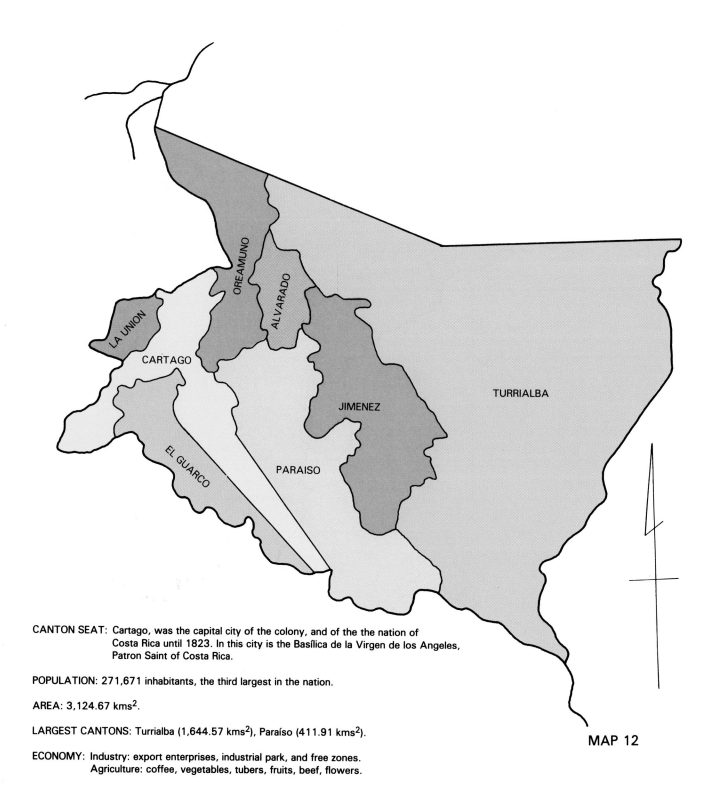

CANTON SEAT: Cartago, was the capital city of the colony, and of the the nation of Costa Rica until 1823. In this city is the Basílica de la Virgen de los Angeles, Patron Saint of Costa Rica.

POPULATION: 271,671 inhabitants, the third largest in the nation.

AREA: 3,124.67 kms^2.

LARGEST CANTONS: Turrialba (1,644.57 kms^2), Paraíso (411.91 kms^2).

ECONOMY: Industry: export enterprises, industrial park, and free zones.
Agriculture: coffee, vegetables, tubers, fruits, beef, flowers.

MAP 12

SCALE 1:500,000

1 0 1 2 3 4 Km.

DESIGN: Sinaí Badilla

DRAWING: Guillermo Navarro

238

CANTONS OF HEREDIA PROVINCE

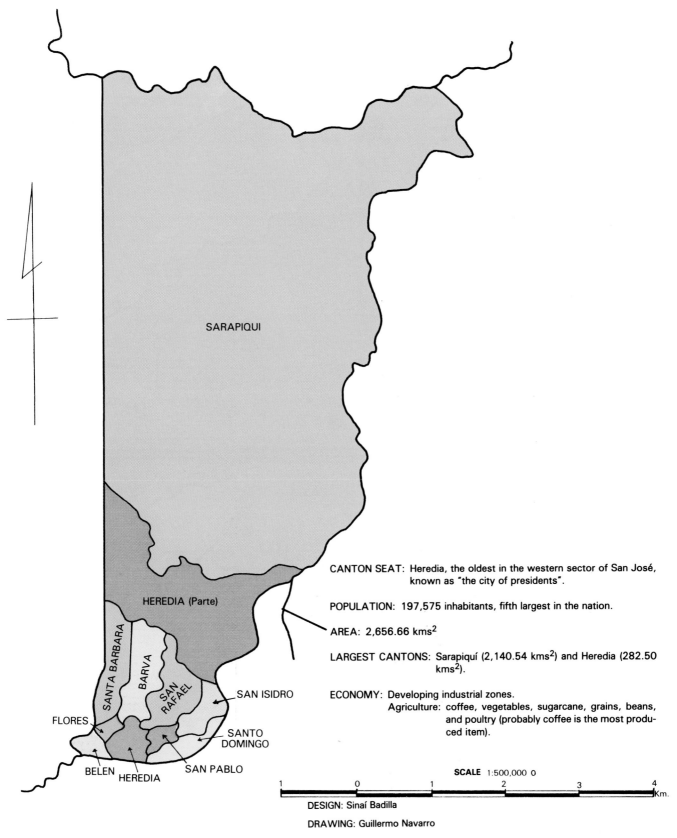

SARAPIQUI

HEREDIA (Parte)

SANTA BARBARA

BARVA

SAN RAFAEL

FLORES

SAN ISIDRO

SANTO DOMINGO

BELEN

HEREDIA

SAN PABLO

CANTON SEAT: Heredia, the oldest in the western sector of San José, known as "the city of presidents".

POPULATION: 197,575 inhabitants, fifth largest in the nation.

AREA: 2,656.66 kms^2

LARGEST CANTONS: Sarapiquí (2,140.54 kms^2) and Heredia (282.50 kms^2).

ECONOMY: Developing industrial zones.
Agriculture: coffee, vegetables, sugarcane, grains, beans, and poultry (probably coffee is the most produced item).

SCALE 1:500,000 0

1   0   1   2   3   4
Km.

DESIGN: Sinaí Badilla

DRAWING: Guillermo Navarro

MAP 13

239

CANTONS OF GUANACASTE PROVINCE

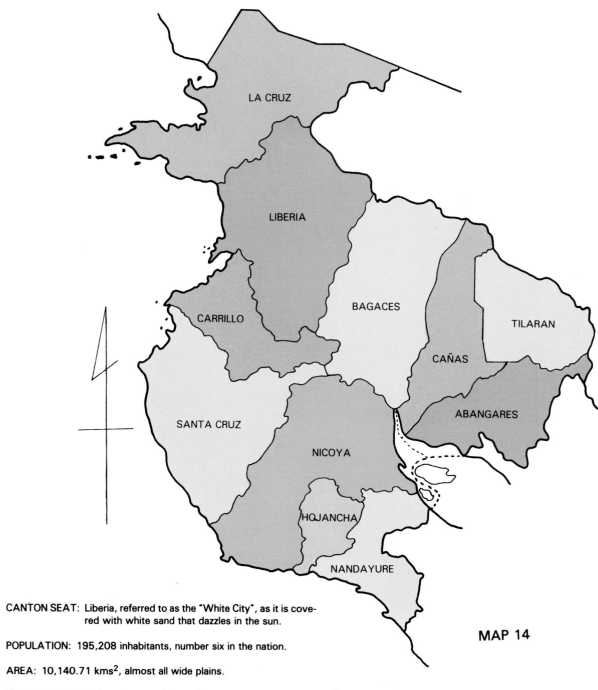

CANTON SEAT: Liberia, referred to as the "White City", as it is covered with white sand that dazzles in the sun.

POPULATION: 195,208 inhabitants, number six in the nation.

AREA: 10,140.71 kms^2, almost all wide plains.

LARGEST CANTONS: Liberia (1,436 kms^2) and La Cruz (1,383.90) kms^2.

ECONOMY: Industry: processing of cotton, rice, and sugarcane
Agriculture: rice, cotton, sugarcane, corn, citrus fruits, sorghum, beans,
vegetables, coffee, other fruits, beef, poultry, and fish.

MAP 14

SCALE 1:1,000,000

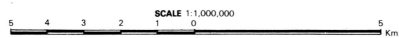

5 4 3 2 1 0   5
                                   Km.

240

DESIGN: Sinaí Badilla

DRAWING: Guillermo Navarro

CANTONS OF PUNTARENAS PROVINCE

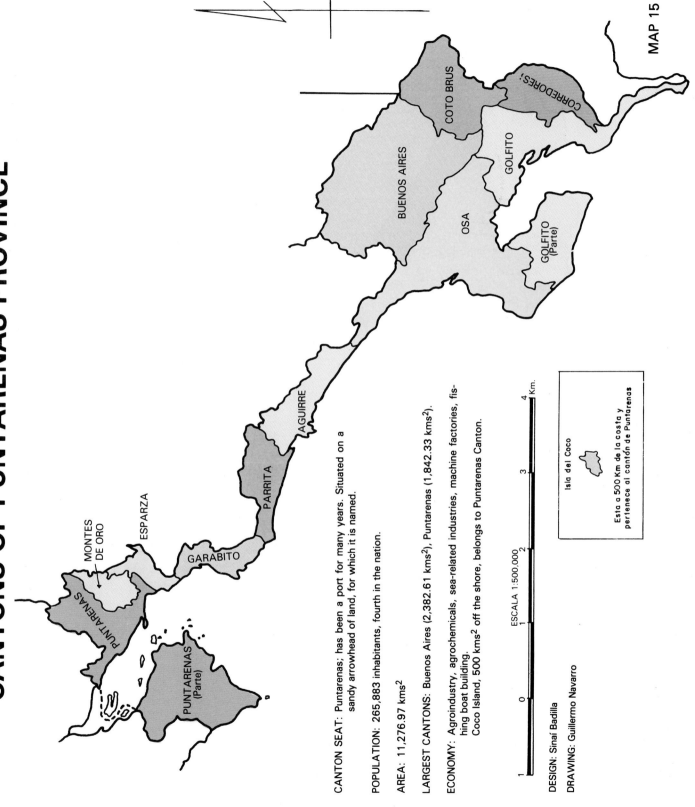

CANTON SEAT: Puntarenas; has been a port for many years. Situated on a sandy arrowhead of land, for which it is named.

POPULATION: 265,883 inhabitants, fourth in the nation.

AREA: 11,276.97 kms²

LARGEST CANTONS: Buenos Aires (2,382.61 kms²), Puntarenas (1,842.33 kms²).

ECONOMY: Agroindustry, agrochemicals, sea-related industries, machine factories, fishing boat building. Coco Island, 500 kms² off the shore, belongs to Puntarenas Canton.

ESCALA 1:500,000

Isla del Coco

Esta a 500 Km de la costa y pertenece al cantón de Puntarenas

DESIGN: Sinaí Badilla

DRAWING: Guillermo Navarro

MAP 15

CANTONS OF LIMON PROVINCE

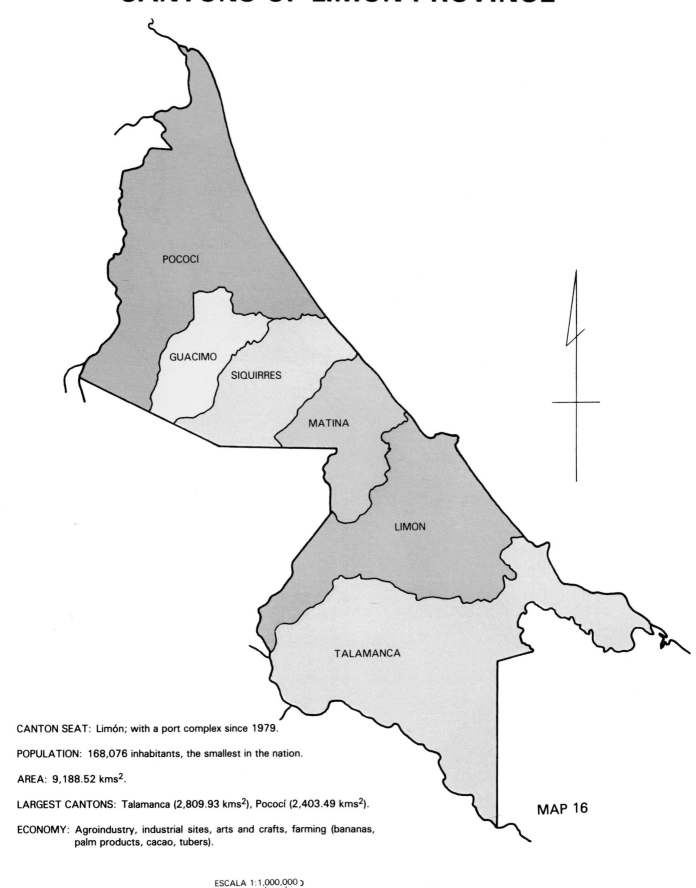

POCOCI

GUACIMO

SIQUIRRES

MATINA

LIMON

TALAMANCA

MAP 16

CANTON SEAT: Limón; with a port complex since 1979.

POPULATION: 168,076 inhabitants, the smallest in the nation.

AREA: 9,188.52 kms^2.

LARGEST CANTONS: Talamanca (2,809.93 kms^2), Pococí (2,403.49 kms^2).

ECONOMY: Agroindustry, industrial sites, arts and crafts, farming (bananas, palm products, cacao, tubers).

ESCALA 1:1,000,000

5 4 3 2 1 0   5
Km.

DESIGN: Sinaí Badilla

DRAWING: Guillermo Navarro

COSTA RICA:
POPULATION PROJECTIONS BY CANTONS
YEARS 1991, 1995, AND 2000

Cantons	1991	1995	2000	Cantons	1991	1995	2000
San José Province				**Heredia Province**			
San José	278 373	281 747	279 751	Heredia	79 543	90 587	104 176
Pérez Zeledón	100 887	109 120	118 675	Sarapiquí	24 265	27 598	31 914
Escazú	43 088	46 728	50 569	Barva	26 952	30 691	35 282
Desamparados	150 573	168 234	188 649	Santo Domingo	32 007	35 319	39 150
Puriscal	24 416	23 879	22 737	Santa Bárbara	24 641	28 667	33 831
Tarrazú	10 659	11 124	11 449	San Rafael	31 464	35 152	39 518
Aserrí	43 142	49 500	57 365	San Isidro	11 941	13 535	15 507
Mora	14 727	15 441	16 054	Belén	16 345	18 184	20 368
Goicoechea	102 647	109 472	115 986	Flores	12 198	13 489	14 984
Santa Ana	25 617	28 078	30 760	San Pablo	18 179	21 936	27 147
Alajuelita	40 399	43 483	46 308				
Coronado	33 541	37 433	41 771				
Acosta	15 646	15 449	14 826	**Guanacaste Province**			
Tibás	85 401	98 228	113 759	Liberia	32 779	34 474	35 902
Moravia	49 779	57 952	68 068	Nicoya	38 415	37 899	36 807
Montes de Oca	45 262	45 774	45 292	Santa Cruz	31 112	30 782	30 020
Turrubares	4 581	4 388	4 046	Bagaces	10 823	10 789	10 589
Dota	5 843	5 954	5 926	Carrillo	21 117	22 188	23 182
Curridabat	53 472	66 869	86 146	Cañas	20 650	22 236	23 935
León Cortés	8 914	8 923	8 680	Abangares	12 913	12 919	12 755
				Tilarán	15 934	16 284	16 451
Alajuela Province				Nandayure	10 940	10 487	9 825
Alajuela	160 601	174 122	188 696	La Cruz	13 063	13 734	14 275
San Carlos	94 094	103 699	115 102	Hojancha	6 809	6 442	5 926
Upala	34 597	39 666	46 152				
Los Chiles	18 197	23 135	30 661				
Guatuso	8 473	9 522	10 833	**Puntarenas Province**			
San Mateo	4 277	4 600	4 966	Puntarenas	84 698	89 180	93 449
Orotina	11 757	12 604	13 544	Esparza	21 456	24 270	27 869
San Ramón	49 248	52 348	55 373	Montes de Oro	8 065	8 234	8 335
Grecia	46 393	49 092	51 636	Aguirre	13 591	13 174	12 461
Atenas	18 370	19 455	20 529	Parrita	10 704	10 265	9 595
Naranjo	28 880	30 661	32 376	Garabito	3 461	3 539	3 582
Palmares	22 748	24 279	25 760	Buenos Aires	37 194	42 109	48 419
Poás	18 555	20 605	22 995	Osa	29 209	29 980	30 552
Alfaro Ruiz	8 215	8 453	8 577	Golfito	36 310	39 650	43 638
Valverde Vega	13 520	14 595	15 733	Coto Brus	45 609	54 200	66 215
				Corredores	38 791	44 379	51 695
Cartago Province							
Cartago	114 659	124 870	135 490				
Paraíso	34 587	36 964	39 192	**Limón Province**			
La Unión	64 463	77 508	95 082	Limón	71 345	79 891	90 850
Jiménez	13 017	13 069	12 830	Pococí	60 877	71 459	86 232
Turrialba	60 159	62 723	64 544	Siquirres	42 202	50 736	63 100
Alvarado	9 596	9 904	10 062	Talamanca	19 029	25 021	34 781
Oreamuno	32 114	35 510	39 309	Matina	19 187	21 939	25 664
El Guarco	28 573	32 359	36 843	Guácimo	21 807	25 089	29 572

Source: Ministry of Planning and Economic Policy and the Latin American Demography Center (CELADE).

ESTIMATES OF CURRENT POPULATIONS
OF SOME WILD ANIMALS IN COSTA RICA

MAMMALS

ENDANGERED	THREATED	COMMOM
Ocelote	Honey Aunteater	León breñero
Jaguar	Tapir	Anteater
Margay	Squirrel Monkey	Perezoso gris
Puma, Mountain Liom		Tepezcuintle
Giant Aunteater		Ring-Tailed Cat
Manatee		

BIRDS

ENDANGERED	THREATED	COMMOM
Jobiru Stork	Angler Eagle	Quetzal
Harpic Eagle	Pava granadera	
	Pavón	
	Scarlet Macaro	

REPTILES

ENDANGERED	THREATED	COMMOM
Tortuga lora	Crocodile	
Leatherback turtle	Iguana	
Green turtle		
Tortuga Carey		

AMPHIBIANS

ENDANGERED	THREATED	COMMON
Golden Toad		

Source: *National Biodiversity Data Base, National Biodiversity Institute.*

BIBLIOGRAPHY

Aguilar-Bulgarelli, O. *La Constitución de 1949* [The Constitution of 1949]. San José: Editorial Costa Rica, 1974, 2nd edition, p. 188.

———*Estudios Sociales para 7mo grado* [Social Studies for 7th Grade]. San José, Librería: Imprenta y Litografía Lehmann, S.A., 1975. 3rd edition, p. 140.

"Provincia eclesiástica de Costa Rica" [Ecclesiastical Province of San José]. *Anuario Eclesiástico 1987* [Ecclesiastical Yearbook 1987]. San José: Secretariado Conferencia Episcopal, p. 120.

Araya-Pochet, C. "Los factores demográficos y su incidencia en la evolución económica y social (1821-1843)" [Demogrphic factors and their effect on economic and social evolution (1821-1843)]. *Revista de Costa Rica*. San José: Ministry of Culture, Youth, and Sports, No. 8, January 1975, pp. 7-27.

Avila, O. *La sociedad de Costa Rica (1843-1854)* [Costa Rican Society (1843-1854)]. University of Costa Rica. Graduate thesis, 1971. Mimeographed, p. 470.

Bolaños, Rafael Angel and Lemistre, Annie P. *Santo Domingo de Heredia. Su historia desde la perspectiva del Valle Central Occidental de Costa Rica* [Santo Domingo, Heredia: Its history from the perspective of the Western Central Plateau of Costa Rica]. San José: Center for Social Studies and Research. Edited by I.F.A.M., 1984. p. 158.

Bonilla, H. H. *Los Presidentes* [The Presidents]. San José: Editorial Universidad Estatal a Distancia and Editorial Costa Rica, 1979. 2 volumes.

Boza, M. *Los Parques Nacionales de Costa Rica* [National Parks of Costa Rica]. San José: Ministry of Agriculture, INCAFO, 1978, p. 80.

Borbón Z., Jorge. *¿Cómo evitar el colapso de San José?* Revista Actualidad Económica. San José. Editorial Trejos Hnos. Sucs., S.A. agosto-setiembre 1988.

Bontempo, José A., *Coyuntura Industrial*. Revista Actualidad Económica. San José: Editorial Trejos Hnos. Sucs., S.A., marzo-abril, 1989.

Cardoso, C. "La formación de la hacienda cafetalera en Costa Rica (siglo XIX)" [Formation of the coffee plantation in Costa Rica in the Nineteenth Century]. *Revista de Costa Rica*. San José: Ministry of Culture, Youth, and Sports, No. 12. September 1976, pp. 153-196.

Carvajal, María E. "¿Cómo modernizar la C.C.S.S.?" [How can the Costa Rican Social Security System be modernized?]. *Revista Actualidad Económica*. San José: Editorial Trejos Hermanos Sucesores, S.A., March-April, 1989.

Cevo-Guzmán, J. *Modelos de análisis geográficos en Costa Rica* [Models for geographical analysis in Costa Rica]. Heredia: Publications Dept. of the National University, 1974, p. 230.

———*Magallón-Molina, Florencio, et al. Costa Rica, nuestra comunidad nacional* [Costa Rica, our national community]. Seventh Grade Social Studies. Textos Modernos Cattleya, 1989, p. 256.

———*Recopilación de datos climáticos de Costa Rica* [Compilation of climatic data for Costa Rica]. Heredia: School of Geographic Sciences. National University, 1975 (mimeographed).

Hartshorn, *et al. Costa Rica, Perfil Ambiental* [Costa Rica, Environmental Profile]. San José, Trejos 1983, p. 152.

Chinchilla, E. *Atlas Cantonal de Costa Rica* [Canton Atlas of Costa Rica]. San José: IFAM. National Printing Office, 1987, p. 396.

Atlas Estadístico de Costa Rica No. 2 [Statistical Atlas of Costa Rica No. 2], 2nd ed. General Statistics and Census Office and the National Economic Planning and Policy Office. San José, Costa Rica: LIL, 1981.

———*1984 Population Census*. General Statistics and Census Office. D.G.E.C.-MEI, 1984. p. 500.

Administratative Territorial Division of Costa Rica/National Commission of Administrative Territorial Division, San José: National Printing Office, 1989.

Población de Costa Rica y orígenes de costarricenses [Population of Costa Rica and origins of Costa Ricans]. San José: Editorial Costa Rica (Biblioteca Patria No. 5), 1977, p. 404.

Facio R. *Estudio sobre economía costarricense* [Study on Costa Rican Economy]. San José. Editorial Costa Rica. 1972, p. 415.

Fernández-Guardia, R. *Historia de Costa Rica: El descubrimiento de la conquista* [History of Costa Rica: The discovery of the conquest]. San José, Costa Rica: Editorial Lehmann, 1941.

Flores-Silva, E. *Geografía de Costa Rica* [Geography of Costa Rica]. 2 volumes. San José: Editorial Universidad Estatal a Distancia, 1979, p. 352.

Gil-Pacheco, R. *Ciento cinco años de vida bancaria en Costa Rica* [One hundred five years of banking life in Costa Rica]. San José: Editorial Costa Rica. 1974. p. 415.

González, L.F. *Historia del desarrollo de la instrucción pública en Costa Rica. Tomo 1* [History of the development of public education in Costa Rica, Volume 1]. *La Colonia* [The Colony]. San José, Costa Rica: National Printing Office, p. 145.

González-Víquez, C. *Historia financiera de Costa Rica* [Financial history of Costa Rica]. Editorial Costa Rica, 1977, p. 207.

_____*El sufragio en Costa Rica ante la historia y la legislación* [Suffrage in Costa Rica in the context of history and legislation]. San José: Editorial Costa Rica (Bibilioteca Patria No. 11), 1978, p. 315.

Guardia-Quirós, J."Discriminación y cambio en la agricultura" [Discrimination and change in agriculture]. *Revista Actualidad Económica*. Editorial Trejos Hermanos y Sucesores, July 15, 1987.

Gustafsson B. Westermark A. El Sector Forestal en Costa Rica, El Proyecto de Integración Bosque Industria, Proyecto de Fin de Carrera, Universidad de Gotemburgo, Escuela de Ciencias Económicas y Empresariales, octubre 1988.

Hall, C."La expansión de los transportes en Costa Rica" [The expansion of transportation in Costa Rica]. *Revista Geográfica de América Central*. Heredia: National University, 1975, Semester II, pp. 9-26.

_____*El café y el desarrollo histórico-geográfica de Costa Rica* [Coffee and the historical-geographical of Costa Rica]. San José: Editorial Costa Rica, 1976, p. 208.

_____*Costa Rica: Una interpretación geográfica con perspectiva histórica* [Costa Rica: A geographic interpretation with a historical perspective]. San José: Editorial Costa Rica, 1984.

National Housing and Urban Development Institute. Some issues concerning the Metropolitan Area Study. OPAM, 1975, p. 50.

Liga Agrícola Industrial de la Caña (LAICA = Industrial Sugarcane Farmers League). "Lo que no todos sabemos sobre el azúcar" [What we all don't know about sugar], 1982.

Meléndez, C. *Historia de Costa Rica* [History of Costa Rica]. San José. Editorial Universidad Estatal a Distancia, 1979, p. 175.

Minisry of Public Works and Transportation. General Planning Office. *Reseña histórica de los transportes en Costa Rica* [Historical summary of transportation in Costa Rica]. 2nd edition. San José: MOPT, 1984, p. 175.

Nuhn, H. *Regionalización de Costa Rica* [Regionalization of Costa Rica]. (MIDEPLAN, OFIPLAN). Revised edition, 1973.

_____*Atlas Preliminar de Costa Rica* [Preliminary Atlas of Costa Rica]. San José: National Geographical Institute, 1978, p. 47.

_____*Costa Rica en la Independencia de la Federación* [Costa Rica in the Independence of the Federation]. San José: Editorial Costa Rica (Biblioteca Patria No. 8), 1977, p. 254.

"Problemas del Cantón de Los Chiles" [Problems with Los Chiles Canton. Possible Solutions." Paper presented by the community of Los Chiles to the Government of Costa Rica, July 1986, p. 85.

Sáenz, A. *Historia Agrícola de Costa Rica* [Agricultural History of Costa Rica]. San José: U.C.R. Publications. Agricultural Series No. 12, 1970, p. 1087.

Sander. G. *La colonización agrícola en Costa Rica* [Farm settlement in Costa Rica]. San José: National Geographical Institute (IGN). Minisry of Public Works and Transportation, 1964. 2 volumes.

Thomas, F.S. and Gallardo, C. *Nuestros presidentes del Poder Ejecutivo* [Our presidents of the Executive Branch]. San José: Editorial Texto Ltda., 1979. 3rd edition, p. 49.

Trejos F., José Joaquín. *Ideas Políticas Fundamentales* [Fundamental Political Notions]. San José: Editorial Libro Libre, 1985.

Woodbridge, Jorge. "Cambio estructural en las exportaciones industriales" [Structural changes in industrial exports]. *Revista Actualidad Económica*. Editorial Trejos Hermanos y Sucesores, July 15, 1988.

Zelaya, C. *et al. Costa Rica Contemporánea* [Contemporanean Costa Rica]. San José, Editorial Costa Rica, 1979, Volume 2.

GEOGRAPHIC INDEX

A

U

V

Y

Z

PHOTOGRAPH INDEX

GENERAL INDEX

9. Political and Administrative Organization.. 81